The Dead Past

Sir Edmund Trelawny Backhouse

Haec olim meminisse juvabit.[1]

Peking, 1943

ALCHEMIE

---

[1] From Virgil's *Aeneid*. "One day, this will be pleasing to remember." Commonly rendered as "One day, we'll look back on this and smile".

The Dead Past
By Sir Edmund Trelawny Backhouse
Edited by Dr Reinhard Hoeppli
And Peter Jordaan

With thanks to William Backhouse.

Cover photo: Jardin du Luxembourg, Eugène Atget, 1902.

CONTENTS

INTRODUCTION

This is the first publication of *The Dead Past* by Sir Edmund Trelawny Backhouse, Bart.

Born in 1873, he was a British oriental scholar and linguist who authored, with journalist J.O.P. Bland,[1] the books *China Under The Empress Dowager* (1910) and *Annals And Memoirs Of The Court Of Peking* (1914). Both works greatly influenced the way the West viewed Peking. Sir Edmund was also – and this must be stated at the outset – an unmitigated rogue and liar. Possibly, like some, a charming one, but an untrustworthy, fleecing criminal nonetheless.

The Dead Past forms the first part of his fictionalised memoirs, and was completed only some months before his death in 1944. Like an opium dream, it blends truth and fantasy to bring alive a youth spent in the company of the leading personalities of the *fin de siècle*. Those featured include Oscar Wilde, Lord Alfred Douglas, Walter Pater, Paul Verlaine, Lord Rosebery, and the courtesan La Belle Otéro, some of whom are described as his lovers.

Sir Edmund's other volume of memoirs, *Décadence Mandchoue*, details his later life in China, describing real or imagined affairs with nobles and commoners, and also with the Empress Dowager Cixi (Tz'u Hsi). It was first published in

---

[1] John Otway Percy Bland (1863–1945), British writer and journalist.

2011 by Earnshaw Books (and in a Chinese version by New Century Press), and was written prior to *The Dead Past*.

He was born into a wealthy Quaker family: the Backhouses were bankers, missionaries and botanists, and established the Backhouse Bank which financed the world's first passenger train service. Sir Edmund's father, Sir Jonathan Edmund Backhouse, 1st Baronet, was a director of Barclay's Bank.

Despite this background, Quaker frugality was not initially part of Sir Edmund's character. While still at Oxford he ran up extraordinary debts of £23,000. He fled England, and in 1895 was declared bankrupt. His family settled his debts, stringing out the case in the courts over four years, and managing to settle his creditors at ten percent. Given the family's public profile and respectability, the affair was managed discreetly, and he was provided with a modest allowance.[1]

Sir Edmund turned up in China in 1899. Soon after arrival in Peking he undertook translation work for George Ernest Morrison, the Australian-born Peking correspondent for *The Times* of London. Morrison wrote that Sir Edmund "possesses extraordinary abilities. He is one of the greatest scholars England possesses". However, they later fell out, and Morrison was the first to doubt the authenticity of a diary of a high Manchu official, Jing Shan (Ching-Shan), which Sir Edmund claimed to have found, and which became the centrepiece for *China Under The Empress Dowager*.

Undoubtedly Sir Edmund's linguistic ability and his homosexuality, which recognised no barriers of station or

---

[1] Hugh Trevor Roper, *A Hidden Life*, pp18-20, 118.

class, gave him intimate access to a far broader range of individuals than might otherwise have been the case.

Despite inheriting the baronetcy upon the death of his father in 1918,[1] apart from occasional visits to Britain, Europe and North America, Sir Edmund remained in China for the rest of his life, surviving on his family allowance and piecemeal work,[2] including for Lord ffrench, whose company was building railways for the Chinese government. For a decade he was also a part-time professor at Peking University.

In 1913, Sir Edmund began to donate a great many Chinese manuscripts to the Bodleian Library, hoping to receive a professorship in return. This endeavour was ultimately unsuccessful. Several of the manuscripts were discovered to be forgeries by unknown hands.[3]

During the First World War he was secretly commissioned by the British Government to purchase rifles from Chinese sources: they were never delivered, and either he was duped, or more likely, masterminded the fraud. During this period he was certainly responsible for a series of other serious criminal scams.

Sir Edmund witnessed the last days of the Manchu dynasty, the turbulent Republican period that followed, and the Japanese invasion in the 1930s. As he grew older he adopted Chinese dress and customs, and avoided the foreign legation quarter except in times of crisis.

---

[1] The baronetcy was inherited by a nephew and is still extant.
[2] Charles Austin Thomas Robert ffrench, 6th Baron ffrench of Castle ffrench, Galway, Ireland (1868–1955). Head of the firm Pauling & Co.
[3] Hugh Trevor Roper, *A Hidden Life*, pp118-119.

Following the Japanese invasion in 1937, Sir Edmund's family sent him a ticket for England but he sold it. When the Pacific war began he moved into the British Legation Compound. Due to his age and fragility the Japanese did not intern him. In 1942 he converted to Catholicism and spent the last months of his life in a French Catholic hospital where he died.

During the Japanese occupation, Sir Edmund was befriended by his Swiss physician, Reinhard Hoeppli, an eminent parasitologist and Honorary Swiss Consul. Hoeppli has been described as a sophisticated intellectual, blessed with an acute sense of humour, and sense of the absurd.[1] Like Sir Edmund, he was also rumoured to be homosexual.[2]

Hoeppli described Sir Edmund as sporting "a long Chinese gown of dark colour which made him timeless." He found him to be an engaging conversationalist, gourmet, and bibliophile. Beyond the exterior of an elderly scholar, he also found there lurked an old satyr. Entertained and no doubt titillated by Sir Edmund's more erotic tales, he encouraged and paid him to write his memoirs, promising not to publish them in his own lifetime.

Following Hoeppli's death in 1973, the manuscripts were handed over by his executor to Sir Hugh Trevor-Roper, Regius Professor of Modern History at Oxford University. Trevor-Roper initially considered preparing the works for publication, but as his researches revealed their fictions, he chose instead

---

[1] Alistair Morrison, Defending Dr Hoeppli, *New York Times*, 15 September 1977.
[2] Hugh Trevor-Roper, *A Hidden Life: The Enigma of Sir Edmund Backhouse*, Macmillan, London 1977, p267.

to write a biography, *A Hidden Life: The Enigma of Sir Edmund Backhouse*, which was published in 1976,[1] and republished the following year with corrections.

Hoeppli had wished that, following his death, the original manuscript be given to the Bodleian Library at Oxford University, and duplicates left to the British Museum in London, the Bibliothèque Nationale in Paris, and Harvard University in Cambridge, Massachusetts. Only the first two bequests to British institutions were made: the other copies were given to the University Library in Basel, Switzerland and the National Library of Australia. It is from the Australian copy (NLA MS 3670) that this published text has been prepared.[2]

Despite *The Dead Past* being completed in Peking in 1943, it has only been available to readers in typescript form, upon application to one of the four institutions that hold copies. This is despite Trevor-Roper's biography and the continued referencing by scholars of Sir Edmund's writings.

So until now, *The Dead Past* has lived up to its title, mouldering in just a handful of typescript copies locked away in archives — over seventy years since Sir Edmund laid down his pen. It is a most curious circumstance, and suggests, if not suppression, then deliberate neglect. It is the desire to remedy this regrettable situation (which at this juncture has assumed

---

[1] Published in America and later English editions as *The Hermit of Peking: The Hidden Life Of Sir Edmund Backhouse.*

[2] For the byzantine story of how a copy ended up in Australia see: Andrew Gosling, 'Sir Edmund Backhouse and How His Scandalous Chinese Memoirs Came to Canberra', *ALRA (Asian Library Resources of Australia) Newsletter*, No 70, July 2017.
[https://web.archive.org/web/20210620150821/http://www.alra.org.au/newsletter1707/1707_gosling_1.pdf]

the shape of an injustice), which has prompted the current publication.

Trevor-Roper, who demolished Sir Edmund's reputation, termed the memoirs pornographic and snobbish, and by dint of them being fictionalised, implied they were historically worthless. [1] This may partially account for the long non-publication of *The Dead Past*, but heterosexual fascism, with its active and passive suppression of alternative histories, has undoubtedly also played its traditional part.

Snobbish *The Dead Past* most certainly is. Sir Edmund preened himself on his linguistic talents, and employs French and Latin copiously throughout the manuscript even for common terms. It would have appeared affected even when the general English reader was schooled in those languages.

As a professional historian, Trevor-Roper's first standard was that of Truth: Sir Edmund's sly inventions, indicative of the vain and psychopathic fraudster he was, were an insult to everything he honoured. If they and Sir Edmund's protestations of honesty irritated him, it would be entirely understandable.

However, once Sir Edmund's claims to absolute truth are dismissed, it is possible to take a pragmatic view of him (particularly given his deep love of France and its literature) as a typical fantasist perpetrator of the *roman-à-clef* — the novel with elements of truth. Textural promiscuity, in every sense of the word, is a Gallic tradition.

---

[1] For Trevor-Roper's approach to the material, see: Adam Sisman, *Hugh Trevor-Roper: The Biography*, Weidenfeld & Nicolson, London 2010.

10

So where did truth end, and fantasy begin? To employ the phrase Sir Edmund regularly uses in his work – "Who knows?" In his post-script essay, Hoeppli wrote that his rickshaw-puller spontaneously mentioned there existed a rumour that Sir Edmund had been the lover of the Empress Dowager, and a document has revealed that Sir Edmund assisted a British Army officer, Major Noel Du Boulay, in returning looted treasures to the Manchu court.[1]

However J.O.P. Bland, who later investigated his collaborator's frauds for himself, would later write: "Backhouse is notoriously untruthful...I can only explain it by ascribing it to a kind of morbid psychology, that delights in mystification."[2] The assessment of the O.E.D. seems very fair: "there may be many small truths in those manuscripts that fill out the picture of his life, but we know now that not a word he ever said or wrote can be trusted."[3]

Trevor-Roper noted the similarity of Sir Edmund to that other homosexual fantasist Frederick Rolfe – Baron Corvo.[4] Charles Masson Fox,[5] to whom Rolfe had written the infamous

---

[1] Gosling, 'Sir Edmund Backhouse and How His Scandalous Chinese Memoirs Came to Canberra' See: Anthony du Boulay, 'The Summer Palace, Beijing 1900: An Inventory By Noel Du Boulay', *Transactions of the Oriental Ceramic Society*, The Oriental Ceramic Society, London 1990, pp85-89.
[2] Trevor-Roper, *A Hidden Life*, pp203-204.
[3] Robert Bickers,' Backhouse, Sir Edmund Trelawny, second baronet (1873–1944)', *Oxford Dictionary of National Biography*, Oxford University Press, 2004.
[4] Frederick William Rolfe, aka the self-styled Baron Corvo (1860–1913), writer, artist, photographer and eccentric.
[5] Charles Masson Fox (1866-1935), a Cornish businessman who was a part of the circle surrounding painter Henry Scott Tuke. In 1912-13 Fox was blackmailed by a woman who accused him of seducing her 16-year-old son.

pornographic 'Venice Letters', [1] and offered to write two similar frank memoirs for money, was Sir Edmund's first cousin.[2] As Trevor-Roper speculated, it's possible Sir Edmund may have seen Rolfe's letters, and they had encouraged his fantasies. A further inspiration, which Sir Edmund mentions, was possibly *Adventures of a Younger Son* by his namesake Edward John Trelawny.

Referencing Hoeppli's postscript essay, Trevor-Roper, noted that in the first draft of *The Dead Past* Backhouse had mentioned Rimbaud, "but when Hoeppli pointed out an insuperable chronological difficulty, he deftly changed the poet into a cobbler called Rimbot whose name had occasioned a temporary and pardonable confusion."[3]

As Trevor-Roper deduced,[4] Sir Edmund wrote the section on Verlaine in *The Dead Past* with the biography of Verlaine by Edmond Lepelletier to hand – because he quotes page references. Lepelletier left a blank in Verlaine's life from February to July 1886, which Backhouse used to fill with his own fiction of having Verlaine leave Paris to teach at his school. Unfortunately for Backhouse, research by later scholars revealed Verlaine never left Paris.

Likewise, Sir Edmund's account of Lord Rosebery seems a confection derived from information in the public domain – Rosebery's insomnia, night drives, and personal collecting

---

[1] Frederick William Rolfe, *The Venice Letters*, Cecil & Amelia Woolfe, London 1974.

[2] Hugh Trevor-Roper, *A Hidden Life: The Enigma Of Sir Edmund Backhouse*, Macmillan, London 1977, p299.

[3] Trevor-Roper, *A Hidden Life*, 1977, p245.

[4] Hugh Trevor-Roper, *A Hidden Life*, p261.

interests had all featured in the press – and possibly homosexual gossip.[1] Perhaps even informed gossip. Members of Sir Edmund's family were closely associated with the Liberal Party, and he was a member of the National Liberal Club.[2] Talk of Rosebery's orientation in at least the Turf Club, to which he also belonged, was rife.[3] However, there is no mention of Sir Edmund in Rosebery's papers[4] – at least those which survived the sorting out undertaken by his youngest daughter, Lady Crewe.[5]

As a wealthy and spendthrift Oxford student, Sir Edmund had been obsessed with the theatre, lavishing expensive gifts on the leading ladies of the day. What is also apparent is that he felt himself to be a social outsider — perhaps even from those circles which might otherwise have accepted him.

As a sensitive young man, conscious of his appearance, he may have flaunted his linguistic skills and tendency to pedantry like a proud fur. There is, as Trevor-Roper observed, an "empty elitism" in the degree of his intellectual and social snobbery. This may have alienated him from his peers and made him an easy target for mockery. He writes in *The Dead Past* that Oscar Wilde supposedly told him: "My poor Trelawny, you are simply banal. I am sorry for you, because

---

[1] e.g. One of Lord Ronald Gower's still unpublished diaries describes in precise detail a visit to Rosebery's Scottish seat of Dalmeny, and of the interior of his private retreat on the estate, Barnbougle Castle. [Diary of Lord Ronald Gower, September 1901, D6578, Staffordshire Record Office.]

[2] Hugh Trevor-Roper, *A Hidden Life*, p18-19.

[3] Paul B. Remmey, Jr., 'Lord Spencer's Recollections of Balfour, Curzon, Rosebery, and George V', *Research Studies*, Volume 38 (4), December 1970, Washington State University, p312-318.

[4] Leo McKinstry, *Rosebery: Statesman In Turmoil*, John Murray, London 2005, p414.

[5] Remmey, Lord Spencer's Recollections.

you are so ugly!" Whether the words were said by Wilde or another, they have the sting of authenticity: of something painfully recalled and long chewed over. Indeed, the section on Wilde in *The Dead Past* reads like the revenge for past snubs.

Sir Edmund could certainly hold a grudge. As he makes clear in the closing passages of *The Dead Past*, he relished the Japanese takedown of British colonialism: a sentiment no doubt fuelled by the myriad slights he'd totted up from its representatives, be they officious clerks or snooty officers' wives.

And so he lingered on in a garden house in Peking, surviving on the family remittances, and whiskey, caffeine crystals and sleeping pills: dignified, scholarly, curious, and enraptured by the golden silk caresses of the seductive East. In the end, Sir Edmund was one of those eccentric English expatriates that add so much to the local colour of foreign locales, and become a legend in themselves.

Yet the old Peking recluse in his Chinese robes had been young once, and it is this lost youth in England and France that *The Dead Past* summons.

This edition includes every word in the manuscript, including Dr. Hoeppli's Postscript. Antiquated spellings for Michelangelo and Shakespeare have been updated, and a handful of obvious but minor errors corrected.

As well as convoluted syntax, Sir Edmund had a penchant for page-long paragraphs. While some have been retained, where paragraph breaks naturally suggested themselves, they have been inserted for easier reading. Where missing commas might lead to confusion, they have also been added, including in Hoeppli's Postscript. Biographical footnotes and translations of the many French and Latin passages have been provided: any mistakes are the editor's own. The handful of original footnotes by Sir Edmund himself are indicated by his accompanying initials.

Given it has spent over seven decades cruelly locked away in the dusty shadows, I'm delighted to be able to bring Sir Edmund's *The Dead Past* into the light and the living present where it belongs.

P.J.

June 2021

Frontispiece

The Author in His Seventy-first Year. March 1943.

Photo S. Vargasoff.

Lectoribus Salus![1]

I, Sir Edmund Trelawny Backhouse, a Baronet of the United Kingdom and a Baron (honorary) of the former Russian Empire, a Marquis of the Manchu Dynasty, Doctor of Letters, member of the Academy of Paris, hereby swear (and were it with my latest breath I should swear to the same) that my papers on Paul Verlaine,[2] Stéphane Mallarmé,[3] Aubrey Beardsley[4] and Walter Pater[5] are faithful records of my friendships with these eminent persons, not one syllable being added nor invented (much whereof I was not sure being omitted) in my narratives; except that the exact time may have occasionally escaped my recollections, writing as I am some fifty (ay and more) years after the events described, without a scrap of written chronicles, and with only the beacon light of an old man's memory (and with the hand of fate already heavy on him), to guide me across the labyrinthine and weed-ridden paths of the relentless past. I certify to this dedication on my

---

[1] Reader's Salvation!

[2] Paul-Marie Verlaine (1844–1896), major French poet associated with the Symbolist and Decadent movements. Married Mathilde Mauté with whom he had a son, but is noted for his stormy love affair with fellow poet Arthur Rimbaud, whom he shot and wounded. Later as an English teacher, he had an affair with a pupil, Lucien Létinois, which inspired more verse.

[3] Stéphane Mallarmé (1842 –1898), pen name of Étienne Mallarmé; major French symbolist poet and poet.

[4] Aubrey Vincent Beardsley (1872–1898) illustrator, author, and leading figure of the Aesthetic movement.

[5] Walter Horatio Pater (1839–1894), Oxford don and highly influential essayist, and art and literary critic. His *Studies in the History of the Renaissance* (1873) was the bible of arty young men, and a novel *Marius the Epicurean* (1885), embodied its spirit in an Ancient Roman setting. A romance with the Balliol undergraduate and future novelist William Money Hardinge damaged Pater's academic career.

bounden and solemn honour, as one who has received recognition from his own sovereign, and from other potentates of this world, or even he goes into (as he soon must) the darkness of dusty death to pass before a greater than any earthly throne.

E.Backhouse
Peking, 17.VII.43.

PAUL VERLAINE

1. The Poet as Preceptor

Take it for all in all, my life has not been unhappy. We all know Sophocles' aphorism at the climax of his Oedipean tragedy: "Call no man happy till the end of his life;" it might apply to potentates fallen on evil days or to the ruin of great persons; but for one who was neither born great, nor achieved greatness, nor yet had greatness thrust upon him except perhaps for a brief hour under my great mistress, Tz'u Hsi, the Empress Dowager, won from the sands of time, I do not know that the shadows of a sad decline, imposed, as it were, by the inexorable law of averages (it is a just law, it is 'God's law'), should be allowed to shut out remembrances of halcyon days which gild old age with the after-glow of youth, even as an Ode of the agnostic to immortality.

Certainly my childish years were ideally unhappy, for I was born of wealthy parents who had everything they wanted and were miserable *par conséquent* in its possession; a father of good family indeed, but of the earth earthy, pedestrian, false to the fingertips, lewd as a satyr, hating me for what was, even then, the promise of an admittedly exceptional intellect; a mother from an ancient Cornish house, which predated the Norman Conquest by centuries, a she-wolf of Celtic blood, whose cruel eyes unsated with torture, petrified like a Medusa my early years with pallid terror, a 'raksha' incarnate, half Medea, half Jezebel, arrogant despot, ignorant and overweening, from whom in the twenty and more years of our dolorous acquaintance, or rather inveterate hostility (for I never saw her (nor wanted to) after 1894 till her death eight years later), I heard not a kind word nor received a grudging dole of sympathy, but hate and hate alone throughout the livelong days, the while she mocked childish tears.

Aged thirty, I accompanied my father to her grave and, as he reverently bared his head, I cursed her detestable memory in ten different tongues much to my sire's edification. In fact, to my unholy joy, tears came into his eyes! "The gods remember ever-lastingly: by their great memories the gods are known."

Aged nine, I was sent to a school, St. George's, at Ascot, the 'Head' (as we called him) being a certain Reverend Dr. Herbert Sneyd Kynnersley,[1] a sadistic tyrant of colossal self-adulation who loved to flog his pupils, stimulating himself before each cruel birching with copious draughts of *vin de Xérès*.[2] The boys, aged eight to fifteen, were prigs and snobs, but Winston Churchill, Maurice Baring,[3] Niall Campbell (now Duke of Argyll),[4] Lawrence Palk, afterwards Lord Haldon[5] (whose sad

---

[1] Rev. Dr. Herbert William Sneyd Kynnersley (1848–1886). Author of *Greek Verbs For Beginners*, etc. Married Flora Georgiana Macdonald. His reign at St. George's is described, with a wide range of opinion as to his sadism and arousal by flogging, in: Winston Churchill, *My Early Life* (1930); Maurice Baring, *The Puppet Show Of Memory* (1922); Viriginia Woolf, *The Life Of Roger Fry* (1940), and Count Harry von Kessler, *Gesichter und Zeiten* (1935). Kessler, who was homosexual, looked upon him fondly, but being German, perhaps had a greater respect for *die Disziplin*.
[2] Sherry.
[3] Maurice Baring (1874–1945), polyglot man of letters, popular novelist, war correspondent, and highly-connected homosexual bachelor son of the 1st Baron Revelstoke, of the Baring bank family.
[4] Niall Diarmid Campbell, 10th Duke of Argyll (1872–1949); an eccentric bachelor laird.
[5] Lawrence William Palk, 3rd Baron Haldon (1869–1933). The Palk family had been wealthy landowners, particularly at Torquay. However, burdened by debts, their fortune imploded, with the 2nd Baron declared bankrupt in 1891. The 3rd Baron was constantly short of money, and notorious for lending his name to promote crooked companies. He married twice, ending

and tragic life makes me all the more conscious of his kindnesses to me when he was a big boy, and I a small one), caused the misery of those drab term-days of ungenial discipline, *taquinerie et brimades*,[1] whence imagination and affection were remorselessly shut out, to be, if not bearable, at least easier to be borne.

How shall I forget the occasion which was a *péripétie*[2] in my miserable fortunes! It was the afternoon, about sunset had there been any sun in that gloomy realm of Dis[3] that is England in winter: we boys were waiting before lessons in the entrance ball which served as our 'recreation' room and the scene of the Head's draconian harangues of his pupils, a judge like God almighty from whose decision lies no appeal, who worked himself into a Salvini-like[4] (without the genius) crescendo of frenzy over some imagined dereliction, pending his inevitable "you must be flogged". (It is a satisfaction to be able to add that this detestable Orbilius[5] suffered from aortic disease of the heart and constantly recurring fainting periods.

---

up living "in straightened circumstances in Brixton", and latterly in a labourer's cottage in Cornwall. He described his near-destitute son and heir, who was charged with theft in 1928, as "hopeless". [Special London Letter, *The Star* (Guernsey) 18 July 1891, p1; Lord Haldon Hauled Down, *John Bull*, 12 April 1924, p10; Soldier, Actor, Farmer and Cook, *Shields Daily News*, 16 August 1938, p5; Past Life Of Peer's Heir, *Sheffield Daily Telegraph*, September 1928, p5; Iain Fraser, *The Palk Family Of Haldon House And Torquay*, Sylverwood Publishing, Newton Abbot 2008, pp77-82.]
1 Teasing and bullying.
2 Turning point.
3 In Dante's *The Divine Comedy* the city of Dis encompasses the sixth through to the ninth circle of Hell.
4 Tommaso Salvini (1829–1915), Italian tragedian.
5 Horatius Flaccus' pedagogue. E.B. (A flogging schoolmaster—from Horace's master.)

23

A famous London physician, Dr. Ringer,[1] used to come down to Ascot occasionally after these seizures and, we had heard, warned him against the effort entailed by over-flogging his pupils (I believe that he also received a cogent *avertissement*[2] on humanitarian grounds from the Ministry of Education). It affords to me an evil joy to state that the *dominie* ignored the physician, administered to a certain Dermot Howard Blundell,[3] with whom he was supposed to have homosexual intercourse and to whose room (for we all had cubicles with doors attached) he often repaired at strange hours, the most terrible birching of his career and dropped dead at the final stroke. We boys were so thrilled by the tidings of his fatal syncope that, with the friendly co-operation of a kindly house-maid who "laid him out" in his coffin, we managed to have the broken rod inserted in his shroud, like the Egyptians who buried familiar objects with their dead; so birch and crucifix (for he was an extremely high English churchman) found place together in his dishonourable grave.

Revenons à nos moutons:[4] in the gloom that overshadowed heaven and earth on that winter's afternoon (February, 1886) which was to begin a new life for me, the news of Mr. Gladstone [5] having "kissed hands" on his appointment by Queen Victoria as prime-minister had just been received in suburban Ascot, for Windsor which was always in telephonic touch with Osborne is only six miles distant. Dr. Kynnersley used the occasion for a seditious tirade against the great

---

[1] Sydney Ringer (1835–1910), clinician, physiologist and pharmacologist.
[2] Warning.
[3] Dermot Howard Blundell-Hollinshead-Blundell (1874–1910), first-class cricketer and British Army officer. Married Eugenie Sybil Ward; one son.
[4] Back to the subject at hand.
[5] William Ewart Gladstone (1809–1898); four times Liberal Prime Minister between 1868 and 1894.

statesman, whom he accused (as did Queen Victoria) of being indirectly Charles George Gordon's [1] murderer and incidentally denounced some six or more of us lads as embryo liberals, semi-accomplices with Mr. Gladstone, and sinners against the Tory faith without which none can be saved.

He had just ended his address, when a cab drew up at the front door which led to our hall and a visitor was announced with a couple of shabbiest carpet bags. He was bald as a coot; his skull was as full of protuberances as an old copper saucepan; he had tiny, oblique eyes which sparkled, a flat nose and a swollen nostril. Looking back, I can see that he resembled Socrates with his short, wiry beard, a Socrates however who erred like a vagabond on the roads, without self-mastery or philosophy.

As he introduced himself to the Head who was expecting him, as the new French usher, some cruelly-minded boys laughed at his broken, if very fluent, English. To me he seemed most fascinating, all the more because of the novelty of a type which had not yet come into my ken. He was half shy and half caressing, half dour and half intimate: like a faun or a satyr, a sort of Caliban, part brute, part god, a force of nature which knows no law and therefore appalls the observer, a species of tramp who had been through the *via dolorosa*[2] of the streets and would never find refuge on earth till he reposed in her soft arms. I remember that he was in deep mourning and knew later that it was for his dear mother's death.

---

[1] Major-General Charles George Gordon (1833–1885), the 'Hero of Khartoum', and national icon. His homosexual desires may have played a part in his martyrdom.
[2] The path that Jesus walked to his crucifixion.

Another usher showed him to his room and after shaking off the dust of travel he returned to our hall for the forty or fifty boys to be presented. I saw at once that I attracted him, as did young Churchill: without particularly good looks and suffering from a life-long shyness, I have often been conscious that a certain type of brain felt an appeal from my personality, why I don't know, except perhaps that there exists a magnetism unbeknown to myself, a gift of God which might lay me open to unfair charge of insincerity. As a child of five, I was taken to the Vatican by my cousin, the then Mr. Nicholas O'Connor, later Sir Nicholas O'Connor G.C.M.G., Minister at Peking, Ambassador to St. Petersburg, who was an ardent Catholic, by His Holiness' gracious consent, to an audience. Pio Nono[1] only a year before his death still retained the wonderful sparkle and lustre of his eyes which had made suspicious Italian *contadini*[2] (and still more *contadine!*[3]) attribute to him the evil eye: he blessed me with what seemed real paternal affection, *"Caro fanciullo! Sia ricevuto nella fede."* "Dear child: may you be received into the faith!" It was strange to me to be honoured with that saintly benediction; and even then I thought ruefully of home tyranny and the negation of justice that life connoted to my helpless childhood, guarded as I was by monsters outshadowing the Minotaur.

Amidst the audible jests of my school-mates (for if there is one thing an English boy deems the sin impossible to be forgiven, it is the attempt to speak French with an accent somewhat (even if remotely) resembling a Frenchman's, and not the

---

[1] Pope Pius IX.
[2] Peasant.
[3] Female peasant.

French of Stratford Atte Bowe[1] which Chaucer holds up to ridicule. So I said M. Verlaine: *"Monsieur le Professeur, cela me fait bien du plaisir que de faire votre connaissance"*, and he to reply, *"Cher enfant, tu es charmant, déjà je t'aime tendrement"*.[2] In other words, I had inspired him with attachment: happily Dr. Kynnersely was innocent of French but one or two of the boys had had French *bonnes* and sniggled slightly at the affectionate mode of address, which suggested a sort of love at first sight.

After the introductions, Verlaine called me to his side to inform me that *"l'art doit être de glace: il faut toujours ciseler les mots comme des coupes,"*[3] a dictum of great pith and moment but, as may be supposed, rather above the head of a school-boy of thirteen!

Then he asked me: *"Est-elle en marbre ou non, la Vénus de Milo?"* And I replied: *"Mais pour sûr elle est en merbre, Monsieur le Professeur,"*[4] which reply seemed greatly to please him. *"Nous allons faire le causette tous les jours: si tu ne dors pas trop tôt, je passerai ce soir à ta chambre à coucher et tu me donneras de tes nouvelles."*[5]

I could not say him nay, while reflecting that nightly visits to the boys were the Head's special apanage. However, as

---

[1] "She spoke the French of Stratford atte Bowe and not the French of Paris." EB

[2] "Professor, it gives me great pleasure to make your acquaintance". "Dear child, you are charming, already I love you tenderly".

[3] Art must be like ice: one must always chisel the words like cuts.

[4] "Is it in marble or not, the Venus of Milo?" "But for sure it is marble, Mister Professor."

[5] "We're going to chat every day: if you do not sleep too early, I'll come to your bedroom tonight and you can tell me about yourself. "

Kynnersley never honoured me with nocturnal calls and he knew no French except *bonjour* etc. pronounced in an accent unrecognisable to any Frenchman, I thought he might attribute the visits to a benevolent wish on Verlaine's part to give private tuition to an apt pupil. And so he came that very evening, sat on my small bed and played with me most lovably and sweetly but quite without sensual intrusion, as he quoted from his *Clair de Lune*:

> "*Votre âme est un paysage choisi*
> *Que vont charmant masques et bergamasques,*
> *Jouant du luth et dansant et quasi*
> *Tristes sous leurs déguisements fantasques.*
> *Tout en chantant sur la mode mineur,*
> *L'amour vainqueur et la vie opportune,*
> *Ils n'ont pas l'air de croire à leur bonheur,*
> *Et leur chanson se mêle au clair de lune,*
> *Au clair calme de lune triste et beau*
> *Qui fait rêver lee oiseaux dans les arbres*
> *Et sangloter d'extase les jets d'eau.*
> *Les grands jets d'eau sveltes parmi les marbres.*"[1]

---

[1] Your soul is a delicate landscape
Where roam masqueraders and dancers
Playing the lute and dancing and seeming almost
Sad under their whimsical disguises.
While singing in minor key
Of victorious love and easy life
They don't seem to believe in their happiness
And their song is mingling with the moonlight,
With the sad and beautiful moonlight,
Which sets the birds dreaming in the trees
And the fountains sobbing with ecstasy,
The great slender fountains among the marble statues.

I admired the magic of the words, but only quote them now because long afterwards I read and appreciated the poem, and not that, as a boy of thirteen. I was able then to retain the lines in my childish, if retentive, memory. He stayed with me for half an hour, graciously correcting mistakes in my accent and conversation: when he asked me if I were catholic, I reminded him that this was a Church of England school and that the Holy Father was regarded as worse than Mephisto himself. "I have repented." said Verlaine, "and returned to the God of my baptism and first communion. The day will come when you too shall be received in the true faith." Verlaine was all emotion and never indulged in reflection: but he erred not in his prophesy. Thank God and the Blessed Virgin for their sovran grace! *Que tu étais joliment prophétique, char Lélian, à mon égard.*[1]

Child as I was, I felt not a little proud that *Pauvre Lélian*[2] (for so he bade me call him *dans nos momenta d'intimité*[3]) had discovered *un attrait*[4] in my personality, but did not at the time associate (in fact should not have understood) any erotic stimulus with his marked advances. I doubt it a boy of fourteen would have possessed any sense appeal to him. I could imagine the merciless mockery or my school-fellows it they heard me addressing him as Lélian: boys of that age are absurdly sensitive about Christian names, and I remember as a child of nine how I shrank with embarrassed wrath when my mother came down to the school, entered the hall and called

---

1 "You were beautifully prophetic, Lélian, in my regard."
2 Poor Lélian.
3 In a moment of intimacy.
4 An attraction.

me by my *nom de baptême*[1] before the other boys, as I thought, just to wound my sensitive shyness.

Next morning Verlaine took the French class: some of the boys were insufferably rude and called out in vulgar blatancy "Waterloo" half a dozen times; but happily the English accent rendered the gross insult pointless. I do not know how English teachers fared on the continent but am certain that no country in the world could produce such discourteous license as the British boy exhibits toward his modern language master hailing from abroad. Ay! Waterloo, that "glorious" victory for Blücher, what time *l'empereur avait l'offensive, presque la victoire; il avait Wellington acculé au coin d'un bois,*[2] but for Grouchy's fatal inaction.

On that first morning he gave us for dictation:

> *"Le ciel est par dessus le toit:*
> *Si bleu, si calme:*
> *Un arbre, par dessus le toit*
> *Berce sa palme.*
> *La cloche, dans le ciel qu'on voit*
> *Doucement tinte.*
> *Un oiseau sur l'arbre qu'on voit*
> *Chante sa plainte*
> *Mon Dieu, mon Dieu, la vie est là*
> *Simple et tranquille,*
> *Cette paisible rumeur-là*
> *Vient de la ville.*

---

[1] Christian name.
[2] The Emperor had the offensive, almost the victory; He had Wellington cornered at the corner of a wood.

Qu'as-tu fait ô toi que voilà,
Pleurant sans cesse,
De ta jeuneese?"[1]

The master complimented me on my accurate copy and bade me read it aloud. So far as I understood them, the beautiful lines touched me and my voice trembled as I read. No doubt, the tears were in my eyes and those insufferable boys mocked me audibly as Verlaine patted me affectionately on the shoulder. When the class was dismissed, I passed a bad quarter of an hour: "What price Frenchy spooning you! he's 'keen' (salacious in school parlance) on you: congratulations. Sucking up to him, are you?" I had perforce to listen to *un flot d'ordures*[2] for the whole of the so-called recreation hour. It became a standing joke that never became outworn or hackneyed. As I expected, it was not long, before I acquired the elegant *sobriquet* of "Mrs. Frenchy"; many years later I happened to run across a former school-mate who had been one of my most persistent tormentors and he called out:

---

[1] The sky is here above the roof,
So blue, so calm!
Above the roof a tree,
Waving its foliage
The bell-tower in the sky that one sees,
Gently chiming
A bird upon the tree
Sings his complaint.
My God, my God, how life is there
Simple and tranquil
How peacefully are borne there
Sounds of the city.
What have you done, O you,
Weeping incessantly
With all your youth?
[2] A stream of garbage.

31

"Hullo: Mrs. F." Is there anything so cruel as an English boy'? I doubt it.

That Easter term proved for me a period of unalloyed content: Lélian's stimulating teaching helped me wonderfully with my French. It is true that he provided me with an equipment of vocabulary which was scarcely appropriate to a boy of thirteen, e.g. expressions like *il était soûl comme un pore*:[1] but apart from that he introduced me to *les grands écrivains*,[2] beginning with *Le Cid*:[3] where the line *'Et pour leur coups d'essai veulent des coups de maitre'*[4] as read by him was a veritable revelation of tragic emphasis.

Racine like Corneille, was naturally over my head, but the enchanting harmony of the verse marked ineffaceably for me the characters of Phèdre, Bérénice, Andromaque. He read with me *Paul et Virginie*[5] which was more on my level and delighted me with its exotic colour. Verlaine took infinite pains as stage manager of an attempt by us boys to perform *Le Bourgeois Gentilhomme*,[6] with me in the part of Le Philosophe. It was quite a success and my performance pleased him, though many of the boys thought me *maniéré*,[7] probably because I tried to pronounce as Verlaine taught and not as the English usher who had previously directed our French course and

---

[1] Drunk as a pig.
[2] The grand writers.
[3] A French tragicomedy by Pierre Corneille (1606–1684), based on the legend of Rodrigo Díaz de Vivar ('El Cid Campeador'), a military figure in Medieval Spain.
[4] 'And for their test strokes want some master strokes.'
[5] A novel (1788) by Jacques-Henri Bernardin de Saint-Pierre (1737–1814).
[6] The famous play by Jean-Baptiste Poquelin, aka Molière (1622–1673).
[7] Mannered.

pronounced every word with accent on the first syllable, *à l'anglaise.*

Often he invited me to his room, and I vividly remember the inseparable *verte* by his desk. During that time, intimate as we became, there was nothing between us that was not pure as ice and chaste as snow. Occasionally he read to me letters which arrived in abundance from Mallermé and Dierx[1] an well as many others though I fancy only the two former knew of his Ascot address, and I was pleased when one of the former's communications bade him bring *ton enfant prodige*[2] to Paris *pour les beaux jours pascals.*[3]

Verlaine asked me if my parents would permit my accompanying him to Paris for French tuition, and to my great surprise, the Head approved and obtained their consent. I think dear Lélian was really glad of my company apart from the tutorial honorarium, which may have meant a temporary solace to his penury.

Paname[4] is never so beautiful as in the month of April, for Easter fell very late that year, on April 25, when the chestnuts on the Boulevards are bursting into leaf and the new buds are sweet with spring: Verlaine's rooms were on the top floor of 16 Rue Saint Victor, but my father had taken a room without pension, giving me funds to pay, as the English say, "my own shot" with Verlaine, at a nearby hotel, though I spent the day and a good part of the night with Lélian.

---

[1] Léon Dierx (1838–1912), poet.
[2] Your child prodigy.
[3] For the beautiful Easter days.
[4] Slang term for Paris.

I had no regular lessons but venture to differ from those who deny that it is possible to "pick up" a language by living in the country: frequent excursions with Verlaine introduced me to places like *La Bonne Hôtesse*, rue du Mont Cenis, where Marie Vizier[1] reigned, or Père Fréde[2] at *Le Lapin* and La Mère Adèle in *Boul Miche*,[3] all of whom without exception took kind notice of the humble little *écolier*[4] from *Perfide Albion*,[5] but I was too young then to be able to record impressions of those exoteric resorts where starving artists and literary men managed by exercise of personality to have *une ardoise.*[6]

Verlaine was often *entre deux absinthes*[7] but never encouraged, nor indeed allowed, me to drink with him (in fact I had no wish then for the delectable *Népenthès* which Honor makes Helen, *dia gunaikôn*, divine of women, offer to the Greek heroes from Troy as an anodyne); that time came some years later. I vividly recall his taking me frequently to see '*Le Solitaire de la Rue de Rome*',[8] Stéphane Mallarmé: his austerity, like something carved in marble, was exactly the reverse of the theatrical Verlaine with his strange loves, his drinking bouts, his unconsciousness of material questions. I remember Mallarmé saying: *"Un jour ton jeune ami sera aux nouvelles: il a du cran; vois comme il est crâne."*[9]

---

[1] A buxom blonde who ran the cabaret. Renoir had a brief affair with her.
[2] Another bohemian cabaret owner-manager.
[3] Boulevard Saint-Michel. The Latin quarter.
[4] Schoolboy.
[5] Perfidious Albion i.e. England.
[6] To have credit. (Literally: a slate.)
[7] Between two absinthes.
[8] Mallarmé's epithet.
[9] "One day your friend will be in the news: he has a gutsy look: see his skull."

Le lecteur bénévol [1] will understand, for suggestions and attacks *de malhonnêtes personnes* [2] are for me but sound and fury, signifying nothing, that in recording events of 57 years ago an old man's memory may betray him into ante-dating a conversation. For example, in 1886 and again in 1891 - 92 - 93 - 94 I certainly often met Mendès, [3] Barrès [4] and Huysmans; [5] but as to my first visit to Paris in Easter 1886, I have no accurate recollection of what they said.

It is otherwise with Villiers de l'Isle Adam [6] whom Verlaine took me to see at a café where he would spend most of the night and disappear like a ghost with the daylight. I remember his aspect of terrible poverty, like a tramp who spends his night on a public bench: his face was livid but tinged with red spots, his eyes glassy, his shoulders bent like a porter's. But he was of those who dream dreams and see visions: the tobacco and beer-ridden effluvia of the *café* table were for him an enchanted palace: his lacklustre eyes saw things that to the rest of us are invisible: of short and ungainly figure, with long floating hair, his whole face became transfigured as he rose from table like an oracle and uttered prophecies.

"For me the external world means nought; my soul is an enchanted palace. He who searches for a treasure is happy till he finds it. This wretched café is grander than the Louvre:

---

[1] The benevolent reader.
[2] Of dishonest persons.
[3] Catulle Mendès (1841–1909), poet and man of letters.
[4] Auguste-Maurice Barrès (1862–1923) novelist, journalist and politician.
[5] Charles-Marie-Georges Huysmans (1848–1907) novelist and art critic who published as Joris-Karl Huysmans. Author of the iconic decadent novel *À rebours*.
[6] Jean-Marie-Mathias-Philippe-Auguste, Comte de Villiers de l'Isle-Adam (1838–1889) symbolist writer.

sublime hallucinations have been my reward and I have written of them, here and there, by fragments, at hap-hazard, as in my unfinished romance *Axel*."

> "Beware, beware his flashing eyes, his floating hair:
> Weave a circle round him thrice:
> Close your eyes with holy dread:
> For he on honey-dew has fed
> And drunk the milk of paradise"

Which was as true of Villiers as of Samuel Taylor Coleridge,[1] poet and philosopher drowned in a mist of opium, that brain frozen at its marvellous source.

As we parted from Auguste Villiers de l'Isle Adam, Verlaine told me that he possessed the grand style and that his probe was unequalled in harmony or *éclat*: "a fellow of infinite jest." He died in the summer of 1886,[2] well cared for at the end by *les frères hospitaliers de Saint Jean de Dieu*. Verlaine often told me how generous both Mallarmé and Dierx had been toward him, although the former, at least, was by no means affluent. In after years, when I was better able to appreciate his confidences, he would read to me notes from Stéphane who gave pathetic, but perfectly futile, advice to poor Lélian regarding his divine insouciance in money matters, for I fancy that his *bonne à tout faire*,[3] or rather mistress, named Eugénie Krantz, *faisait danser l'anse du panier*[4] with considerable

---

[1] Samuel Taylor Coleridge (1772–1834) poet, literary critic, philosopher and theologian. With William Wordsworth, a founder of the Romantic Movement in England.
[2] Actually, 1889.
[3] Dogsbody; general help.
[4] Conducted small villainy by rounding out expenses. (Literally: danced the handle of the (shopping) basket.

success. Mallarmé certainly obtained through Dierx a sort of literary pension for the worn out genius (physically, not mentally) and *le vagabond des chemins*.[1]

And so the *pascal*[2] holidays came to an end, and Verlaine took me back to the prison of the Ascot boarding school. I am glad to think that the £50 per term of his usher's salary besides his tuition fees seemed to render him externally more prosperous; he continued the pleasant intimacy but, whatever his proclivities may have been and I knew that I attracted him, he never made at that time an advance that the greatest hypocrite in Albion could have misunderstood.

We acted under his aegis and inspiration, a considerable number of plays, and I earned his warm approval as Don Fernand in *Le Cid*, the latter part being well taken by a boy named Bertie Pearse,[3] rather my senior, who was certainly attractive and who did attract the susceptible Lélian, but to what extent I know not, probably only partial and midway. I think we were rather jealous of each other: he was a very handsome boy, mischievous but not bad-hearted (poor fellow! he was drowned in 1934 on a motor-boat excursion in an Irish lough!), although he 'chaffed' me mercilessly, especially one day at dinner when the school *échanson*[4] plied me with a glass of *vin de Porto* medically ordered for my anaemia, but Pearse's merciless bantering on Bacchus, god of wine, a play on my name, quite deprived me of any exhilaration from the wine

---

1 The vagabond of the pathways.
2 Easter.
3 Major (Beauchamp) Albert 'Bertie' Thomas Kerr-Pearse (1871–1934). Aide-de-camp to the Governor of Madras; private secretary to the Governor of Western Australia. Married Lily Assheton Drummond, and had issue.
4 Butler.

cup. Dante (who loved well because he hated; hated wickedness that hinders loving), once prepared to paint a 'picture; but, perchance being ill-content with the result, said the poet "then I stopped my painting."

Buonarotti [1] wrote a century of sonnets which equal Shakespeare's;' if indeed the latter is the author of the hundred or more attributed to him. "With this key Shakespeare unlocked his heart: did 'Shakespeare?, then the less Shakespeare' he." Leonardo, the genius *qui nihil tetigit quod non ornavit*,[2] was equally great in invention as in verse, (leaving his paintings for the moment out of account). Dante Gabriel Rossetti[3] (Lélian condemned Rossetti for exhuming his poems whereof he owned no copy, from his wife's coffin, six years after her death: as is known, he had driven her by his cruelties to self-slaughter and Lélian thought that the poet had better done to leave these monuments of his remorse in her tomb) excelled no loss in painting than in poetry: Morris[4] painted before he made verse; I believe that Burne Jones[5] wrote creditable rhymes; Ruskin's poetry was certainly lamentable but his drawings, while below the level of his majestic prose, would probably have been marked by Mathew Arnold,[6] who loved to separate the sheep from the goats, with a good second class. Aubrey Beardsley wrote some respectable translations of Catullus' most erotic verses as well

---

[1] Michelangelo.
[2] Who touched nothing which he did not adorn.
[3] Gabriel Charles Dante Rossetti (1828–1882), poet, illustrator, painter and translator.
[4] William Morris (1834–1896), textile designer, poet, novelist, translator and socialist activist associated with the Arts and Crafts Movement.
[5] Sir Edward Coley Burne-Jones, 1st Baronet (1833–1898), artist and designer associated with the Pre-Raphaelite movement.
[6] Matthew Arnold (1822–1888) poet, cultural critic, and school inspector.

as of the famous lines *"Ave atque vale"*[1] to the letter's dead brother: Max Beerbohm [2] equally great as essayist and caricaturist has written a delicious parody of Swinburne:[3]

> "Was't heaven, my brother, did send us
> Locked bliss and ineffable blending?
> Thy tool in a challenge stupendous,
> Encroaching and ever ascending!"

Paul Verlaine had conjointly a pretty talent of caricature which he freely exercised during his Ascot ushership and, I believe, in the years that followed. "So to be the man and lose the artist; win the man's joy, lose the artist's sorrow." Aubrey saw some of these drawings and thought that they indicated a natural untrained gift of design, as wayward as his verse.

His pen and ink sketches of his colleagues were unkind but delicious: Mr. Herbert Martin Cooke [4] B.A., with his huge 'piton' [5] and favoured gesture of thumb biting toward a recalcitrant boy: Mr. Robert Estcourt Macdonald[6] B.A. of Oxon, the Head's brother-in-law, with streaming sentimental eyes sentencing a boy to be "sent up to the Head" for posterior treatment; Reverend Thomas Cadwallader Sanders [7] M.A.,

---

[1] Hail and farewell.

[2] Sir Henry Maximilian 'Max' Beerbohm (1872–1956), essayist, parodist, caricaturist, and dandy.

[3] Algernon Charles Swinburne (1837–1909), poet, playwright, novelist, and critic.

[4] Herbert Martin Cooke, later Cooke-Cross (1858–1931), son of a Ely landowner. Married Sarah Jane Cross; divorced.

[5] A climbing spike. Here: penis.

[6] Robert Estcourt Macdonald (1854–1923), of a prominent Wiltshire gentry family.

[7] Rev. Thomas Cooke Sanders (1843–1892), son of a Northamptonshire vicar.

bearded and high-stomached, at the wicket plying the cricket ball which indeed he did with success; the Reverend Herbert William Sneyd Kynnersley LL.D. himself, wan, blue as lead, with drooping whiskers and fishy eyes, wearing a ghastly sadistic grin, thin as a whipping post, salacious and lustful, probably boasting a cyclopean orgasm, birch in hand with flogging block draped in solemn black and a spare rod intended to overawe and impress, with a hideous rug thoughtfully disposed for the doomed candidate of the *fessée*[1] to kneel upon, his naked buttocks upturned for the encounter; the pantry *échanson*, proffering to me (by the Head's direction) a glass of port wine and my childish expression of shrinking horror, for I dreaded the mockery of my school-mates and the inevitable Shakespearean 'tag' that the Head had taught them: "Come thou Monarch of the Wine, Plumpie 'Bacchus' with Pink eyne."[2]

Flora Macdonald Sneyd Kynnersley appeared in a coloured chalk sketch *Une expérience manquée on le dénoûment imprévu.* [3] In 1886 electric light was in its infancy, but Kynnersley had installed a rudimentary plant at St. Georges' School under an engineer named Robey. We boys all had light turned on and off at destined hours in our cubicles but were forbidden under pain of the following 'sanction' neatly printed and framed for each room: "Any boy in-fringing this rule not to tamper <u>under any circumstances whatsoever</u>" (thrice underlined in red) "with this electric light and (or) switch will at once and without further warning receive <u>a most severe</u>" (in red) "punishment across the bared breech." I disobeyed

---

[1] Spanking.
[2] From Shakespeare's *Antony and Cleopatra*: Act 2 Scene 7.
[3] A missed experience is the unforeseen outcome.

the order and my steeled buttocks paid a terrible penalty; as did *les derrières d'autres patients.*

The Head loved experiments in matters of which he knew little; so, with Robey's help he devised a tiny battery and lamp for Flora's hair on occasion of a dinner party to which Lélian was invited. All began well; her rather pretty, russet hair seemed to be tenanted by glow-worm *locataires*; [1] and Verlaine exclaimed: *"Comme vans êtes ravissante, Madame la Principale, ce soir-ci!"* [2] Alas: someone had blundered, I presume, knowing less of electricity than of aeroplanes or conic sections,[3] that the tiny battery had fused. At any rate, the resultant 'tableau' was an appalling shriek, "Herbert, I am on fire," and small flames darted from the nest of hair which concealed the apparatus. 'Lélian, *en galant homme*, applied his napkin to the spot, extinguished the little conflagration and burned his own hand. The caricature of his heroic gesture was admirably to the life; equally so the Head's air of dignified aloofness and nonchalance, as it the episode scarcely concerns him a whit; while the rector of Ascot, The Reverend Beauchamp Kerr-Pearse D.D.,[4] an aristocrat to the finger tips, a High Anglican, occupies himself in making the sign of the Cross on the party in general and on Flora and Lélian in particular, a supererogatory, if ornamental, *procédé* or outward visible sign, which lent *éclat* to the miniature drama and had, I suppose, as much efficacy *vis-à-vis* the immortal

---

[1] Lodgers.
[2] How lovely you are, Madame Principal, this evening! "
[3] In mathematics, a conic section is a curve obtained as the intersection of the surface of a cone with a plane. The three types of conic section are the hyperbola, the parabola, and the ellipse; the circle is a special case of the ellipse, though historically it was sometimes called a fourth type.
[4] Rev. Beauchamp Albert Thomas Kerr-Pearse (1836–1900). Of Batts Park, Taunton, Somerset. Married Geraldine Henrietta Guinness.

gods, as common sense would expect or sentiment aspire to, in view of Heaven's masterful Lucretian indifference to mortal joys and griefs or trembling earthly fears.

I have spoken of Bertie (Bertram Algernon Trevelyan) Pearse,[1] son of the Reverend Doctor who held in honour the crucifix whose:

> "Pallid burden sick with pain
> Watches the world with wearied eyes,
> And weeps for every soul that dies;
> And weeps for every soul in vain."

Lélian greatly loved his sparkling mischievous eyes, his dainty upturned nose, his short upper lip worthy of Apollo, his smile half mockery, half allurement. I admired his high spirit but *il me faisait toujours le taquin*[2] and mercilessly mocked my over-delicate and highly sensitive temper; "Like sweet bells jangled, out of tune and harsh;" who am so tender to all hardness, whom the slightest hint of sarcasm or of unmerited reproof repels and wounds far, far more than the multitudinous whippings so familiar (ay! and so welcome) to my hinder topography.

I have spoken elsewhere of my youthful *éreutophobie*, or dread of morbid blushing, which suffused my face with crimson for the passionate sins of others as well as for mine own. Well, Bertie's blushes exhibited themselves elsewhere than on his facial cheeks, for another part, that which

---

[1] Incorrect. As per the note on page 35, his full name was Beauchamp Albert Thomas Kerr-Pearse. Having possibly known him only by his common name of 'Bertie', it seems Backhouse is guessing or his memory has failed.
[2] He always teased me.

Xanthippe's husband [1] loved in Charmides, [2] assumed a rubicund hue which we boys admired when standing naked around the swimming pool.

Lélian claimed that this quality of local blushing propensity was innate in man, as it still is in apes (so he declared wrongly, I am told), but that civilisation had robbed humanity of the gift. Perhaps it resembled the ear "waggling" of the Countess Russell, wife of Lord John, later Earl Russell, Prime Minister of Queen Victoria. The latter was interested in the feat and demanded an exhibition at a tea party: Lady Russell partially succeeded but was seized in the august little lady's presence with an attack of nerves and thereafter lost for good and all the convenient and coveted faculty.

Verlaine sketched Bertie standing naked on the diving board; years later I could see that "'twas redolent of amorous suggestion;" the delicate line of the boyish undeveloped but beautiful organ, like a rosebud awaiting the sunlight:

"If nature put not forth her power,
About the opening of the flower,
Who is it that shall live an hour?" [3]

the delectable curve and pink-hued presentment as of the morning sky touched by Aurora's fingers of those twin Normandy pippins, *le mole*, the buttocks (as Italy calls them).

---

[1] Socrates.
[2] The handsome and popular youth of whom Socrates says in one of Plato's dialogues: "I saw inside his cloak and caught fire".
[3] Wordsworth. E.B.

43

Lélian gave to his sketch the legend: *"Ganymede dans l'attente de Zeus."* What the exact relations between them may have been I can surmise but dare not pronounce: Bertie was older than I and puberty had already announced itself; but I should not suppose a great sympathy between the gay Lothario in embryo that was Pearse and the stranger nature more akin to mine own of dear Lélian. Bertie played Le Cid to my Don Fernando, and Verlaine sketched us in the final scene which I venture here to quote from memory:

> *"Rodrigue. Pour posséder Chimène at pour votre service,*
> *Quo peut-on m'ordonner que mon bras n'accomplisse?*
> *Quoi qu'absent de ses yeux il me faille endurer,*
> *Sire, et ce m'est trop d'honneur de pouvoir ospérer.*
>
> *Don Fernando. Espère en ton courage, espère on ma promesse;*
> *Et possédant déjà le coeur de ta maîtresse,*
> *Pour vaincre un point d'honnour qui combat contra toi*
> *Laisse faire le temps, to vaillance et ton roi."*[1]

It was a delicate drawing of Bertie as the fearless knight in his impetuous *élan at le fougue de le jeunesse*,[2] of me as the hidalgo king endeavouring, at least, to present him in his sovereign dignity. The picture is today, I hope, still to be found among

---

[1] "Rodrigue To gain Chimène, and for your service,
What command can be issued that my valour cannot accomplish?
Yet, though absent from her eyes I must endure
Sire, I have too much happiness in being able to hope.
Don Fernando. Hope in your courage, hope my promise;
And already possessing the heart of your mistress,
To defeat a point of honor that fights against you
Let time, your valour, and thy king exert themselves. "
[2] Momentum at the ardour of Youth.

my masses of papers in London unless incendiary bombs have paid to my bank a visit.

I must not omit to mention Herr Doktor Wolfgang Kym (he always insisted upon the k in Doktor even in English) whose father had migrated from Weimar to Zurich after the revolution of 1848. With kindly blue eyes and bushy eyebrows (the latter suggestive of a fierceness entirely alien from his dispositions), an even, if ironical, temperament and a passionate love for music, he took issue with me for what he called the "unpatriotic" spelling of my surname, dubbing me "Max," because, said he, I resembled a portrait of his hero, Max Piccolomini,[1] as a boy. He and Lélian were great friends and their favourite topics were the crimes of 'La Gueuse',[2] (as they always denominated La Troisième République, after the fashion of the times) a common hatred of President Grévy[3] and a devoted admiration of Wagner [4] and his artistic, disastrous king.[5]

Now that the Comte de Chambord (Henri V)[6] was dead, Lélian had become Bonapartist: Saints' days were always half holidays at Ascot; and on one such anniversary (it may have been "Barnaby the Bright", June 11) Dr. Kym and Lélian took

---

[1] A character in Wallenstein, a trilogy of dramas by Friedrich Schiller (1759–1805).
[2] The beggar-girl/whore.
[3] François-Judith-Paul Grévy (1807–1891), President of the Republic of France, 1879 to 1887.
[4] Wilhelm Richard Wagner (1813 –1883), German composer, theatre director, polemicist, and conductor.
[5] Ludwig II of Bavaria (1845–1886).
[6] Prince Henri, Count of Chambord, Duke of Bordeaux (1820–1883), disputedly King of France from 2 to 9 August 1830 as Henry V, although never officially proclaimed as such. Afterwards, Legitimist pretender to the throne of France from 1844 until his death.

me with them on a pilgrimage to Farnborough and Chislehurst *où nous nous inclinâmes devant la dépouille de l'empereur Napoleon III et de son fils.*[1] Some eleven years later I recall telling the Empress Eugénie[2] of our homage to her dead: she was touched and remembered how Lélian had made *amende honorable*[3] to her for his vulgar invectives against her son before the fall of the empire. *"Un sublime poète"*, she called him, *"qui fut aussi volage qu' une girouette."*[4]

I read *Die Piccolomini* and *Wallensteins Tod*[5] with Dr. Kym and remember his dramatic rendering of the final scene, where Piccolomini, heart-broken by Max's death, receives the fateful missive from his emperor "Dem PRINZEN Piccolomini," and the curtain falls on anguish and on remorse for a title gained at such a cost. Lélian drew a clever sketch of Dr. Kym, not a caricature but a portrait, which showed to you the man in his habit as he lived. I was a favourite of the doctor, as indeed of all the ushers, partly, perhaps, in pity for Dr. Kynnersley's vindictive hatred, favoured, I shall over believe, by my wicked parents now, I trust, burning in a warmish corner of hell.

In particular did Dr. Kym and Lélian sympathize with my much enduring posterior, the unsatiated, never glutted prey of the Head's relentless, unconscionable birch-rod. In fact, Dr. Kym, in his chivalrous anger, proposed (no doubt not seriously) to lend to me a small loaded pistol which I was to fire at Kynnersley's abdomen after the termination of my next

---

1 Where we bowed before the remains of Napoleon III and his son.
2 Eugénie, Empress of France (1826–1920), wife of Emperor Napoleon III, who reigned 1852 to 1870.
3 Honourable amends.
4 A sublime poet who was as fickle as a weather vane.
5 The second and third plays in Schiller's Wallenstein triology.

flogging. He said (and I took his words in solemn earnest and was quite prepared to play my part for better or worse) that, if I succeeded *par accroc*[1] in wounding the headmaster, the police would naturally hold an enquiry: Dr. Kym and Verlaine would give evidence of his barbaric maltreatment and my bleeding buttocks, streaming with "infant gore" would tell the tale more eloquently than any Counsel as a speaking testimony in acquittal of my childish vengeance.

However, 'Herr Wolfgang Kym,' of course, never lent to me the weapon which would have been a damaging *pièce de conviction* against himself. He and Lélian did write to the Journal of Education and to Mr. Henry Labouchère,[2] the owner of *Truth* and a violent Republican, to ventilate the scandal (also, I think, to the Society for Prevention of Cruelty to Children).[3] In fact, Dr. Kym, an expert photographer in those infant days of the art, most obligingly took pictures of my wounded hinder quarter with splintered twigs *"des tronçons de bouleau"*[4] embedded in the flesh and that of a fellow victim named Stuart Menzies; both counterfeit presentments requiring, owing to being surreptitiously taken in a dark outhouse, a very long exposure, but the result was distinctly adequate, and the doctor sent them an evidence of our outrageous and bestial chastisement to Mr. Labouchère.

Who shall wonder then if I am still an admirer of German *Grossmut*,[5] as I found it in the days of my youth? Thanks to Dr.

---

[1] By misadventure.
[2] Henry Du Pré Labouchère (1831–1912). English politician, writer, publisher of the influential journal *Truth*.
[3] Nothing was published.
[4] As Montesquieu calls them. EB Sections of birch.
[5] Magnanimity.

Kym's thoughtfulness, I fancy that certain stops (the exact nature whereof I ignore) were taken which compelled the Head to moderate his birchings, so far as his vaulting and bounding *Sadismus*[1] could be curbed or trammelled. But, as I have elsewhere said, orgastic impulsion gained the day at the last and he fell dead of a cardiac attack immediately after a ferocious castigation of Dermot Howard Blundell,[2] for whom he was said to have conceived and materially consummated a strong homosexual affinity, such as he most surely did not entertain toward me. God's latest curse upon his wicked soul!! May his Gitonian proctal cavity be seared in Hades with rod-hot iron like Edward II of England in 1327!

Of a surety was myself his chiefest *bête noire,* always excepting the present prime minister of Great Britain. Mr. Churchill's veridical autobiography in its *élan* and vivacity makes abundantly clear the drab misery of those Ascot days, from which he suffered scarce less than I under that beast in human form who was le croquemitaine de notre jeune âge.[3]

After Dr. Kynnersley's death which occurred (*albo lapillo notanda dies*[4]) on July 16, 1886,[5] the school broke up for a premature vacation and Lélian's ushership terminated, while I went to Winchester College and the school was to be run under different auspices hereafter. (As for Kynnersley may his

---

[1] Sadism in a medical sense.
[2] Captain Dermot Howard Blundell-Hollingshead-Blundell (1874–1910). Served in the Boer War; A.D.C. to the Governor of Malta.
[3] The bogeyman of our youth.
[4] Noting the tombstone. (Literally: Noting the white stone.)
[5] False. As Trevor-Roper noted (p265), Sneyd-Kynnersley died four months later, on 1 November 1889 in Birmingham. He was on a visit to his father when the heart attack occurred.

pale ghost suffer perennial interstitial prods in Hades on and within the seat of his homosexual exuberances.)

NOTE

The heirs of all the ages of that great and glorious European tradition in which England has never had much part, *Britannia Magna* the last outpost of Roman civilization, as is writ in Virgil's[1] Eclogue: *"et penitus toto divisos orbe Britannos"* "the northern island sundered from all the human race," occasionally speak of London as synonymous with Albion (may one not retort "what can they know of 'England' who only London know?"); but in fact *le Pays de Cocagne*[2] is far less England than Paris is France (which no provincial admits), or Berlin (when I knew it) is Germany, or ever the 'Führer' became paramount and blessed *Gross Deutschland* with *Saturnia Regna*.[3]

There are other routes to England besides the old Kent or Sussex road to Charing Cross, Strand and Victoria in Pimlico, and fully half of the passenger traffic and very much more than half of the freight never set eyes on the Cross of Gold that hangs o'er city and river, Wren's stately monument that so far surviveth the changes and chances of a wanton iniquitous war.

Verlaine came to Ascot in February 1886 via Dieppe and Southampton, the longer sea route connoting a cheaper fare.

---

[1] Publius Vergilius Maro, aka Virgil (70 BC–19 BC) Roman poet who wrote three of the most famous poems in Latin literature: the Eclogues (or Bucolics), the Georgics, and the epic Aeneid.
[2] The Land of Plenty.
[3] A golden age. (Literally: The reign of Saturn.)

49

From Southampton he journeyed by the South Western Railway through Winchester and Basingstoke to Woking, where he changed trains to the loop-line for Ascot via Frimley, Camberley and Bagshot, never coming within 30 miles of "famous London town." The weather on that day was inclement and he had a rough crossing with delays both at Dieppe and on entering the Solent with its mysterious double tides. He and I took the same Channel route together to Paris on April 21, 1886, for the *pascal*[1] holiday, and it was likewise the road which he travelled in November 1892 when he came to Oxford and returned home by, some weeks later. Hence, his statement in 1893 quoted by Lepelletier[2] that he had not set foot in London for twenty years may conceivably be accurate, though apparently contradicted by his visit thither in that cold snow-laden winter of 1880-81 in company with that sweet youth, Lucien Létinois. [3] Dearest Lélian was by no means strong on dates; but I do not know of any visits which he paid to London between 1886 and 1893.

Certain is it that he never went "up to town" during his Ascot tutorship: the partly pedestrian *pèlerinage*[4] of 10 miles or more which he, Doktor Kym and I paid to the graves of Napoléon III and of Louis Napoléon his son in June 1886 led us through the lush meadows of Berkshire and the golden expanse of broom *genêt épineux*[5] and gorse to Chislehurst near Woking through Bagshot heath and Frimley birch woods.

---

[1] Easter.

[2] Edmond Lepelletier, Paul Verlaine, *Sa Vie, Son Oeuvre* - nouvelle edition. Paris, Mercure de France, 1923. E.B.

[3] Lucien Létinois (1860–1883). Until his untimely death at the age of twenty-three from typhoid fever, a love of Verlaine, who devoted twenty-five poems to him in *Amour* (1888).

[4] Pilgrimage.

[5] Spiny broom.

Well do I recall how Dr. Kym, always full of fun, suggested our plucking a large supply of birch twigs for the sadistic Kynnersley's delectation and their future application to my hardened latter end. We knew not then that our *plagosus Orbilius* — that flogger Orbilius — was even at that hour treading the unconscionable road of dusty death which called him a month later from the scene of his truculent birchings and delivered our unhappy buttocks from the Neronian horror of his sadistic persecution.

PS

My belief is that Verlaine purposely suppressed much reference to his Ascot days; because he did not wish his creditors, the Létinois family and others as well as Mme. Verlaine his former wife, to know that he was earning a regular income which might have been *mis en séquestration*.[1] Verlaine on one occasion, as M. Lepelletier says on page 504, *"tout a coup disparaissait."*[2] This particular disappearance occurred in 1887 but his sojourn at Ascot in 1886 may have been equally unknown to others than Mallarmé and Léon Dierx. My old friend, Arthur Symons, [3] poet, essayist, homosexual, Catholic, and charming, quoted *Pauvre Lélian* as saying that between 1873 and 1893 he had never once revisited London. Symons was a genius but none who know him would regard his *obiter dicta* [4] as settling the matter,

---

[1] Placed under administration.
[2] All of a sudden disappeared.
[3] Arthur William Symons (1865–1945).
[4] Remarks.

seeing that he himself refers to Verlaine's "honeymoon" in January 1881 to London with dear Lucien Létinois.

2. Last Memories of Lélian and Other Common Friends

While at Winchester, I had frequent letters from Verlaine and am happy to think that in the holocaust of my important correspondence with literary and historic personages that with my dear Lélian still survives (so far as I know) in a London bank's custody. I did not see him again until January 1891 when I was again in Paris, in company of my school-fellow Lord Alfred Douglas,[1] now a devout Catholic but then certainly not of those, "*che la region sommettono al talento,*"[2] whom the Florentine saw in "*cet air épais muet de touts lumière*"[3] dumb to all light, those sinners of the flesh whose lusts outran their intelligence.

Bozie, as he was commonly called (a corruption for Boyzie), would probably not thank me for recalling numerous love episodes at Winchester in which he was usually the ascendant and I the pathic, although positions were sometimes reversed. He has persuaded himself in his old age, perhaps sincerely, that Wilde seduced an innocent pure boy (himself) with *pedicatio*,[4] and its attendant delights.

Having seen the two together and listened to their conversation, I can definitely contradict this admirable,

---

[1] Lord Alfred Bruce Douglas (1870–1945), poet, journalist, lover of Oscar Wilde.
[2] From Dante's *Inferno*.
[3] From Verlaine's *Les Fêtes galantes.*
[4] Rectal titillation or copulation.

although possibly disingenuous, rehabilitation of his character. Bozie, though many years younger, beguiled and seduced Oscar, quite apart from the latter's own by no means negligible *luxure des plus lubriques*.[1] He (Douglas) was a *coquet*[2] of the first water, who would leave Paris and Oscar for an unknown address and then telegraph from his temporary sojourn: "Oscar! if you do not come to me, I shall die," what Wilde denominated "passionate telegrams." And the latter, the incarnation of selfishness, arrogance and intransigence, allowed himself to be fooled by this clever beautiful boy with the pale face and the golden hair, who has since learned to write admirable religious poetry but who certainly achieved Oscar's ruin.

My friend, Robbie Ross,[3] Oscar's literary executor, who later quarrelled with Bozie Douglas, knew the facts better even than I: in fact the *De Profundis* original manuscript in the British Museum reveals them for all time. I will not say a great deal of my personal relations with Oscar: he, Bozie, Harry Stanford (an actor and a catamite) and I stayed together in l'Hôtel des Deux Mondes on the Avenue de l'Opéra. The unbiased reader will not be astonished to hear that sexual relations were frequently commemorated between us; although Oscar admitted to me that he derived greater pleasure from association with the type of *laquais, la canaille et la lie du peuple*,[4] "because their passion was all body and no soul!" In my opinion M. Lepelletier[5] is mistaken (from a

---

[1] Lust of the most lewd.
[2] Flirt.
[3] Robert Baldwin Ross (1869–1918), Canadian-British journalist, art critic, art dealer, and lover and friend of Oscar Wilde.
[4] Lackeys, the rabble and the dregs of the people.
[5] Edmond Lepelletier, *Paul Verlaine sa vie, son oeuvre*, édition, Paris, Mercure de France, 1923. E.B.

laudable motive) in denying to Lélian all carnal homosexual commerce; it is contradicted by his own admissions to me and also by his tragic endeavour to pedicate upon me in January 1895.

I must add one reminiscence of Robbie Ross (whom Lélian admired) in the tragic summer of 1895, when Oscar was awaiting inevitable condemnation and poor Ross' rooms near St. Mary Abbott's Church, Kensington, were under watch from detectives. I went (not without risk) to see him late one night and he promptly locked the door of his sitting room. "Trelawny," for so he loved to call me, "you know I am impotent; but let me 'have' you on that sofa if I can: between the legs if you prefer, but don't refuse me." (There was no doubt which posture he preferred, and 'twas not intercrural!).

Poor Robbie: he did his best which was not saying much, and managed to effect an inadequate copulation (from behind, gladly accorded by me) which, I hope, gave to him some solace in that very dolorous time. At least, he was a gentleman, which is a good deal more than can be said of Oscar and Bozie! Toward the end of his artistic life I believe that he foreswore all his homosexual interests (in fact persuaded himself that he had never had any, much as the Old Buddha[1] really convinced herself that she had saved many missionaries in the Boxer year, or George IV announced that he had commanded a brigade at Waterloo), for he had run through the full gamut of that exoteric emotion which he once savoured with so great a zest!

---

[1] Empress Dowager T'zu-his of China (1835–1908).

55

It was about 10 January 1891 (a date which M. Lepelletier's excellent biography p.522 appears to confirm) during *une vague de froid*[1] unusual for 'Paname' (or shall so be vulgar and say 'Pantruche'[2] like *les faubouriens*[3] of that day), and a virulent epidemic of what was then called Russian influenza in England, that Verlaine came to the Deux Mondos chiefly to see me; but we all went off together and after *apéritifs* dined at Paillard's.[4]

Verlaine had been given a day's exeat from the hospital where he was being treated (so he told me), for bubos of the legs and a syphilitic sore in the rectum: certainly he looked the part and was a pitiable spectacle. M. Lepelletier, p.350 (and I think other biographers of Lélian) have made allusion of his and Arthur Rimbaud's readiness to submit to a medical examination (*"se soumettro à une expertise médicale"*[5]) with a view to refuting the allegations of pathic and interstitial commerce.

It is, I think, worth mentioning that Lélian, in [the] course of a short private chat *chez* Paillard that evening, spoke bitterly of a certain *interne*, whom he named, a Dr. Du Boulay, at his hospital, who had twitted him regarding the abnormal conformation of his anus which he stigmatized as "bottle shaped," insinuating, I daresay, that sexual intrusion had been frequently achieved. But (I presume) the frequent use of "anal dilators" of box-wood would have had a similar effect on the

---

[1] A cold snap.
[2] Another slang word for Paris and its suburbs.
[3] The people of the suburbs.
[4] A fashionable restaurant frequented by the elite of Europe. Amongst the specialities was Pomme Otero, named after the noted courtesan.
[5] Submits to medical expertise.

expansion of the cavity as the entry of an intromittent fleshly organ.

I think that perhaps one of my saddest recollections is when I called him aside that night on some pretext and presented him with 100 francs: his pathetic gratitude brought tears to my eyes. At Oscar's request he read to us poems from his *Parallèlement*, [1] where he records the aspirations of his genuine conversion and *'les blandices du crime'* [2] in joint association. *Comme le chien de l'Écriture, il retourne à son vomissement;*[3] and his relapse inspired him with verses no less exquisite than those of his conversion in:

> *"Void mes pieds, frivoles voyageurs,*
> *Pour accourir au cri de votre grâce,*
> *Voici mere pieds, frivoles voyageurs."*[4]

I seem to hear Oscar, with his slight Irish accent but excellent French, lavishing insincere compliments: *"vous êtes le meilleur poète de votre temps."*[5] We all had the wine leaves in our hair, as Wilde loved to say, for with all his wit, he was over repeating himself, so that his *mots* lost much of their point. We spoke of Salomé which Wilde had just "completed"; I don't think that it is the betrayal of a secret (except *Celui de Polichinelle*),[6] if I mention here that, while much of the idea of the play is due to Wilde, the French was heavily revised and

---

[1] Verlaine's seventh anthology, published 1889.
[2] The blandishments of crime.
[3] Like the dog of writing, he returned to his vomit.
[4] "Here are my feet, vain travellers,
To run to the cry of your mercy.
Here are my feet, vain travellers."
[5] "You are the best poet of your time."
[6] Except that of an open secret.

repolished (even rewritten from A to Z) by Maurice Barrès;[1] although I believe that the striking *"j'ai baisé to bouche, Iokanaan, j'ai baisé to bouche"*[2] was Wilde's own. Oscar's supreme egoism was considerably ruffled when Lélian told him how Huysmans had denied much originality to *Dorian Gray* and claimed that the purple passages regarding Dorian's collection of jewels were all *obérés de dettes*[3] to *A Rebours.* *"Il dit,'* said Verlaine, *"quo vous donnez comme vôtre ce que vous avez pillé chez lui: c'est un plagiat des plus effrontés."*[4]

Wilde was the most touchy of men, and I suppose that none can read the passages in the two books without perceiving his debt to Huysmans; in my judgment, his bloated adiposity and badly curled hair rendered him at best unprepossessing, but when *pris de vin*[5] he became *rouge comme un coq ou comme une amarante,*[6] and his green eyes radiated the cunning of an apache. I greatly expected him to vomit, like Marc Antoine *si cruellement malmené*[7] and maligned in Cicero's Second Philippic.

"I shall challenge him to a duel," shouted he. "Don't do that," said Verlaine, "because Huysmans will accept your challenge and that is hardly what you want!" "Sir, you are insolent," retorted Wilde; but in his heart, coward as he was, though he

---

[1] Auguste-Maurice Barrès (1862–1923), novelist, journalist and politician.
[2] "I kissed your mouth, Iokanaan, I kissed your mouth."
[3] Overwhelmed by debts.
[4] "He says," said Verlaine, "that you give as yours what you plundered at home: it is a plagiarism of the most impudent."
[5] Taken of wine.
[6] Red as a rooster or amaranth.
[7] So cruelly maltreated.

took lessons from a Parisian *maître d'escrime*,[1] he knew that bluff was his only weapon and might fail him now.

We who were mutes and audience to this act patched up a sort of reconciliation between Lélian and Oscar, the latter being the more drunken of the two. I remember being the most sober, or rather the least intoxicated of the party, having to pay the very substantial 'addition,' something, in those dear days of cheap prices, like 800 francs (for we had consumed seven or eight magnums of *Moët et Chandon*). And we all adjourned au Moulin Rouge, no great distance from Paillard's, where it happened that the heir to the Throne of England, Albert Edward Prince of Wales, was conferring the honour of his presence, and to my disgust the performers and all *faisaient des révérences à cet ivrogne envieilli.*[2]

After the performance, we all formed a sort of line of honour for the passing of the great man. Oscar told us, purring with high satisfaction: "you'll see that His Royal Highness will stop and speak to me," but he was too optimistic, for, although Albert Edward evidently recognised Wilde, he absolutely ignored him and passed out to his waiting brougham without a bow. It reminded me of Henry V, as King, when he unkindly ignored the boon companion of his heir-apparent's days of wild debauchery, Sir John Falstaff, as the latter stood acclaiming his passage to Westminster (Shakespeare: *Henry IV*, last part). Poor Oscar: we parted with Verlaine who, I expected, would have to pass a *mauvais quart d'heure*[3] at the hospital, as he had broken *la consigne*,[4] and returned to the

---

1 Fencing master.
2 Were making a bow to this aged drunkard.
3 Bad quarter of an hour.
4 Instructions.

Deux Mondos. Wilde had had two bad figurative *camouflets*[1] in one evening and was so much upset that I believe his couch was really virgin on that one occasion only, until prison bars shut out copulative encounters.

It must have been about November 10, 1892 that Lélian came to visit us at Oxon. I recall a luncheon party at Christ Church given in his honour by Dr. Haverfield,[2] the great archaeologist of Roman Britain, whom Mommsen,[3] never over-ready to bestow praise on a rival, still less on an Englishman, once called *"Der berühmte Haverfield"*:[4] there were present my cousin, Dr. Thomas Hodgkin[5] D.C.L., the author of *Italy and Her Invaders*; a Quaker banker like George Grote,[6] and a great antiquarian; Walter Pater; Lord Warkworth, heir to the dukedom of Northumberland (later Earl Percy),[7] whose mysterious death in Paris in December 1905 as the result of a duel gave rise to a colossal sensation in which a British prime minister played a dubious part;[8] scholar, visionary and orator, Niall Campbell,[9] his cousin, now Duke of Argyll, who had been

---

[1] Snubs.

[2] Francis John Haverfield (1860–1919), ancient historian, archaeologist, and academic.

[3] Christian Matthias Theodor Mommsen (1817–1903), German classical scholar, historian, jurist, journalist, politician and archaeologist.

[4] The famous Haverfield.

[5] Thomas Hodgkin (1831–1913), historian and biographer. Married Lucy Ann Fox, and had issue.

[6] George Grote (1794–1871), banker, radical M.P., historian, scholar, and philosopher, who is buried in Westminster Abbey.

[7] Henry Algernon George Percy, Earl Percy (1871–1909), until 1899, Lord Warkworth, Conservative politician.

[8] The official cause of death was pleurisy, although there were rumours of a duel over a woman, fought with pistols; Winston Churchill supposedly being the opponent, which he denied. [Charles Petrie, *A Historian Looks at His World*, Sidgwick and Jackson, London 1972, p190.]

[9] Niall Diarmid Campbell, 10th Duke of Argyll (1872–1949), was a gossipy confirmed bachelor, and eccentric scholar of the family genealogy and

my *camarade d'école*[1] at Ascot, known today as an eccentric and quarrelsome recluse; Viscount Balcarres, later Earl of Crawford,[2] a distinguished authority on art; York Powell,[3] the historian of early England whose premature death was a sad loss to research; Earl Beauchamp,[4] president of the Oxford Union, later Governor General of Australia,[5] elegant, aesthetic and *maniéré* as any son of Eton; Dr. Charles Lewis Dodgson,[6] the mathematical genius, author of *Alice in Wonderland* under the pseudonym of Lewis Carroll, who resented any mention of the latter's identity and pretended to be a scientist pure and simple; F. E. Smith,[7] later Lord Chancellor of England as Earl of Birkenhead, the Junior Treasurer of the Oxford Union, even at

---

recondite subjects. Possessing "a woman's voice, very eunuchy," he hated modern life: "he was a king in his own land, at least in his own opinion, even in the days of austerity and Socialism." He once threatened the Commissioner of Works, Sir Alfred Mond, with the dungeon, should he or an underling ever step foot on his soil. [Brian Masters, *The Dukes*, Frederick Muller, London 1988, p293; James Lees-Milne, *Ancestral Voices*, Chatto & Windus, London 1975, p242-247; A London Newsletter, *The Sphere*, 3 September 1949, p4; Duke Of Argyll, *Falkirk Herald*, 24 August 1949, p4.]

[1] Schoolmate.

[2] David Alexander Edward Lindsay, 27th Earl of Crawford (1871–1940), Conservative politician and connoisseur. Married Constance Lilian Pelly, and had eight children. His collection of erotic books was bequeathed to the British Library.

[3] Frederick York Powell (1850–1904), historian and scholar. Powell took an interest in French poetry, and Paul Verlaine and Stéphane Mallarmé lectured at Oxford under his auspices. Married Florence Batten Silke, and had issue.

[4] William 'Boom' Lygon, 7th Earl Beauchamp (1872–1938), Governor of New South Wales 1899–1901, Liberal politician, Lord Warden of the Cinque Ports. Married Lady Lettice Grosvenor, with whom he had seven children. In 1931, in lieu of arrest for homosexuality, he was forced into self-exile until 1937.

[5] Incorrect. See note above.

[6] Charles Lutwidge Dodgson (1832–1898), better known by his pen name Lewis Carroll, writer of children's fiction. Bachelor.

[7] Frederick Edwin Smith, 1st Earl of Birkenhead (1872–1930), Conservative politician and barrister.

that time colossal in his arrogance and acridity of tongue, last and least myself. Will Rotherstein,[1] then staying with York Powell and working at a series of "Oxford Portraits" for John Lane,[2] the publisher, was invited but was not *des nôtres*,[3] if my memory serves me.

Pater delighted in Lélian, though he was certainly not a kindred spirit, the orderly disposition and the formalism of the aesthetic ascete contrasting with the slipshod topsyturvydom of the absinthe addict and irresponsible vagabond that was Verlaine, bless him! I recollect York Powell saying to me that he deemed Lélian the greatest of living poets. Alfred Lord Tennyson[4] had died in the previous month and Verlaine greatly admired William Watson's[5] ode to the dead poet, "Lacrimae Musarum," saying that he would fain translate it into French, especially commending the lines "The singer of undying songs is dead" and "Lo: in this season pensive-hued and grave." In fact, *Pauvre Lélian* cherished the hope of translating *Maud* and *Dream of Fair Women*, but Macmillans, Tennyson's publishers, did not encourage the idea. Mallarmé might probably have compassed an acceptable version into French, but Hippolyte Taine's[6] prose translations could hardly be bettered and I doubt if a metrical rendering of Maud would have been a feasible undertaking in view of the prosodical trammels of French verse.

---

1 Sir William Rothenstein (1872 –1945), painter, printmaker, draughtsman, lecturer, and writer on art.
2 John Lane (1854 –1925), co-founded The Bodley Head imprint with Charles Elkin Mathews.
3 With us.
4 Alfred Tennyson, 1st Baron Tennyson (1809 –1892), Poet Laureate.
5 Sir William Watson (1858 –1935) poet, popular in his time for the celebratory and controversial political content of his verse.
6 Hippolyte Adolphe Taine (1828 –1893) critic and historian.

Very few verse translations satisfy me; and I have never been able (perhaps wrongly) to join in the universal chorus of admiration in Germany (among intellectuals, some of whom even claim that the translation surpasses the original) for the classic rendering of Shakespeare, accurate and erudite, but, as it seems to me, sterile, cold and shorn of the magic utterance and the inspiration. How terribly the translator fails with Prospero, Lear, Brutus and Cleopatra!

Some days later, Pater gave a dinner party at Brasenose[1] (B.N.C.) in honour of Lélian: Hilaire Belloc [2] also an ex-President of the Union and a great debater, and Bobbie Phillimore,[3] who had been with me at Ascot before Verlaine's arrival, a leading orator of the "Varsity" debating society, grandson of Sir Joseph Phillimore Bt.,[4] Mr. Gladstone's college contemporary at Christ Church, member of a famous legal family, Bobbie whose early death deprived Parliament of valuable talents (an inheritor of unfulfilled renown, peradventure?), were among the chosen guests. Poor Lélian partook not wisely but too well of the multitudinous *gamme*[5] of wines and 'liqueurs' (for absinthe, burgundy and benedictine do not blend), and Pater and I had perforce to help him home to his neighbouring lodging. The sight of the drunken but ineffectual satyr that Verlaine presented on that occasion greatly shocked the fastidious Pater who dubbed him

---

[1] One of Oxford University's colleges.
[2] (Joseph) Hilaire Pierre René Belloc (1870–1953) British-French writer, historian and political activist.
[3] Hon. Robert Charles Phillimore (1871–1919), son of the 1st Baron Phillimore. Married Lucy Fitzpatrick, no issue.
[4] Sir Robert Joseph Phillimore, 1st Baronet PC (1810 –1885), judge and politician.
[5] Range.

for the nonce Caliban in the toils. It was a sort of passive, dumb intoxication which harmed none, though in itself repellent to an admirer of the illustrious poet. The time-honoured medieval tag *Corruptio optimi pessima*[1] holds good today as much as when Alexander Pope wrote:

"Who would not smile if such a man there be?
Who would not weep if Bolingbroke were he?"

After Mallarmé, Dierx, and I had arrived separately at 39 Rue Descartes, on a Sunday morning of January 1895, Lélian favoured us with the following philosophic comments: "Religion has hardened me morally and intellectually, has provided me with the background that I required and brought to my style a more variegated pattern, a more passionate and realistic force. It is untrue to say that I have been a prey to conflicts of art and religion, of sensuality and asceticism. What interests me is the strange, the original; conventional manners and ways are fructiferous to some and I myself, indeed, hate eccentricity as opposed to originality. My mind has been of too delicate a texture to grapple with the rougher elements of life. Feeling and love are the moving power of poetry; the person I am in love with does indeed stir my heart, but I regard it as a sacrilege to compose verses out of my love. I love the Jesuits, because the rule of Saint Ignatius compels the need of scientific accuracy in self-examination; Loyola's[2] exercises are a military handbook of sanctity with the rules and discipline though he disapproved *les flagellations religieuses* whether self-inflicted or administered by another. I detest the sight of

---

[1] Corruption of the best is the worst.
[2] St. Ignatius of Loyola, born Iñigo López de Oñaz y Loyola (1491–1556), beatified Basque Catholic priest and theologian; one of the founders of the Society of Jesus (Jesuits).

moral or physical evil; the filthy are filthy still, but I believe in an intimacy between Christ and myself. Sometimes I have fits of melancholy which resemble madness; disappointment ends everything I endeavour to do. Although my poetry has been acclaimed, I think of myself as a eunuch; life is so weary and each day dies with sleep."

I am only making a discovery of the obvious in saying that sanctity and the lusts of the flesh are nearer neighbours than any geographical or arbitrary frontiers: St. Ignatius Loyola, the chastest of men, warned his companions against the danger of devotion degenerating into salacity: Swinburne (who was, of course, *incroyant*[1] but friendly) wrote that the sensuous ritual of the Catholic Church engenders sensual desire. Even so, whenever I heard Lélian discoursing in this semi-penitent, semi-life-weary strain and proclaiming himself not only to me (who did not matter) but to others, like Mallarmé and Dierx (who thought him on these occasions *poseur*) that he was a "eunuch," I foresaw that the mood of the moment would be replaced by something not only erotic but as torrential as a salmon river in spate.

It was so on this occasion (January 1895): poor Paul Verlaine became violently amorous of myself: Mallarmé and Dierx (both of whom had lately been financing him, the former with his wonted magnanimity out of his own resources and the latter, by grace of the Minister — I think of Public Instruction — out of some eleemosynary[2] funds for derelict victims) certainly not scandalised, but vastly amused, said to him: *"Hé! Lélian: nous allons te laisser tranquille: que nous filions à*

---

[1] A non-believer.
[2] Charitable.

65

l'anglaise (passe-moi, mon cher Trelawny, cette façon de parler au figuré) et toi, tu peux y aller 'ubi trahit sue quemque voluptas'." [1] And off they went: I thought of accompanying them but fatal curiosity held me.

What happened? Almost nothing! Poor Lélian exposed an organ shaking *comme un tremble (aspen)*,[2] enormous and ill-looking; for his 'tool' was syphilitic, if not gangrenous. I was certainly not inclined to submit to his onset and thus to ensure to myself a venereal contagion which I have always, perhaps undeservedly, escaped. But nature came to his rescue and he ejaculated (*"bûché"* [3] said he) before my eyes, then sank exhausted on the settee and rehearsed his *chapelet*[4] to "my dear Mother, Mary." It was a sad spectacle, that of genius in the trammels of most ineffectual and inadequate lust. He began to weep and knelt to beseech my pardon.

Poor Lélian, the most honest of men, assured me that he should inform Stéphane and Dierx that no homosexual programme had been accomplished so far as I was concerned; it was a task of supererogation, as both of them knew me well enough to trust to my *finesse* to shake off his erotic hircine onslaught. In fact, they returned almost immediately, comforted Lélian who told them what had happened and we all talked of other things over the absinthe. Lélian's health (he died some eleven months later) was such that I dreaded his religious ecstasies and still more the occasions when he was

---

[1] "Hey! Lélian: we will leave you alone: let us escape quietly (give me, my dear Trelawny, this way of speaking figuratively) and you can go 'where he draws his own pleasure'."
[2] Like a trembling aspen.
[3] Worked.
[4] Rosary.

66

pessimistic as to his *salut*;[1] for the doctors of the hospital (where he was treated free) had warned him that an ejaculation was dangerous owing to the aortic disease of the heart and that the reversion to normal after the orgasm might prove fatal.

The reader need not be told that I am not of those who submit 'concupiscence to reason' (to vary Dante's description of those sad souls in the Inferno who are paying the penalty for sins of the flesh); it is, however, the simple truth to say that Lélian never excited in me the least spark of passion. In many ways I honoured him; in all ways I admired his genius; but sensual attraction there was none.

It was during that arctic winter of 1895, such as Paris had seldom known, on a Sunday after hearing High Mass at Notre Dame that he told me of his long liaison from 1871 to 1875 with *l'athée*,[2] as he was at pains to designate, him by whom he signified Rimbaud: he, Lélian, had entreated him, "les fois ne se nombraient plus," [3] as he expressed it, times without number, to permit the penetration of his active desires, but Rimbaud still denied him, ruthless as the goddess Athena who withhold from Agamemnon, *anax andron*, King of men, her divine visits; what caused Rimbaud to relent and to permit to the frenzied brother poet the access, the intrusion, that was so near his heart, Verlaine hardly knew; but one night the passive resister came to him, *"j'ai changé d'avis,"* [4] and the two indulged in fertile, reciprocal coitus with the accompaniments that poets' imaginings would be sure to suggest. It was not

---

[1] Hello.
[2] The atheist.
[3] The times were no longer counted.
[4] I changed my mind.

Rimbaud (so he said; was it so or not, *chi lo sa?*[1]) to whom Lélian dedicated *Monradieux péché* "thou that art my sin and my light," but it was certainly Rimbaud on whose account Verlaine was sentenced for attempted homicide in a jealous frenzy to two years of *travaux forcés*,[2] by the Belgian law courts, during which period and for some considerable time after, he vanished, like Villon, an suddenly as Ariel departs from Prospero.

He talked to me of his youth spent in the Batignolles quarter of Paris with a widowed mother in comparative comfort and an atmosphere of deep affection. After passing his *baccalauréat*, he was allotted a clerkship in the municipality of Paris and attracted Baron Haussmann's patronage. It was during office hours that he wrote his *Poèmes saturniens* and became intimate with François Coppée,[3] Léon Valade[4] and other poets, especially José Maria de Hérédia[5] whose sonnets Paul greatly loved. Verlaine, Catulle Mendès, Léon Dierx were all regarded as future poets of genius: he, Verlaine, proclaimed the doctrine of impassibility which his career sadly belied, for carnality and hot blood were his undoing.

It was in 1867 that *Poèmes saturniens* appeared, synchronous with *Le Reliquaire* of Coppée; Emile Zola[6] predicted great things of both poets and spoke of *Poèmes saturniens* as

---

[1] Who knows?
[2] Hard labour.
[3] François Edouard Joachim Coppée (1842–1908) poet and novelist. Rimbaud published numerous parodies of his verse.
[4] Paul-Valmir-Léon Valade-Gabel (1841–1884), poet and playwright.
[5] José-Maria de Heredia (1842–1905), Cuban-born French Parnassian poet.
[6] Émile Édouard Charles Antoine Zola (1840–1902), novelist, journalist, playwright; best-known practitioner of the literary school of naturalism.

redolent of *"un génie étrange et tourmenté."*[1] Lélian always spoke gratefully of Zola and, as I have mentioned, believed that the latter with Alphonse Daudet[2] (a most improbable combination) had been responsible for *le denier d'aumône*[3] through the Crédit Lyonnais, which other admirers had provided.

After *Fêtes galantes* appearing in 1868, a slender volume which mentioned in my first paper on Verlaine, with the exquisite *Clair de Lune* that he had recited by my bedside at Ascot in 1885, Verlaine fell in love "with a woman" (as Shakespeare says in *Romeo and Juliet*, an esoteric touch of the poet that will not escape the notice or those 'steeped' in homosexual pleasures), publishing in commemoration of the occasion *Bonne Chanson*, which contains many beautiful, if unintelligible lines. This was in 1869 just before the war; after the fall of the empire, as is well known, he took part, while very young, in the Commune and was fortunate to escape being shot by Thiers'[4] party when the Commune was suppressed. He told me that Gambetta[5] had befriended him and was grateful to the great Tribune's memory, although he wrote a sarcastic epigram on Gambetta's statue.

---

[1] A strange and tormented genius.

[2] Alphonse Daudet (1840–1897), novelist.

[3] The last of alms.

[4] Marie Joseph Louis Adolphe Thiers (1797–1877), second elected President of France, and the first President of the French Third Republic. When the Paris Commune seized power in March 1871, Thiers gave the orders to the army for its suppression.

[5] Léon Gambetta (1838–1882) lawyer and republican politician who proclaimed and played a prominent role in the French Third Republic.

Verlaine spoke to me much of François Villon[1] some of whose verses he quoted to me, so I repeat them here. Villon's first offence was the murder of a priest, Philippe Sermoise, in a drunken brawl over a woman in 1455, he was granted a special pardon for this crime, as later at Meung by Louis XI's grace, judged once more by the Châtelet, condemned this time to be hanged, but pardoned by *Le Parlement*, he composed *Le Lais* (Legs):

> *"Et puis que departir me fault*
> *Et du retour ne suis certain*
> *Je ne suis homme sans défault...*
> *Vivre aux humains est uncertain."*[2]

In *Le Testament*:

> *"Et s'esté m'a dur et cruel,*
> *Trop plus que cy ne raconte,*
> *Je vueil que le Dieu eternel*
> *Luy soit donc semblable a ce compte!*
> *Et l'Eglise nous dit et compte*
> *Que prions pour noz ennemis.*
> *Je vous diray: J'ay tort et honte,*
> *Quoi qu'il m'ait fait, a Dieu remis!"*[3]

---

[1] François Villon (c.1431–c.1463), best known French poet of the Late Middle Ages. Noted for his criminal behaviour.
[2] And since I have to depart
And I can't be sure of returning
I'm a man not without weaknesses...
Life for humans is uncertain.
[3] "And if he was hard and cruel to me,
Even worse than I can say here
I pray that the eternal God
Will deal with him accordingly
And the Church asks and expects

In *La vieille en regrettant le temps de sa jeunesse*:

"Ces gentes espaules menues,
Ces bras longs et ces mains traictisses,
Petiz tetins, hanches charnues,
Eslevées, propres, faictisses
A tenir amourouse lices;
Ces larges reins, ce sadinet[1]
Assis sur grosses fermes cuisses
Dedans son joly jardinet?....
Du sadinot, fy! Quant des cuisses,
Cuisses ne sont plus, mais cuissettes
Grivelées comme saulcisses."[2]

In the famous *Ballade des dames du temps jadis:*

"Où est la très sage Heloys[3]
Pour qui chastré fut et puis moyne

Let us pray for our enemies.
I'll reply: I was wronged and shamed
Whatever he has done to me, let God repay!"
[1] Perhaps I ought to add as a footnote that 'sadinot' is the Vulva. EB
[2] "These graceful slim shoulders
These long arms and fine hands
Small breasts, rounded hips
High, neat, in perfect state
To hold love smoothly
These broad loins, this cunt
Resting on big firm thighs
Nestled in a pretty garden
Of the cunt, ha! As for the thighs,
Thighs are no more than drumsticks
Mottled like a sausage."
[3] The reference to Héloise and her poor emasculated Abelard (Esbaillart) and to Buridan, whose name survives in the adage *"ressembler a l'âne de Buridan,"* (to be lacking in will of one's own) will be obvious. EB

Pierre Esbaillart à Saint Denis?
Pour son amour et ceste essoyne.
Semblablement, où est la royne
Qui commanda que Buridan
Fust gecté en ung sac en Seine?
Mais où sont les neiges d'antan?"[1]

I write out these familiar lines, because Lélian preferred them; Verlaine and Villon had many features in common and were each the best poets of their age. It was M. Jules Lemaître[2] who said that the former like François Villon was *"un barbare, un sauvage, un enfant. Seulement cet enfant a une musiquo dans l'âme et à certains jours il entend des voix que nul avant lui n'avait entendues."*[3]

Take these verses:

"Voici mon coeur qui n'a battu qu'en vain,
Pour palpiter aux ronces de calvaire,
Voici mon coeur qui n'a battu qu'en vain."[4]

---

[1] Where is that wise girl Eloise,
For whom was gelded, to his great shame,
Peter Abelard, at Saint Denis,
For love of her enduring pain,
And where now is that queen again,
Who commanded them to throw
Buridan in a sack, in the Seine?
Oh, where is last year's snow?

[2] François Élie Jules Lemaître (1853–1914), critic and dramatist.
[3] A barbarian, a savage, a child. Only this child is a musician at heart and on certain days he hears voices that no one before him has heard.
[4] Thus, my heart, which has beaten in vain,
To throb with brambles of Calvary,
Here is my heart that beat in vain. "

72

Like Saint James' dog, he "returns to his own vomit again" and in his *Parallèlement* he places in opposite columns the blandishment of vice and the gloom of despair. Count Tolstoi[1] in a tale called *Mudrost* (Wisdom) recounts the history of a vagabond and drunken violinist who sees visions of heaven and plays the most adorable music. After tramping the roads throughout a winter's night, he falls dying in the snow and hears a voice from heaven calling: "'Tis thou that art the happiest and that host chosen the better part."

Verlaine talked to me of Barbey d'Aurevilly[2] whom he used to visit in his squalid room of La Rue Rousselot, so dear to Parisians, that narrow, dirty lane, bordered with gardens where Madame de la Sablière[3] came over two hundred and fifty years ago to devote her remaining years to the service of the sick and to hearken to the admonitions of her confessor, abandoned by her lover and dying of cancer of the breast, near the gardens of the Brothers of Saint Jean de Dieu. François Coppée and Paul Bourget[4] were frequent visitors and brought to Barbey d'Aurevilly the admiration of young writers for his talent.

Barbey, clad in a red dressing gown in his tiny, bare room, *splendide mendax*,[5] would say: "I have sent all my household effects into the country." (Poor man, he had none:) "It is a good

---

[1] Count Lev Nikolayevich Tolstoy (1828–1910), Russian author.
[2] Jules-Amédée Barbey d'Aurevilly (1808–1889), novelist and short story writer. He specialised in mystery tales that explored hidden motivation and hinted at evil without being explicitly concerned with anything supernatural.
[3] Marguerite de la Sablière (c.1640–1693), salonist and polymath, wife of Antoine Rambouillet, a financier and poet entrusted with the administration of the royal estates.
[4] Paul Charles Joseph Bourget (1852–1935), novelist and critic.
[5] Nobly false.

thing that Jesus was a god; as a man he would have lacked character; Hannibal[1] was a much greater personality." He never went out of his way like Baudelaire,[2] to shock people out of sheer animal mischief, nor was he malicious, but he loved sin in an abstract way and was quite devoid of passion. He wrote a review of *Fleurs du Mal* which attacked Baudelaire as a man, while exalting his verse: the latter called upon him, pretending to be very angry, while actually delighted with the review: "Sir, you have attacked my character: if I challenged you to a duel, you would not be able to fight owing to your religious views." "Not at all," said Barbey, "my passions" (which were non-existent) "are always placed by me above my convictions. I am at your disposal," and Baudelaire roared with delight. Barbey was a strong Catholic but blasphemed as a sort of compliment to the faith, saying the most sacrilegious things just to annoy God.

Like Baudelaire, Verlaine sometimes loved *esbrouffer les bourgeois*,[3] as when at Charleville in 1871 he paid extravagant compliments to some Bavarian officers in a cafe, comparing them to French *militaires* in terms far from complimentary to the latter.

In becoming Christian, he wished to put off 'the old man,' that is to exchange his previous opinions for new ones: from being republican or communist, he becomes royalist and partisan of the 'Comte de Chambord.' Thus he writes:

---

[1] Hannibal (247–c183 BC) Carthaginian general and statesman who commanded Carthage's forces against the Roman Republic.
[2] Charles Pierre Baudelaire (1821 –1867), poet, essayist and art critic. Most noted for the book of lyric poems, *Les Fleurs du Mal* (The Flowers of Evil).
[3] Shock the bourgeois.

"Et je dis, réservant d'ailleurs mon voeu suprême
Au lys de Louis Seize:
Napoléon qui fus digne du diadème
Gloire à ta mort française."[1]

in reference to the death of the prince impérial whom he had
once attacked as *"Charognard."*[2] He sent a copy of *Sagesse* to
the Empress Eugénie in atonement for his former expressions
of hate:

"Ma jeunesse élevée aux doctrines sauvages
Détesta ton enfance."

(My youth, reared in wild doctrines, loathed thy childhood.)

I wrote in my autobiography of my meeting in 1886 with
Villiers de l'Isle Adam; nothing that Verlaine wrote surpasses
his *Hymme funèbre chanté sur son cercueil*:

"Tu nous fuis comma fuit le soleil sous la mer,
Derrière un rideau lourd de pourpres léthargiques,
Las d'avoir splendi seul sur les ombres tragiques,
De la terre sans verbe et de blind éther."[3]

---

[1] "And I say, reserving moreover my supreme wish
To the lily of Louis sixteenth:
Napoleon who was worthy of the diadem
"Glory to your French death"
[2] Scavanger.
[3] "You are fleeing from the sun under the sea,"
Behind a heavy curtain of lethargic purples,
Tired of being splendidly alone over the tragic shadows,
"Of the land without verb and of blind ether."

Verlaine's Ode to Wilhelm II[1] contains:

> *"Je t'aime quand même, et même c'est bête,*
> *Mais pas bourgeois;*
> *Parceque vous êtes un honnête homme,*
> *Bien que Prussien,*
> *Parceque vous êtes un fou tout comme*
> *Moi, ce Messin!"*[2]

To his dead love, Lucien Létinois, of whom we will speak:

> *"Ami, je viens parler à toi.*
> *- Commence par prier pour moi.*
> *Alors, ta belle âme est sauvée*
> *- Mais par quel désir éprouvée?*
> *Le désir sans doute de Dieu?*
> *- Oui, rien n'est plus dur que ce feu.*
> *Comme tu dois souffrir, pauvre âme?*
> *- Rien n'est plus doux que cette flamme.*
> *Âme vers Dieu pensez à moi!*
> *- Commence par prier pour toi."*[3]

---

[1] Wilhelm II (1859–1941), German Kaiser 1888-1918.
[2] "I love you anyway, and even it's silly,"
But not bourgeois;
Because you're an honest man,
Although Prussian,
Because you're a madman just like
"Me, this native of Metz!"
[3] "Friend, I come to talk to you.
- Begin by praying for me.
So your beautiful soul is saved
"But by what desire?"
The desire no doubt of God?
"Yes, nothing is harder than this fire."
How must you suffer, poor soul?
Nothing is softer than this flame.

With more chivalry than accuracy biographers of Lélian have denied all homosexual relations between him and Lucien Létinois: Verlaine himself told me that during their short intimacy he had copulated with him times without number, *se dépensant sans compte*, [1] spending himself without limit. Lucien was above middle height, lithe and agile, with regular manly features, somewhat sunburnt, keen brown eyes which looked you straight in the face. His Ardennes origin scarcely showed itself in his speech which for a peasant was cultured. The tragic intimacy was brief, for poor Létinois was attacked by typhoid and died in a few days at the Hospital de la Pitié. Verlaine writes in *Amour* (Lucien Létinois):

"Tu me tenais, d'une voix trop lucide, des propos dour et fous, 'que étais mort, que c'était triste,' et tu serrais très fort ma main tremblante." [2]

The coffin was draped in white as for a virgin; Lucien was buried at the cemetery of Ivry at Lélian's expense. At this date he became a chloral [3] addict, and his mother, always devoted, purchased a small house at a village named, Coulommes, where unfortunately Verlaine's sociability makes enemies by political opinions too freely expressed; he is accused of being a Jesuit, a priest in disguise. Evil gossip seeks to separate mother and son; there is a quarrel between them and poor Paul is accused by neighbours of threatening to kill his mother,

---

Soul to God think of me!
"Begin by praying for yourself."
[1] Spending without counting.
[2] "You held me, in a voice too lucid, words dour and crazy, 'that was dead, that it was sad,' and you squeezed my trembling hand very hard."
[3] Chloral hydrate, the first (1832) synthetically produced sedative-hypnotic drug, commonly used in the late 19th century to treat insomnia.

when in fact he menaced suicide, with the result that Verlaine is sent to prison for a month.

Returning to Paris, he suffers from *hydarthrose au genou*,[1] has to spend months with leg encased in plaster in a miserable room of La Cour Saint François (facing la rue Moreau): *Pour comble de malheur*,[2] his mother dies and he cannot even pay to her *les derniers soins*.[3] It was then that he returns to *'la Sorcière Vert', saumonée dans un nid de flames*.[4] He wishes for death:

> *"La main droite est bien à ma droite,*
> *L'autre à ma gauche; je suis seul,*
> *Les linges dans la chambre étroite*
> *Prennent des aspects do linceul."*[5]

I am not writing the biography of Lélian, could not if I tried, for I lack any documentation and am merely here recording, so far as I recall them, his own words, except as regards the last year (or so) of his life respecting which Stéphane gave me an abridgement. If I mention Verlaine's episode at Coulommes and his unjust imprisonment for threats which he never delivered to his mother, it is because he acutely felt the imputation on his filial devotion to a woman who, one should suppose, must have been a beautiful character, always cheerful, always full of hope for the future, single-souled in her

---

[1] Arthritis of the knee.
[2] To make matters worse.
[3] Her last care.
[4] The Green Witch (i.e. Absinthe), salmon in a nest of flames.
[5] "The right hand is right on my right,
The other to my left; I am alone,
The linens in the narrow room
Take shroud aspects."

love for a wayward son with whom *les seine ménagers*[1] must have been such as to try even a Saint Theresa.[2] Lélian in his random descriptions gave to me no dates; but I imagine that the Lucien Létinois digression occurred in the early eighties, while the Coulommes imprisonment was in the spring of 1885; his Ascot ushership starting in early February 1886 and my pascal sojourn as a *Parigot* in Paname being from about April 20, 1886 to May 18.

As to Rimbaud, Lélian told me that on his enlargement (in spring of 1875) from the life *cellulairement* spent at Mons (to quote the title of his little volume bearing on the imprisonment), he sought to get in touch with him again through a common friend's good offices. Rimbaud was then in Stuttgart acquiring German – it is of course familiar ground to traverse in speaking of his extraordinary linguistic flair that none is better qualified (peradventure) to admire than the present chronicler. M. Delahaye (the friend, I believe, above mentioned), did not tell to Lélian the actual whereabouts of Rimbaud and in fact (so Verlaine fancied), was most unwilling to forward letters, fearing, only too correctly, a sinister development, but ultimately acquiesced.

Rimbaud, on learning Paul Verlaine's wish, wrote back to Delahaye that *"cela m'est égal"*[3], adding, I believe, that if 'Le Loyola' (an opprobrious nickname which mocked Lélian's faith) chose to come to Stuttgart, events could take their course. And indeed they did. The two former lovers met for

---

[1] The Seine household.
[2] Therese of Lisieux, born Marie Françoise-Thérèse Martin (1873–1897), beatified French Catholic Carmelite nun venerated for her sanctity, and practical simplicity of her approach to spiritual life.
[3] I don't care.

what Lélian called to me *"un colloque de Poissy"*[1] (referring to the futile conference between Catherine de Médicis[2] and the Protestants early in her regency) which *"n'était pas dans un sac"*[3] (as Verlaine remarked), but on the contrary began in a *brasserie* where both, but particularly Lélian, became morosely intoxicated. From the beer-garden, arguing and gesticulating, they took a long night walk out of Stuttgart and found themselves in the moonlight on the banks of the Necker with an admirable distant view of the Black Forest. Lélian took advantage of the solitude to demand of Rimbaud a nocturnal pedication, in those idyllic (almost Theocritean) surroundings, a sort of wild Eclogue: Rimbaud refused; the two fought with fists (albeit, perhaps, the climate of Stuttgart in December is hardly ideal for open air sexual manoeuvres). Verlaine was beaten and sank unconscious on the river bank, while the former, not undamaged in the encounter, left him there, as he supposed, to die.

He was found in what seemed a moribund condition by some worthy peasants, truly good Samaritans, who convoyed him to their hut and nursed him back to life, refusing all remuneration. Speaking from my own experience, I doubt if anywhere in Europe one would find kinder people than the peasants of Württemberg and Bayern: the suspicion of strangers so prevalent in France, Prussia, Italy, to say nothing of Poland or Russia is entirely absent. Parts of Albion (such as Cornwall and Wales) compare with them, but it is certainly not an 'English' characteristic.

---

[1] A Poissy symposium.
[2] Catherine de Medici (1519–1589), Queen Consort of King Henry II of France.
[3] Was not in a bag.

After *la bataille de Stuttgart*, as poor Lélian denominated it, the two protagonists exchanged rude letters, mainly on religious differences, which only added fuel to the flame of hate. The tragedy of their relationship was played out and thereafter Lélian poured out the stream of his invective and sarcasm against Rimbaud, imitating (in exaggerated form) the latter's pronounced *ardennais* dialect. As Rimbaud's worldwide Odyssey progresses, Lélian addresses a series of Martial-like[1] stinging epigrams *à son intention*[2] for example (Rimbaud is supposed to be speaking):

"J'ai promené ma gueule infecte au Sénégal,
Et vu Cinq-Hélèn' (zut à Badinguet).
Un' rud' noce!
Mais tout ça c'est pas sérillieux;
Je rêve et négoce..."

(I have taken my stinking mouth to the Senegal and seen Saint Helena – pish for Napoléon III. I had a great time, but that's not the serious part of it all: I dream and do business). Verlaine exaggerates *le grasseyement*[3] of Rimbaud.

An old man, alone with his memories, in destitution and (perhaps in causeless) dread of losing his reason, confuses dates and unconsciously may even misremember occurrences. It is a fact that I met Rimbaud but it was not *chez* Lélian. There was a certain Bibi Rimbot, a cobbler of artistic and scholarly instincts, whom Verlaine affected, until the jealousy of Eugénie caused his exclusion: 'twas he of whom I had thought,

---

[1] As per Marcus Valerius Martialis aka Martial (c38–c102 AD), Roman poet best known for his twelve books of Epigrams.
[2] To him.
[3] The burr of his accent.

but my meeting (once only) with Rimbaud was *chez* Mallarmé in Rue de Rome during my *pascal* holiday of 1886, on an evening when Verlaine was otherwise preoccupied. I was too young to derive much impression, but recall a giant stature, thick lips which disclosed, when he chose, a frank smile, a slightly tilted nose, a high forehead concealed by ample chestnut hair, rosy cheeks, deepest blue eyes that suggested an innocent child-like nature. That he limped slightly (but it may have been affectation). I remember but recall not traits of illness. He must have been *de passage*, perhaps from Sumatra or Cyprus, in Paris, took very little notice of me except to smile slightly (making a gesture which, though it conveyed nothing to me then, recalled Caligula's *vis-à-vis* Chereas) (*vide* Suetonius' Life of Emperor Caius Caesar) when Stéphane told him I was Verlaine's English protegé. The latter made no comment on this accidental encounter and at that time, of course, I knew nothing of the tragic history which divided the two forever.

To conclude this appreciation, I must add a word about Lélian's last days: Eugénie bullied him most mercilessly except when he was able to glean a little money from his publishers or from the subventions of Le Ministre d'Instruction and the subscription raised by *Le Figaro* (at François Coppée's suggestion). The ill-assorted couple moved from 16 Rue Saint Victor to slightly more affluent surroundings at 39 Rue Descartes which Eugénie had furnished *à bon compte*.[1] It is said that the chairs were all gilden in some magic fluid which stained the nether garments of visitors with a shade of gold,

---

[1] Cheaply.

provoking the *bon mot*: *"Croirait-on que chez un poète on se oeuvre d'or?"*[1]

Rue Descartes saw many visitors during those last months, Mallarmé, Léon Dierx, Huysmans, Catulle Mendès, Mornand,[2] Mme. Maurice Bernhardt,[3] Jules Gautier,[4] 'chef de cabinet de M. Combes.'[5] In October 1895 Verlaine developed bronchitis and lung congestion; he lingered on for three months but knew that he was dying and asked for a priest. Medical charges had again exhausted his funds and he was dead before Fr. 500 accorded to him *d'urgence*[6] by *l'Administration des Beaux Arts*[7] arrived in time to pay a portion of the funeral expenses. Mallarmé told me that M. Raymond Poincard[8] contributed an equal sum, *un beau geste*[9] which would have gratified dear Lélian whose hatred of the republicans was notorious.

Late in the evening of that January 8 he was lying exhausted on his *grabat,*[10] when suddenly the agony began. Eugénie entered the room, in her obtuse, though cunning, crassness, failed to take in the situation and hurled invective at the

---

[1] "Would it be believed that a poet would work with gold?"
[2] Henri Eugène Mornand (1852–1921), journalist and literary critic.
[3] Princess Maria Teresa Wirginia Klotylda Jablonowska (1863-1910), painter. Married Maurice Bernhardt, playwright and theatre director, who was the son of actress Sarah Bernhardt and the Belgian Prince Henri-Maximilien-Joseph de Ligne.
[4] Jules Joseph Alexandre Gautier (1856–1936).
[5] Émile Justin Louis Combes (1835–1921), radical and anti-clerical Prime Minister of France (1902-1905).
[6] Of emergency.
[7] By emergency by the Administration of Fine Arts.
[8] Raymond Poincaré, (1860–1934), statesman who served three times as 58th Prime Minister of France, and as President of France, 1913 to 1920.
[9] A nice gesture.
[10] Bed.

agonisant,[1] who rolled out of bed and in the intervals of the death rattle groaned: *"Un prêtre . . ah! je n'ai même pas de prêtre!"*[2]

Eugénie rushed out to get help: neighbours lifted him back to bed. His last word was "François", by which, Mallarmé believed, he meant Français (but in my judgment he meant François Villon, his prototype of whom he often spoke to me as François.) using the word of old tradition with the o instead of a, in the sense of the old ballade: *"Je meurs français: adieu!"*[3] Be this as it may, Eugénie interpreted the appeal to be addressed to M. François Coppée who had, indeed, years before been one of Lélian's intimates and had, as we have seen, recently induced the ill-fated M. Calmette of *Le Figaro* to solicit a subscription in his columns for the dying genius.

Coppée was touched by what he thought to be this dying remembrance, spoke of it at the funeral oration and brought *une couronne*[4] which he placed himself on Verlaine's breast. He lay there, clad in *l'habit* with a black tie, clasping the crucifix and rosary. His expression bore a frown; but his head reclined peacefully on his shoulder, like a child after a scene with its mother. He was said to have called for "Edmond" at the moment of death, but it was not likely to be I of whom he thought, although perhaps not impossible.

I arrived in Paris too late for the funeral, whereat all parties and schools wore represented, symbolists, naturalists and *décadents.* His two mistresses, Eugénie and Philomèle, were

---

[1] Dying man.
[2] "A priest." Ah! "I don't even have a priest!"
[3] I die Français, goodbye!
[4] A crown.

both there in widows' weeds, shoulder to shoulder in a sort of temporary truce.

"The poet in a golden age was born,
With golden stare above,
Dowered with the hate of hate, the scorn of scorn,
The love of love." (Tennyson).

Dear Lélian: he was not of my dearest friends, but is associated with my dearest memories; and I love him all the more for the erotic emotion of a moment (believe me: the sole occasion) toward myself which I have frankly narrated, as he, who was the soul of candour, would have wished. He was the most tender hearted of men even in his mood of violent invective. Angry with everything, he ended in being angry with nothing: I am happy to believe that should have attracted a temperament unlike my own, except perhaps in economic inexactitude and indifference to *le spese*:[1] I lack his genius, *tout en ayant à rougir de honte jusqu'au blanc des yeux comme lui aussi pour la série de crimes passionels (peut-être?) que j'ai commis au cours d'une vie également maiheureuse, mais plus mouvementée que la sienne, vraiment telle qus peu de gens ont jamais menée. Me trompé-je?*[2]
'Judicabunt alii, non ego.'

"Where are they tending? - A God
Marshall'd them, gave them their goal. -

---

[1] Expenses.
[2] while having to blush with shame until the white of the eyes like him also for the series of crimes of passion (perhaps?) that I committed during a life also happy but more eventful than his, really such as few people have ever led. Did I deceive you?

Ah! but the way is so long!
Years they have been in the wild!" (Arnold)

8. VI. 43.

3. SUPPLEMENT
Oscar Wilde and Others

Oscar had no noble traits: he was jealous of rivals' successes and I recall one evening in May 1894 on the Boulevard des Capucines when the London journals had just arrived with the news of a triumph at the Saint James' Theatre of a play by Henry Arthur Jones[1] named *The Masqueraders*, Wilde started his favourite theme of the stupidity of the English race, to which William Watson had retorted: "Would any but a stupid race have made the fuss about you that we did?" One evening, when he had "the vine leaves in his hair", or at least *avait décidément le casque* (mildly the worse for wine), he became brutally frank, looking like the satyr he was, telling me that I was commonplace. "My poor Trelawny, you are simply banal. I am sorry for you, because you are so ugly!" "But the other day (*'fis-je'*), you hyperbolised in informing me that I was *coruscant d'esprit*:[2] you don't like people who stand up to you: as long as I am a sort of *fidus Achates*,[3] a *comparse*[4] to you as the *protagoniste*,[5] no praise is too high; but just because Maurice Barrès showed the bad taste of preferring to talk to me yesterday, when you wanted to monopolise him, you must needs explain me away as banal and uncomely, though you sang, a different song when you eulogised my "pomegranate lips" and "alluring pedicandial presentment."[6]

---

[1] Henry Arthur Jones (1851–1929), English dramatist.
[2] Coruscant of mind.
[3] Faithful friend.
[4] Stooge.
[5] The most important person.
[6] Alluring sodomitical presentation. From pedico (Latin): sodomise.

Wilde's ego was not interesting like Barrès '*moi*,' nor brilliant as his mother Lady Wilde who was certainly one of the greatest conversationalists of the day. About a year before Oscar's downfall, she told no how she trembled for his future and quite rightly blamed the fatal influence of Bozie: Douglas who now professes to be Wilde's innocent victim.

Max Beerbohm produced a cartoon of Oscar and Bozie copulating, the expression on the former's face resembling the goat of Pompeii, while Douglas the willing pathic was deliciously satirised; R. S. Hitchens [1] wrote *The Green Carnation* with Esme Amaranthe who in every trait, gluttony, self-love, *dénigrement* of friends and foes was an undisguised portrait of Wilde. The latter would say, when Robbie Ross, Henry James,[2] Haldane[3] and myself tried to point out warnings ahead: "The Treasury[4] will always give me twenty-four hours to leave the country just as they did in Lord Henry Somerset's case." [5] After the collapse of his libel action against Lord Queensberry,[6] Haldane did indeed try to exert his unique

---

[1] Robert Smythe Hichens (1864–1950), English journalist, novelist, critic, playwright. A protégé of Sir Alexander ('Alec') Nelson Hood, 5th Duke of Bronté, he later established a domestic ménage à trois with Swiss writer John Knittel and his wife.

[2] Henry James (1843–1916), Anglo-American author.

[3] Richard Haldane, Viscount Haldane (1856–1928), Scottish Liberal and later Labour imperialist politician, lawyer and philosopher.

[4] Prosecutions by the Crown (i.e. the British Government) were then commonly referred to as being undertaken by the Treasury.

[5] Lord Henry Richard Charles Somerset (1849–1932), Conservative M.P. and popular song composer. Second son of the 8th Duke of Beaufort. He lived in exile following an affair, which his wife exposed, with Henry 'Harry' Smith, the seventeen year old son of a shipping magnate.

[6] John Sholto Douglas, 9th Marquess of Queensberry (1844–1900), pugnacious and erratic Scottish nobleman noted for his outspoken views;

influence on Lord Rosebery[1] to connive at Wilde's departure, but the latter delayed several fatal hours and it was then too late.

I had always regarded Oscar as a physical coward; but Charles Freer,[2] the Maecenas of artists, told me that in the eighties he and a friend were staying in the neighbourhood of a mining town near Denver, Colorado, where Wilde was billed for a *conférence*. Freer naturally went to hear the lecture, found an audience mainly composed of the wildest and roughest miner type. When Wilde started his address, a miner from the back benches fired point-blank at the sunflower wearing esthete, missed him by a few inches, and Wilde held up his hand: "Next!" which brought down the audience and he received a stirring ovation.

Oscar was mad with jealousy at Mme. Bernhardt's[3] penchant for me (the fact being that the Diva disliked him). Maurice had told me that his mother wished me to accompany him to meet the steamer which brought her back from her latest tour in America. So we went to Cherbourg together, Queen Sarah displayed *une caractéristique chaleur d'imagination*:[4] as she saw us on the landing peer, she made incomparable histrionic gestures and exclaimed from the deck: *"Ah!: c'est vraiment toi,*

---

for lending his name to the Queensberry Rules that form the basis of modern boxing, and his role in the downfall of Oscar Wilde.
[1] Archibald Philip Primrose, 5th Earl of Rosebery, 1st Earl of Midlothian, (1847–1929), British Liberal politician and Prime Minister from March 1894 to June 1895. Married Hannah de Rothschild, and had issue.
[2] Charles Lang Freer (1854–1919) was an American industrialist, art collector, and patron.
[3] Sarah Bernhardt, born Henriette-Rosine Bernard (1844–1923), famous French actress.
[4] A characteristic warmth of imagination.

Edmond, at toi mon bien aimé Maurice. Comme je suis bienheureuse de vous revoir tous les deux!" [1] Then on descending the gangway: *"Embrasse moi mon Maurice: c'est le rêve: quel bonheur indicible! Viens Edmond toi aussi, je vais t'embrasser."* [2] In any other than Sarah, the scene would have savoured of the foot-lights, but from the point of view of the passengers and crowds on the landing stage, it was *un clou des plus réussis!* [3]

After Wilde's return from prison, it is pleasing to record that both Mme. Bernhardt and Maurice with his dear little wife befriended the now mentally and physically afflicted author by many eleemosynary [4] but anonymous contributions. Yet he died on November 30, 1900 fortified by the last rites of Holy Church in apparent indigence, although the income of Francs 400 *per mensem* [5] with which his friends had provided him should at that time have sufficed to maintain him in moderate comfort; but the money may have been wasted on the wine (ay! and the cocaine) of his predilection. The time was not yet when Robbie Ross, his literary executor, could return to his estate royalties of over £4,500 from theatrical and literary productions and, I believe, they still provide a regular income. Oscar's actual debts only slightly exceeded £2,500, or say £3,500 with accumulated interest.

---

[1] "Ah, it's really you, Edmond, my beloved Maurice. How blessed I am to see you both. "

[2] "Kiss me my Maurice: it's the dream: what unspeakable happiness! Come Edmond too, I'll kiss you. "

[3] A nail of the most successful.

[4] Charitable.

[5] Every month.

STÉPHANE MALLARMÉ

"The tragic tone," Mallarmé pontifically enunciated at a visit to him after Verlaine's death, "which fills so much of the greatest poetry, is increased by the seer's capacity of apocalyptic vision; his dreams render him ever discontented. He who has captured a glimpse of immortal flowers of fancy can only feel a diminished joy in the evanescent and fading."

"An inspired singer sees the gleaming spires of a city not made with hands; he derives his breath from an ampler ether, a diviner air; the common life connotes for him little savour and his secret thoughts haunt him and impel him to loneliness."

"To the poet rhythms fill the head like music and the words which he applies to them are being beautifully sung as an accompaniment. It is the wordless rhythms that entrance him and he hears the poem singing itself as it were by vibrations on the printed page. Poets are musicians who are denied the fullest expression of sound; so must needs avail themselves of the medium which most resembles song."

"My chiefest emotions emanate from the flesh; I am sensuous and sensitive to sound, taste and colour. A great poet has noble things to say and expresses them nobly; a literary artist loves the music of words and is influenced by his predecessors in the art of expression. The mystic seeks agonies of mortification, because pain is a condition of sanctity. It is succeeded by illumination which reveals things hidden. It was said of Baudelaire that he loved to 'tread upon the brink of meaning' and used unfamiliar words which attracted to them the attention due to things."

Mallarmé recounted to me many anecdotes of Charles Baudelaire who loved to shock the bourgeois. One day Mallarmé heard him say to a postal clerk: "Did you ever eat a baby's brains? They are delicious and taste even better than half-ripe walnuts." Dining one evening at a Duval restaurant, Baudelaire shouted at the top of his voice: "The day after murdering my poor father, I...."

Baudelaire, said Mallarmé, was a great Christian: those who accuse him of inventing new types of depravity and strange sins are paying for both him and his times compliments that neither deserve. Primitive man, *la Bête humaine*, [1] the contemporary of the mammoth and the pterodactyl, left to posterity no novelties to invent in the matter of vice. Baudelaire is the poet of sin, not of vice; his morality is as theological as that of Saint Augustine of Hippo.[2] Like a monk before his breviary, he rises from his couch to exclaim:

> "Cedant tenebrae lumini
> Et nox diurno sideri;
> Ut culpa quam nox intulit
> Lucas labescat munere."

(May darkness yield to light and the night to the day star, so that the sin which the night brought with it may fade by favour of the light.)

---

[1] The human beast.
[2] St. Augustine of Hippo (354–430), theologian, philosopher, and the bishop of Hippo Regius in Numidia, Roman North Africa. His writings influenced the development of Western philosophy and Western Christianity.

His sense of carnal impurity never leaves him, and *Les Fleurs du Mal* represent the poetical expression of the doctrine of original sin. He regards sensual aberration with the minuteness of a theologian or a physician. To Baudelaire the smallest of sins connotes the direst of consequences; a drab encountered by night in a mean street is invested spiritually with a tragic grandeur; her soul is in danger and she is peopled by a legion of devils, while the mystic host of heaven trembles for her salvation. For all eternity the vilest sexual commerce shall echo and re-echo; the sensuality of an hour finds place in the chronicles of hell but should deface any human record.

Baudelaire loves the sin and finds pleasure in damning himself, but his sensuality only goes far enough to ensure his damnation. He is debauched because debauchery is so deliciously impious; lust is quite alien from his composition. He desires to offend God and to make the angels weep; were it not for this ambition he would leave the woman alone. But he wishes to interest heaven and hell by his sins; even his smallest impurities must needs take on the appearance of something considerable. His heart and intellect never believed in religion, but his soul was entirely Christian. An idol rudely carved by a native of Ashanti was shown to him by a naval officer who remarked on its hideousness and threw it down with disdain. "Take care," said Baudelaire, "it may be the true God!"

Baudelaire associates love and death; but the corruption which the pulpit dwells upon to inspire loathing of carnal things is for this human vampire a savoury and a *hors d'oeuvre*: the odour of a corpse connotes to him an aphrodisiac aroma. His poems are beautiful like the divinity of the Arabian Nights whose loveliness set men's hearts aflame, but whose nights were spent at graveyards where she battened on the flesh of corpses.

How exquisite are the lines of Baudelaire to the lost "unfortunates":

> "*Descendez, descendez, lamentables victimes,*
> *Descendez le chemin de l'enfer éternel!*
> *Plongez au plus profond du gouffre où tous les crimes*
> *Flagellés par un vent qui ne vient pas du ciel,*
> *Bouillonnent pêle-mêle avec un bruit d'orage.*
> *. . . Faites votre destin, âmes désordonnées,*
> *Et fuyez l'infini que vous portez en vous.*"[1]

Take his lines _Sur un chiffonnier_:

> "*Oui, ces gens harcelés de chagrins de ménage,*
> *Moulus par le travail at tourmentés par l'âge,*
> *Ereintés et pliant sous un tas de débris*
> *Vomissement confus de l'énorme Paris,*
> *Reviennent. . . .* "[2]

---

[1] Descend, descend, lamentable victims,
Descend the path of eternal hell!
Dive deep into the abyss where all crimes
Flagellated by a wind that does not come from the sky,
Bubbling pell-mell with a thunderous sound.
. . . Make your destiny, disorderly souls,
And flee from the infinite that you carry in you.
[2] Yes, these people harassed with household grief,
Milled by work and tormented by age,
Frozen and bending under a pile of debris
Confused vomit of the enormous Paris,
Return. . . .

It is unjust to reproach Baudelaire as the author of our present literary degeneration; true is it that *décadence*, disfigures his verse, but *Les Fleurs du Mal* none the less constitute a luminous image borne on the wings of poetry.

Mallarmé declared that a book should have three distinct significations, for the intellectual giant, the ordinary reader, for the casual person who does not even cut the pages. Reversing the order, the third sense which is infinitely subtle and pleasurable shall be the reward of the esoteric adept who finds hidden meaning in the written page. The second sense will be apparent to the reader who makes use of a paper knife; while the third, purely gross and literal, will apply to the idler who pauses beneath the galleries of the Odéon and besides the book-stalls to read without cutting the pages.

Naturalism began during the second empire with *Madame Bovary*,[1] 'un chef d'oeuvre:' at its inception it was a salutary reversion to nature and a just revenge upon the romantics. Unhappily naturalism became subjected to a talented, virile, but narrow and brutal intellect which was devoid of sober-mindedness and *de la mesure qui est tout l'art*.[2] Was it not M. Zola who declared of his work: "*J'ai divisé mes 'visites' en trois groupes?*"[3]

With Zola naturalism degenerated into ignoble vulgarity. Its platitudes, its lack of intellectual beauty and of plasticity of form, its ugliness and gross (ay crass) stupidity disquieted delicate spirits. The violence of the reaction excited *le*

---

[1] The debut novel of Gustave Flaubert (1821–1880).
[2] And of the measure which is all art.
[3] I divided my 'visits' into three groups.

symbolisme; even as during *la décadence romaine* the grossest sensuality engendered asceticism.

Zola is absurdly easy to imitate; his method is always visible, his effect invariably exaggerated, his philosophy absolutely childish. He believes that by shocking the moral conventions he has achieved perfection. It is pride that hastens literary decadence; Claudian[1] was far better satisfied with himself than Virgil. The truth is that we have too many works of fiction, and they are too long. The shorter stories survive the longest: the world will always read *Daphnis at Chloé, la Princesse de Clèves, Candide, Marion Lescaut, Paul et Virginie*, which are no thicker than the little finger. To soar through the ages requires wings light as Ariel's: it is in *la nouvelle* that is best exhibited *le vrai génie français qui est prompt et concis.*[2] Elegance, facility and quick movement: *c'est là la parfaite politesse d'un écrivain.*[3] A novel ought to be read at a sitting: it suits the publisher that the romances of today run into 350 pages, far more than the subject requires. Remember that our works are not our own: they grow within us but their roots are 'dans le sol nourricier.'

The most original writer borrows more than he invents: there is no individual tendency in the *Iliad* or in the *Odyssey* which have been composed by several hands without a single distinctive imprint. Sophocles'[4] plays avoid presentation of the author's personality; but with Euripides[5] begins the

---

[1] Claudius Claudianus, aka Claudian (c. 370– c.404AD), Roman poet.
[2] The true french genius who is prompt and concise.
[3] This is the perfect politeness of a writer.
[4] Sophocles (c. 497/6 –406/5 BC), Greek tragedian; author of *Antigone, Oedipus Rex, Electra*, etc.
[5] Euripides (c408–406 BC), Greek tragedian; author of *Medea, The Trojan Women*, etc.

personal element and he must needs inform us of his views on womankind and on philosophy. His indiscretion, interesting in itself, makes the beginning of a decadence. So is it with the Middle Ages that M. Leconte de Lisle[1] pursues with his hate: if we knew more about them, we should accord to them more consideration. They contained men who may have done evil, as is inseparable from life, but who did still more good in preparing the better world we are today enjoying. They effected, under conditions which invasions and race diversity rendered difficult, a real new organisation of human society at the price of astounding efforts. Their military victories have never been equalled; above all the spirit of chivalry which more than anything honours humanity. They served great causes without stint, violent perhaps but working to found an order of justice in Europe.

The Middle Ages present jurists redolent with learning and equity: the legislative work of Saint Louis'[2] epoch is admirable: before the Hundred Years' War[3] the condition of the peasants in France was good. There were sublime nameless artisans who built cathedrals; there were monks who were sages, leading a hidden life, book in hand; there were theologians like the Angelic Doctor[4] who pursued through scholastic subtleties a lofty ideal; there was a Shepherdess[5] who led a king and a

---

[1] Charles Marie René Leconte de Lisle (1818–1894), French poet of the Parnassian movement.

[2] Louis IX of France (1214–1270), aka Saint Louis; reigned 1226 to 1270.

[3] The Hundred Years' War (1337–1453) was the series of conflicts waged between the House of Plantagenet and its cadet House of Lancaster, the rulers of England, and the House of Valois over the right to rule France.

[4] St. Thomas Aquinas (1225–1274), Italian Dominican friar who was an immensely influential philosopher, theologian, and jurist.

[5] Joan of Arc (c. 1412–1431), saint and martyr who supported Charles VII to recover France from English domination late in the Hundred Years' War.

chivalry in her train. Their works were the preparation of ours: even their errors were those of courage and simplicity. If we are better than they, is it not the highest eulogy we can offer to them? By their fruits you shall know them. May it be said of us that our descendants are better than we!

Mallarmé told me that as a student of fifteen he had been taken by Flaubert to visit Alfred de Musset[1] *à l'hospice des aliénés*[2] where he was dying, attended by his faithful valet François, of general paralysis. The weather was inclined to rain, and as they walked up and down the garden paths, Musset picked up a number of small pebbles and with his cane poked little holes in the turf for their reception. *"Le temps est à la pluie: je vais semer tous ces cailloux qui devront se transformer en une ribambelle de petits Musset tout en poussant d'une maniere des plus rapides."*[3]

Before M. Guy de Maupassant's [4] insanity had assumed a dangerous form (he died in 1893) Stéphane remembered a call he and I had paid upon him in January 1891 when he was afflicted by painful Priapism and an irreducible state of erection which could find, so he said, no outlet by the obvious channels. Mallarmé animadverted upon an article of his *sur l'Esthétique*[5] which declares that a good novel may be written in a hundred ways but can only be judged in one. The creator

---

[1] Alfred Louis Charles de Musset-Pathay (1810 –1857) dramatist, poet, and novelist.
[2] At the hospice of the insane.
[3] The weather is in the rain: I'm going to sow all these pebbles that will have to transform into a string of small Musset while pushing in a fast manner.
[4] Henri René Albert Guy de Maupassant (1850–1893) author of the Naturalist school.
[5] On Aesthetics.

is a free man, but the critic is a helot. [1] There exists no hidebound rule for producing a work but there are rules for criticising it. The critic is bound to appreciate the result by the nature of the effort; he must search for the qualities which differentiate it from previous romances. He must divest himself of tendencies but at the same time he is bound to understand, appreciate and explain contrary temperaments and opposing trends. In a word, Maupassant deprives the critic of his freedom and his personal sentiment. To the critic is denied all sensual emotion: 'twill be a death in life, a moral law of Draconian rigour.

But, said Mallarmé, how is one to appreciate a writer's effort without considering to what it tends? It is an impossible task to judge by pure reason works which owe their origin to sentiment. Surely criticism is in itself a work of art and is entitled to the same freedom that Maupassant accords to so-called original works. To appreciate works of art critics possess only sentiment and reason, the most inexact and unscientific of instruments; hence our criticism can never be elevated to the rigorous dignity of a science, but must needs ever hover in uncertainty. It can follow no immutable law nor pronounce an irrevocable judgment. After all, criticism is a work of art which distinguishes an intellectual age; it is a branch, honourable and learned, of the tree of learning grown hoary, as befits a decadent society.

Stéphane dilated on the thanklessness of *la vie littéraire et artiste*,[2] how each would like to be the man and leave the artist,

---

[1] Serf.
[2] Literary and artistic life.

"win the man's joy, lose the artist's sorrow." Dante[1] prepared to paint a picture: Rafaello Sanzio[2] wrote a century of sonnets; each of them would fain forgo his proper dowry. Does he write, he would turn to painting; does he paint: he would write a poem. Mallarmé had no love for Albion; in fact, it is the simple truth to say that, except Madame Sarah,[3] I found not a single Frenchman or Frenchwoman who at that time had a kind word for my country, though many, like Stéphane, recognised the individualism of English literature of which he had a very considerable knowledge, sometimes through translations not always very adequate, though he read English with great facility and of course was for thirty years professor of that tongue, besides giving *conférences* at Oxford in English as well as in French. He quoted with approval:

"Who thanks with brief thanksgiving
Whatever gods there be,
That no life lives for ever,
That dead men rise up never,
That even the weariest river
Winds somewhere safe to sea."[4]

Early in 1896, Mallarmé was making a longer sojourn in the Rue de Rome than usual - he was usually restless in Paris and yearned for the sounds of the country, especially Bretagne - and I paid to him many visits, often finding Huysmans sipping absinthe and eager to discuss religion and sex. It is

---

[1] Dante Alighieri, aka Dante (c. 1265 –1321), Italian poet, writer and philosopher.
[2] Raffaello Sanzio da Urbino, aka Raphael (1483 –1520), Italian painter and architect of the High Renaissance.
[3] i.e. actress Sarah Bernhardt.
[4] Swinburne. E.B.

entirely to the honour of Huysmans, who disliked Oscar Wilde, condemned his writings and resented his unblushing *plagiat*[1] (as I have elsewhere recounted from *A Rebours*) to have expressed *la sympathie d'un confrere* for his "persecutions" and to have most chivalrously handed to me Fr.500 *comme un denier d'aumône,*[2] for the stricken man of letters upon his release from Reading gaol, charging me not to reveal the donor. *"Je doute qu'il l'accepte,"* said he, *et moi de répondre: "vous inquiétez pas, it est certain qu'il l'acceptera sans même demander le nom de son bienfaiteur."*[3] And it was so: Oscar accepted the money in due course as a sort of obligation which was his by right: *"une dette due et tardivement ramboursée au génie."*[4] How different was he from my dear Lélian who wept over the eleemosynary doles of his friends "que je ne mérite assurément guère!"[5] It is pleasant *d'avoir affair 'à un homme comme it faut'*[6] like Paul Verlaine: as for Oscar, his misfortunes command my sympathy, but for the man, the less said, the better.

Mallarmé was a distant relative of Gustave Flaubert and was always welcome at the latter's modest abode, Rue de Murillo. Flaubert was of enormous stature, broad-shouldered, sonorous and boisterous of speech, dressed like a pirate of fiction with the ample jersey of a seaman and *des braies amples comme une jupe*[7] which reached to his heels. His wrinkled face, his red cheeks, clear eyes, long drooping sandy mustache, all

---

1 Plagiarism.
2 As a penny of alms.
3 "I doubt he will accept it. " And I answer: "do not worry, it is certain that he will accept it without even asking the name of his benefactor. "
4 A debt due and belatedly paid back to the genius.
5 That I certainly do not deserve!
6 To deal with a good man.
7 Baggy trousers like a skirt.

suggested the Viking, although he was only Norman through his mother, but he was a 'throw back' to the comrades of Rollo,[1] a drunkard full of generosity and elan, a disciple of Odin,[2] chivalrous to the weak while he plundered the strong, one who loved to slaughter priests and to loot the churches of their treasures. He was angry with everything and had always some injustice to avenge. He resembled his favourite hero, Don Quixote. His little 'salon' with its Turkish carpet figuratively ran blood from the multitudinous bourgeois whom the worthy giant had slaughtered with his vituperations. He hated the present day and would like to have lived in the time of Agamemnon, although possibly men suffered from boredom no less than we who are the heirs of all the ages, the latest breed of time. Apart from the barbarous ages, his chiefest predilection was for Shakespeare and the gorgeous East. It was characteristic of him that he loved Caliban![3]

Neither Mallarmé nor Huysmans wore much impressed by Aubrey's decision to enter the Church, the former as a professing but luke-warm Catholic, the latter a *dévot au plus haut degré.* [4] *"On aurait mauvaise grâce de croire,"* said Huysmans, *"que ce bon Beardsley ne soit pas sincère, mais je m'imagine que c'est le côté cérémonial du culte qui lui fait appel."*[5]

---

[1] Rollo (c. 860–c. 930 AD), Viking and first ruler of Normandy.
[2] God of Norse mythology.
[3] Son of the witch Sycorax, in Shakespeare's *The Tempest*. Half human, half monster.
[4] Devoted to the highest degree.
[5] " It would be bad grace to think that this good Beardsley was not sincere, but I imagine that it is the ceremonial aspect of the worship which appeals to him. "

"You and he," said Stéphane to me, "have '*certains penchants en commun: comment va-t-il arranger tout cela avec son confesseur'?"* [1] This remark reminded me of Frederic The Great's *bon mot à propos* the partition of Poland with the Empress Marie Thérèse: "How did Her Majesty satisfy her confessor regarding our joint spoliation?" So I took up the cudgels for Aubrey, pointing out that, if homosexuality is forbidden by Holy Church, he, at least, was not guilty of it, except in the sense that "the world knows of no higher love than that of brother unto brother." Huysmans, a brother convert, was gladly convinced, but Stéphane attributed Aubrey's new ecstatic devotion to the state of his health. "Weak souls and feeble natures derive comfort from religion."

Few actresses, and perhaps no diva of that *genus irritabile* [2] whereof is *decus at dolor theatri*, "the stage's glory and its grief" (Martial), can have been so generous as Mme Sarah Bernhardt toward her comrades who seek the brief *honours des Blanches*. [3] Knowing that I was on my way to Russia, Madame Sarah wished to give to me letters to the artist world of Saint Petersburg and Moscow as (in a humble way) her comrade and collaborator. So in this kindly motive she arranged at her residence for a reading of *Antony and Cleopatra* in translation, graciously allotting to me the part of Antony which I read in English. Mme Bernhardt repeated the reading in May 1897 at the end of the Paris season on a rather larger scale and very kindly assured me (and in fact told the Empress Eugénie the same) that my portrayal had greatly gained in the interval and

---

[1] "...certain tendencies in common: how will he arrange all this with his confessor? "
[2] Irritable race.
[3] Unclear. Possibly: unofficial honours.

acquired a more Oriental suggestion, perhaps due to my stay in Russia.

Parmi les invités[1] on this occasion were both Stephané and Huysmans, but the audience was not exclusively artistic nor professional though in no sense 'Tout Paris'. The Faubourg Saint-Germain was well represented, while no less a person than the great Foreign Minister and historian M. Gabriel Hanotaux[2] honoured 'la lecture'. It was then that I had the honour to meet M. Gaston Boissier,[3] the secretary of the Academy, that exquisite humanist who, next to Pater, influenced me in my Latin studies more than any other. Both *Cicéron et ses amis* and *L'Opposition sous les Césars* were familiar to me as household words; and I loved his *Promenades Archéologiques*. If I err not, la Duchess d'Alencon[4] who perished in the fire at a charity Bazaar not long afterwards, was also of the audience; but I was not presented to her.

Sarah was simply divine; never shall I forget her "I have immortal longings in me" and "Dost thou not see my baby at my breast that sucks the nurse asleep". Perhaps I did not prove utterly unworthy of the compliment she had paid to me, when I read the lines: "The long day's task is done and we must

---

[1] Among the guests.
[2] Albert Auguste Gabriel Hanotaux (1853–1944), statesman and historian.
[3] Marie-Louis-Antoine-Gaston Boissier (1823–1908), classical scholar; secretary of the French Academy.
[4] Sophie Charlotte Augustine, Duchess d'Alencon (1847–1897), daughter of Duke Maximilian Joseph in Bavaria and sister of Empress Elisabeth of Austria, wife of Prince Ferdinand, Duke of Alençon, grandson of King Louis-Philippe I of France. The fire in which she died occurred in large warehouse: started by ether lamps used for a cinematograph installation, it killed 126, including many aristocratic women.

sleep. . . The sevenfold shield of Ajax cannot keep the battery from my heart." Sarah was pleased with me and M. Hanotaux said: *"Je vous en fais mon compliment; vous vous êtes bien tiré d'affaire, c'etait pour vous une situation assez désavantageuse que d'avoir à lire ce grand rôle avec elle pour collaboratrice. Mais votre interprétation d'Antoine m'intéressait."*[1]

Mallarmé thought (and Huysmans also, though - in a measure - complimentary) that I was not sensual enough nor sufficiently Oriental, as Antony was more Dionysiac reveller than Roman, a lover of eastern hyperbole and luxurious metaphor. (Antony who loved Octavian's bon mot: "If my tool – *mentula*, the organ in erection – had been one inch longer, Fulvia would have stopped the civil war.") Turning to a very different subject, after our return to the Rue de Rome, he asked me, as the Old Buddha was to do many years later, wherein the *jouissance*[2] of pathic copulation with a male subsisted. "The active homosexual pleasure is comprehensible, though to me a sealed book; the passive gratification seems simply non-existent, not even a mirage, nor a chimera, but *quelque chose de controuvé.*"[3]

In reply I suggested as the cause some misplacement of the sexual instinct, *une difformité psychologique,* a passion diverted into an alien channel. But how explain the unexplainable? If it be true that *'le seul philosophe qui puisse sonder les gouffres de l'amour est bien lui qui s'en désintéresee',*[4]

---

[1] "I congratulate you on it; you have done well, it was a disadvantageous situation for you to have to read this great role with her as a collaborator. But I was interested in your interpretation of Antoine."
[2] Enjoyment.
[3] Something counterfeited.
[4] The only philosopher who can fathom the abyss of love is he who is disinterested in it.

still less are we (not philosophers) able to account for the unruly wills and affections Which, while bringing zest and savour to life, convey in their train "more pangs and fears than wars or women have." [1] Huysmans, now *fort Catholique*, [2] admitted with true remorse his long apprenticeship as a pathic, particularly, as he told me, the function of third (and last) in a descendant tier! *"Mais tout cela appartient maintenant au passé, car tout est changé en moi."*[3] Stéphane looked the ascetic that he was: he was the most generous of men (as I have indicated in my paper on Verlaine) and his reclusion was simply due to his love of work. It is quite untrue that his death (so untimely and unexpected) was due to syphilis, but I fancy that it was caused by *un coup de sang*[4] after large potations of *Verte*.[5]

I must not omit to mention Mallarmé's delightful cat named 'Lillith' (Lilith), to which he was absolutely devoted, being a confirmed 'catophile', stroking her with exquisite tenderness and talking with her as to a human. She was most inimical to strangers with feminine jealousy of Stéphane's intimates. Huysmans also loved cats and I think his black Siamese was called Saint Paul. The latter (Huysmans, not the apostle!) was in no sense a solitary; but for Mallarmé who shunned visitors as far as possible, Lillith was a tried companion, who during his frequent *voyages on province* made herself at home with the excellent concierge, a *rara avis* among that difficult race with a delightful smile not unworthy of La Gioconda.[6]

---

[1] Shakespeare, *Henry VIII*. E.B.
[2] Strongly Catholic.
[3] "But all of this is now a thing of the past, for everything has changed in me."
[4] A stroke.
[5] Absinthe.
[6] The Mona Lisa.

I do not think anyone (except perhaps Lillian and Baudelaire if they ever) became really intimate with Mallarmé, though I have employed the adjective. His dispositions were taciturn and he made it plain to those who outstayed their welcome that *il en avaint marre*, was 'fed up' to use a vulgar (to match the French) expression. He had never forgotten that first Easter meeting in 1886 when I was a small school-boy of fourteen; and really took a semi-paternal interest in my development; since I had as a child taken his fancy, and he had predicted to Lélian that I might have a future as a writer or perhaps as an artist. He was both right and wrong; for my life, while in no sense being *aux nouvelles*,[1] has been unusual and not unfruitful, if indeed Plato errs not in saying: "No life is wasted, if it connotes originality, even without achievement." "Is life north living?" asks Voltaire, replying in the same breath: "It depends on the liver." *'La vie vaut-elle vivre? C'est une question de foie (ou foi)'*, a witty reply equally appropriate both to French and English. So may it be said of me: "He lived faithfully a hidden life and rests in an unvisited grave!"

And I would add *osément main posément*, boldly but in sober earnest, that *la devise*[2] of J. J. Rousseau *"Vitam impendere vero"*[3] Juvenal: 'To consecrate my life to the truth' is ever my motto also. I shall die happy, could I be worthy of the magnificent eulogy that Marcus Tullius Cicero once pronounced upon his Roman friend: *"Hoc verum est; dixit enim Quintus Catulus."* "Quintus Catulus said so; therefore 'tis true!"

---

[1] To the news.
[2] Currency.
[3] Life for the truth.

AUBREY BEARDSLEY

Aubrey was still a clerk in the Guardian Assurance Company when first I called at his lodging in a shabby Bayswater Street early one Sunday afternoon of January 1892, about the time of that future King *manqué* Prince "Eddie's"[1] death.

I discovered him in a darkened room drawing by the lamp light; it was a study of an armchair. He had discarded a score or more of sketches and in my presence cast away at least another half a dozen. He was quite unconscious of my presence despite a mechanical reply to my knock. "There," said he to himself, "that satisfies me: we will leave it at that for the present." Then he noticed my intrusion: "Oh! of course, you are Trelawny Backhouse; Oscar told me about you. By the way, do you like Oscar?" "Very little; he is so shockingly commonplace; the other day he told me that he resembles Shakespeare, except for his (Oscar's) more sensitive nose and upper lip. He was going to have a picture made of himself beside a bust of Shakespeare." "With himself a little in front of the bust, I suppose," said Beardsley, "I don't mind his morals but his lamentable repetitions bore me to death and give me nausea like an emetic. One night at the Savoy when a lot of us were having an after-theatre supper, he boasted of having had five love affairs and resultant copulations with telegraph and district messenger boys in one night. 'I kissed each one of them

---

[1] Prince Albert Victor aka 'Prince Eddy', Duke of Clarence and Avondale (1864–1892), heir-presumptive to the throne.

in every part of their bodies,' asserted Oscar: 'they were all dirty and appealed to me just for that reason.'"

"Paul Verlaine," I remarked, "wrote a sonnet: *'Sales sont tes parties secrètes, mais je les aime. '* 'Unclean your private parts but dear to me! '" "Yes, but Verlaine does not wallow in the filth of the gutter like Oscar. Tell me, Trelawny, what do you think of this my final (for the moment) drawing of the Morris chair?" "I am wondering", said I, "why you discarded all those beautiful sketches on the floor? In my ignorance they all seem very nearly perfect."

"It is because they lack command of line; only this latest one satisfies me. I try to have command of line and to get all that is possible out of a solitary curve or single straight line. Just look at this drawing of a Pierrot which I made this morning. Did you see *L'Enfant prodigue*?[1] It impressed me more than I can say." This particular Pierrot was a delicious drawing with a garden background, pointed cypresses and conventionalised roses and lilies. "I love the hour-glass in the garden," I said; "but, Aubrey, tell me what are the things that have most influenced you in your work, while you assimilated them so wonderfully to your genius." "First and foremost, the Greek vases which I am never tired of hearing Professor Miss Jane Harrison [2]

---

[1] *L'Enfant Prodigue* (*The Prodigal Son*), a wordless pantomime set to music (book by Michel Carre Fils; music by Andre Wormser) that was the sensation of the 1891 London theatre season. The story involved Monsieur and Madame Pierrot, and their son, who falls in love with a spendthrift laundry maid who reduces him to a beggar before leaving him; he enlists in the army to regain his honour.
[2] Jane Ellen Harrison (1850–1928), classical scholar and linguist. One of the founders of modern studies in Ancient Greek religion and mythology. She was close to classical scholar Francis Macdonald Cornford, and then maintained a relationship with translator, poet and novelist (Helen) Hope Mirrlees.

lecture about: I'll tell you a secret, that I'd love to illustrate Keats'[1] *Ode To A Grecian Urn* ("Cold Pastoral . . . Beauty is art, art beauty, that is all we know and all we need to know."). Next to the vases, come Italian Primitives and Japanese prints. But I try to bring to each of them my own idiom: I contrast the clean firm lines with masses of blotted shadow and spaces of pure white but I own to imitating the rhythm of Japanese composition which leaves so much to the imaginative faculty."

Then he showed to me *La Procession de Jeanne d'Arc* which he had just finished: its decoration obviously owed much to Burne-Jones, but the rhythm of line and balance are entirely his own. I had already seen and loved *Les Revenants de musique* with the man's dreaming face directed toward the phantom forms that the music calls forth. Aubrey told me that his long days in the city were too much for his delicate health, as in addition his evenings were filled by art-classes in Westminster under a professor Brown who, he said, was greatly influencing his technique. "My father died quite young of consumption, you may know, and the doctors tell me that I have not escaped the hereditary tendency."

I was naturally no judge; but it seemed to me that his sunken eyes under their heavy lids, the extraordinary pallor and emaciation, the eager anxious expression were all to the lay mind indicative of a victim of phthisis. [2] Aubrey laughed heartily in telling me Sir Frederick Leighton's[3] *bon mot* about him: "A great artist who can't draw, but that's a wonderful line,

---

[1] John Keats (1795–1821), one of the great romantic poets.
[2] Tuberculosis.
[3] Frederic Leighton, 1st Baron Leighton (1830–1896), known as Sir Frederic Leighton between 1878 and 1896; painter, draughtsman and sculptor; President of the Royal Academy. A bachelor.

all the same." Aubrey certainly did not draw after Leighton's manner.

It is the fashion to speak of the "naughty nineties," but in fact, except for Aubrey's comet-like resplendence, that period in the artistic and literary sense really came to an end in the spring of 1895 with the Wilde scandal, perhaps the most salient example of British hypocrisy in our annals. Social, literary, artistic, political London, ay and the provinces, knew and talked of Oscar's sexual aberrations; yet, so long as the Treasury shut its eyes to the sorry series of love adventures with *le bas peuple*,[1] great ladies and famous London hostesses were fain[2] to lionise him; the beautiful Constance Countess de Grey [3] graciously accepted his dedication to her of *Lady Windermere's Fan*; Lady Eden, protagonist of the notorious Whistler episode *The Knight* (*sic*; properly baronet – Jimmie Whistler called Eden a knight in his pamphlet, but of course to an Englishman a baronet is not a knight) *and the Butterfly*,[4] wrote to him flattering letters; "Albert Edward P."[5] himself received him after witnessing *A Woman of No Importance*, complimenting in his strong German accent the sparkling, coruscating wit of the epigrams: "*Ach! ich* will not have

---

[1] The low people.
[2] Pleased.
[3] Constance Gwladys Robinson, Marchioness of Ripon (1859–1917), an important patron of the arts. Married the 4th Earl of Lonsdale, and following his death, the 2nd Marquess of Ripon, who was known, before his succession to that title, by his courtesy title Earl de Grey. Lady Ripon therefore being Countess de Grey at this time, she was commonly known as Lady de Grey.
[4] Early in 1894 Whistler painted a portrait of Lady Eden, wife of baronet Sir William Eden. Client and artist fought over the price, resulting in a court case brought by Eden, which Whistler won. In 1899 Whistler published an account of the affair: *Eden versus Whistler: The Baronet and the Butterfly: A Valentine with a Verdict*, which skewered Eden for his pride.
[5] (Albert) Edward, Prince of Wales, later King Edward VII (1841–1910).

(pronounced like HAVE in HAVEL, not 'à *l'anglaise'*) *ein Wort*[1] to be changed," referring to a *bon mot* which the censor of plays had erased; "*es ist kolossal!*" declared Bertie Le Gros; and Oscar answered: "Sire," (to a prince!!) "your will is law!"

But within two years the house of cards collapsed and *le beau monde de Londres*[2] shrieked: *Tollé!*[3] in pious Britannic horror at these random recreations of an idler; albeit it had listened with avid curiosity to the man's own embroidered narrative of his strange loves and miscellaneous "ofs and belongings." Small wonder that literary Paris and cultured society in America thought Oscar to be the victim of government persecution in order to shield others in higher place! Was it so? Who shall say! And I would not say, though I knew!

My intimacy with Aubrey developed as rapidly as the Indian conjurer's mango-tree trick;[4] if one attracted him, and in this case the attraction was assuredly mutual, the barriers broke down like the Canaanite well before Joshua's trumpet blasts. That there was homosexual affinity I would not seek to deny; but except on one occasion — *mea culpa, mea culpa, mea maxima culpa'*[5] — there was no concrete manifestation of an affection that remained outwardly platonic; and even the one encounter to which I refer connoted none of the crescendo periods, *cette augmentation graduelle,*[6] sometimes *hélas*[7] terminating in anti-climax rather than in surfeited libidinous accomplishment, with which an outsider might have

---

[1] A word.
[2] The London upper class.
[3] Outcry.
[4] The illusion of generating a mango tree from a seed within few minutes.
[5] My fault, through my fault, through my most grievous fault.
[6] This gradual increase.
[7] Alas.

associated our happy, our almost ideal, union of contrasted natures.

It behoves me to confess that I was responsible for Aubrey's introduction to three persons who greatly influenced his life: John Lane, André Raffalovitch,[1] Leonard Smithers.[2] Lane, a yeoman from the west country, a little, squatty, stout man with cunning, shrewd eyes 'à fleur de tête, and a russet beard, though already partner of Elkin Mathews in the publishing house The Bodley Head had not as yet openly announced his connexion with the firm, although he was the moving spirit that induced the slow moving Exeter bibliopole that was Mathews to place on the market tiny editions of *belles-lettres*, thus inaugurating a definite literary period. Lane lent himself well to caricature and after our return from Vigo Street Aubrey made a delightful sketch of the interview, Lane's pleading expressions before an adamant Beardsley seeming to suggest an appeal for indecent drawings. It was called *"Margaritas ante porcos."*[3]

André Raffalovitch was a Croatian, *fort catholique*,[4] a charming writer in a foreign and exotic English: it was certainly more through him even than through the Jesuit Father Gray that Aubrey was received a year before his death into the Church. André died some years ago: he has spoken of our association in his memoirs and I am therefore betraying no confidence in frankly admitting that the friendship between us was in no

---

[1] Marc-André Raffalovich (1864 –1934), wealthy French poet, writer on homosexuality, and arts patron. He maintained a lifelong relationship with the poet and Catholic priest John Gray.
[2] Leonard Charles Smithers (1861–1907), London publisher associated with the Decadent movement.
[3] Pearls before swine.
[4] Strong catholic.

sense platonic. In the picture *The Flagellation* which I have elsewhere described, Aubrey intended to represent André and myself; he knew, and delighted in, the erotic detail wherewith we both regaled his fancy. In truth, 'twas more a sensuous than a sensual diversion which in no way shut out the "soul-side to our nature."

André revelled in the ritual and vestments of the Church but it was often after confession and communion that he became most emancipated from the fetters of convention and the spate of his over-rolling passion bore away with it the rather attractive reticence that his habitual shyness imposed.

His confessor, so he told me, did not disdain direct interrogatories as to his sexual methods, even (I believe) in controversion of Holy Church practice asking the name of his collaborator and imposing on André a most severe and salutary penance with the 'discipline' (he – or she – who has graciously forborne thus far with my lucubrations may not be astonished to hear that the 'penance' imposed by the good father Vaughan[1] was faithfully performed by me on André's naked lacerated posterior, but 'twas hardly a religious function, save perhaps in honour of Priapus and the Great God PAN), as recommended in that edifying manual *The Spiritual*

---

[1] Rev. Bernard Vaughan (1847–1922), Jesuit priest. Four of his brothers were Catholic bishops. Bernard achieved celebrity through his attacks on luxury, socialism and contraception, the latter which he termed 'race suicide'. A champion of Empire, and opposer of premature peace in World War I, he was noted for the rousing call: "Keep on killing Germans". [See: C.C. Martindale, S.J., *Bernard Vaughan, S.J.*, Longmans, Green & Co., London 1923.]

Life by Rev. Père Tanquerey:[1] "Things written for our learning." He and Aubrey became most intimate and it was to André that the *Last Letters of Aubrey Beardsley* (Longmans Green & Co., 1904) were addressed, telling of his first confession and first reception of the Blessed Sacrament, a sort of spiritual diary without a vestige of pose or of self-pity. Long before, he had told to André and myself the vision recounted by Arthur Symons in *Aubrey Beardsley* (1905), how, as a child of sixteen, he had seen a Crucifix with a bleeding Christ falling off the wall where no crucifix had ever been.

Regarding Leonard Smithers, I have small cause to congratulate myself on having brought Aubrey and him together. Smithers has been well described as Aubrey's evil genius; he battened like a bacillus in congenial environment on his talent, cheated him persistently of remuneration due for his drawings and ignored his pathetic death-bed appeal to destroy the eight drawings for *Lysistrata*, although for his inaction there is excuse on artistic grounds and legally I suppose he and Pollitt[2] were under no obligation to obey the dying behests of religious ecstasy.

---

[1] Adolphe Tanquerey (1854–1932), French Sulpician Catholic priest, professor of canon law and dogmatic theology, author of works on spirituality.

[2] Jerome Pollitt, born Herbert Charles Pollitt (1871–1942), a wealthy golden youth, son of the proprietor of the *Westmorland Gazette*. He collected Aesthetic and Decadent art, including as a patron of Aubrey Beardsley; had a fling with Aleister 'The Beast' Crowley; gained a Cambridge reputation for female impersonation; and inspired E.F. Benson's character *The Babe* in the 1896 novel of the same name: "a cynical old gentleman of twenty years of age." During World War I he served in the Royal Army Medical Corps, achieving the rank of lance-corporal. In 1923, in a series of dramatic trials of a gay circle in Cumbria, he was imprisoned for two years for 'tampering' (as the Judge phrased it) with young men. [Richard Kaczynski, *Perdurabo: The Life of Aleister Crowley* (Revised ed.), North Atlantic Books, Berkeley

He was a Yorkshireman, aged thirty or more, a cocainomane who had abandoned the law for publishing and bookselling. I had translated anonymously for him some of the more indecent of Catullus' poems, including the very gross verses on Julius Caesar's amours with his brigadier, Mamurra, where the poet congratulates the former on a liaison with a *cinaedus* (or catamite) who suffers from inability to defecate more frequently than once a month, thus facilitating the act of coitus as and when desired, especially as his faeces were harder than pebbles.

Like Balzac (not to speak of a certain *ci-devant*[1] Baron of Sachsen-Coburg, who has been mentioned more than once in these pages[2] and owns to the same proclivity on a minor scale: *Deutschland über alles*[3]) Smithers took enormous quantities of caffeine by the mouth, as much as five or six grammes at a time: on one occasion, he achieved a cyclopean erection and was beginning copulation *a tergo*[4] with a male prostitute of the street, when a fainting attack supervened and he was discovered in the state of the Roman soldier surprised for all time by the Vesuvian lava, dying like the latter with an unreduced orgasm, *un orgasme irreductible.*

Aubrey was in no way attracted by Smithers at their first meeting early in 1893: I do not know that the latter made any proposal relative to future collaboration at that time, when in

---

2010, p37; The Kendal Immorality Cases, *The Penrith Observer*, 5 June 1923, p3.]
[1] Former.
[2] Unmentioned, or removed during editing.
[3] Germany over everything.
[4] From behind.

fact Beardsley was already designing for John Lane the cover of John Addington Symonds'[1] *In the Key of Blue*[2] and of John Warren, Lord de Tabley's poems. Before his twenty-first birthday, a Darlington ex-printer, J. M. Dent, had commissioned Beardsley to illustrate *The Morte d'Arthur* in an *edition de luxe*. He never liked the task, but the five hundred drawings therein show a decorative and delicate conventionalisation which revealed his intense preoccupation with the Primitives. Exquisite are the designs for headings and tail-pieces with *leur charme moyenâgeux*.[3] Dent sent to him passionate telegrams and letters demanding greater expedition, for he was always behind-hand with his work and expostulation fell on deaf ears, if the humour of the moment caused his interest to flag, not without spasmodic revivals.

Beardsley's talent never appealed greatly to Burne-Jones, although one had expected the illustrations of *Le Morte d'Arthur* to be after his own heart: he did, however, sincerely admire the "Mrs. Patrick Campbell"[4] now in the Berlin Gallery, which was remorselessly condemned by practically every art critic in London as a *monstrum horrendum, informe*.[5]

It was at the end of 1893 that John Lane, Aubrey and Henry Harland[6] devised *The Yellow Book*:[7] the title was Beardsley's

---

[1] John Addington Symonds (1840–1893), author, literary critic, cultural historian, and activist for homosexual emancipation.
[2] A collection of Symonds writings published in 1893, the last year of his life, which was wholly open in its homosexual intent.
[3] Their medieval charm.
[4] Mrs Patrick Campbell (1865–1940), born Beatrice Rose Stella Tanner, English actress.
[5] A terrible unformed monster.
[6] Henry Harland (1861–1905), American novelist and editor who moved to London in 1889 and fell under the influence of the Aesthetic Movement.
[7] The celebrated English literary periodical published from 1894 to 1897.

suggestion and the prospectus was written by him. It was to be the most "charming" periodical ever published and the distinctly exuberant self-praise lent itself readily to sarcastic comment in the London and provincial press.

Alphabetical accident placed my name, E. Trelawny Backhouse, at the head of the list which mentioned some forty artistic and literary contributors, including highly distinguished names which suggest nothing in the least abnormal: Edmund Goss, [1] Henry James, [2] William Watson, Arnold Bennett, [3] Maurice Baring, John Davidson, [4] with Sir Frederick Leighton (he only became a peer in January 1896 just before his death) and Walter Sickert [5] as illustrators, Aubrey being the art-editor.

I assisted Harland, a genial versatile New Yorker and Parisian resident, as sub-editor and wrote a large number of letters soliciting contributions (in half a dozen European languages) from Ibsen, Björnson, Jokai, Tolstoi (then beginning a valued friendship), Marten Martens (to whom I wrote in careful Dutch, though he spoke English well) Fogazzaro, [6] Annunzio, [7] Anatole France, [8] Aubrey helping me with luciferous suggestions calculated to appeal to each individual

---

[1] Sir Edmund Wilson Gosse (1849–1928), poet, author, critic. Although married, he struggled with homosexual desires.
[2] Henry James (1843–1916), Anglo-American author.
[3] Enoch Arnold Bennett (1867–1931), author, best known as a novelist.
[4] John Davidson (1857–1909), Scottish poet, playwright and novelist.
[5] Walter Richard Sickert (1860–1942) German-born English painter and printmaker.
[6] Antonio Fogazzaro (1842–1911), Italian poet and novelist.
[7] General Gabriele D'Annunzio, Prince of Montenevoso (1863–1938), Italian poet, playwright, orator, journalist, aristocrat, and army officer.
[8] Anatole France;born François-Anatole Thibault (1844–1924), French poet, journalist, and novelist.

idiosyncrasy. Tolstoi was so well satisfied with my letter that an invitation to Yasnaya Polyana followed. It was through my letter of ecstatic admiration for *L'Etui de Nacre* and especially for *Le Procurateur de Judée* that Lane became acquainted with Anatole France and ultimately published an English translation of his complete works.

The periodical duly appeared in the spring of 1894, and to speak of *The Yellow Book* is to speak of Beardsley. His drawings are inseparable from the history of art; but the storm that they provoked not only in Philistine but in artistic and literary circles can only be compared with the "indolent reviewers'" malicious attacks on John Keats. Aubrey remarked to me: "I am nothing if I am not grotesque," after reading a criticism in the London *Star*[1] denouncing the grotesqueness of a female portrait in the first number. He did not then aim at the rare and unique beauty which had characterised his early drawings and were to mark one of his latest productions, *Mademoiselle de Maupin*, with its perfect delicacy of pattern and execution. He had finished this drawing in July 1897, intending it to be the first of a series of twelve. It is slightly tinted (aquatintesque), executed in line and faint wash, being reproduced by the auto-chromatic process. The face is most tender and appealing; the lace of the garment is delicately indicated; the wooded, Corot-like background suggests a haunting mystery. But I am anticipating events, although I needs must refer here to the delicious 'Chopin Ballade' in aquatintesque which he completed within a few months of his death on March 16, 1898.

---

[1] A popular newspaper.

Aubrey, who disliked Oscar, had expressly stipulated that he (Wilde) should not be asked (nor Bozie Douglas either) to contribute to *The Yellow Book*, threatening his own resignation in event of refusal. It is a curious sequel that the Wilde trial terminated Aubrey's connexion with the magazine. John Lane engendered the hallucination that Beardsley's drawings always possessed a homosexual savour; he used to inspect with absurd minuteness (magnifying glass in hand) each and every sketch, searching for hidden suggestiveness, finding it sometimes where none whatsoever was dreamed of by the artist.

There was, however, one drawing which represented Salome contemplating a candle in her left hand with an expression of satisfied salacity; her swollen vulva resembles a drenched lily; the act of masturbation has been accomplished and she is pausing an instant before the reinsertion of this artificial, but pleasingly long, tool. This beautiful sketch determined Aubrey's fate, for Lane wrote to him a letter of dismissal, couched in his unimaginative English of the middle-class, charging him (why, I don't quite see!) of being a partisan of Oscar Wilde, "whose vices" (said Lane) "are to me a physical impossibility." It was a serious blow for Aubrey who was now stranded and penniless, although some friends managed to provide for his small immediate needs. He gave to me a delicious caricature of "A physical impossibility," presenting fat, squatty little Lane of the large paunch endeavouring vainly to insert a flaccid, inert organ into the *proctodaeum*[1] of his office boy, named Shelley,[2] a good-looking catamite who had

---

[1] Anus.
[2] Edward Shelley. See: Neil McKenna, *The Secret Life Of Oscar Wilde*, Century, London 2003, pp174-179 and *passim*.

been mentioned in the Wilde case as one of Oscar's collaborators in his revels *à l'instar de Tibère*[1] at the Blue Grotto of Capri.

Leonard Smithers did not fail to profit by the occasion and offered to Beardsley the art-editorship of a rival to *The Yellow Book*, *The Savoy*, on a salary of £26-5 a week, but all rights in his future drawings were to become Smithers' property as well as the originals. *The Savoy* had only an ephemeral career, but Aubrey's drawing, *The Rape of the Lock*, displayed a masterly preoccupation with the artificiality of the eighteenth century. After the disappearance of *The Savoy*, Aubrey accepted a commission from Smithers to illustrate the English translation of *Salome* by Lord Alfred Douglas.

I suppose that no work of genius, not even Percy Bysshe Shelley's *Alastor*, has been so maliciously assailed in Albion's reptile press (though his work was acclaimed in Paris, in German art-circles and even in New England, William James consecrating a brilliant article in *The Bookman* to this 'weird genius' too good to be true), but none who knew 'literary' London in that *fin de siècle* interlude will deny the paramount and sinister influence of a handful of dictators whose word was law, even as in another sphere the English (less so the Caledonian) press is controlled by Jews and alien financiers today. I think that it was *The Spectator* (a relatively honourable weekly) that referred to those "evil, nightmare, negroid faces with their hideous suggestion of repulsive magic and hellish witchcraft," hateful to God and to God's enemies, betraying a foul, morbid imagination, like a new disease unknown to men.

---

[1] Like Tiberius.

Time healeth all things and I can imagine the panegyrics of deathless eulogy that the same weekly would lavish on those drawings today. They have been praised by the most eminent connoisseurs of the world; from me laudatory words are an impertinent superfluity. Beardsley shows to us the infamy of that luxurious, miniature Court, the decadence which was the very being of the harlot princess, her addiction to *soi-disant* unnatural diversions, *moitié Lucrèce Borgia, moitié Médée,*[1] the spirit of evil incarnate in degenerate womanhood.

Aubrey did not usually allow his friends to watch him at work; but in my case (perhaps he thought that my comparative nescience of the *métier* in which, indeed, I had dabbled long years ago, rendered my presence innocuous!) he seemed to welcome my patient adoration, the while I "hasted and blessed myself with silence." It appeared to me that it was the lines and curves of Giotto that most stimulated (to vary the metaphor) Aubrey's fertile imaginings. I watched him draw Salome's dance before the tetrarch; he began by blotting out a cast mass of shadow which so boldly contrasted with the pure white spaces of the remaining design; a few clear, firm lines in perfect economy and rhythm and the very spirit of the unchanging east was evoked, the swaying, lithe little body, the Terpsichorean cadence of those lust-provoking and delectable bared limbs. Six (I counted them) adorable curves and straight lines portrayed to my astonished eyes the evolution of the Dionysiac dance. Aubrey had never visited the Orient with which, sooth to say, I had then only a nodding acquaintance; but what he drew was the very spirit of Byzance and Le Caire,[2]

---

[1] Half Lucrezia Borgia, half Medea.
[2] Constantinople and Cairo.

127

ay and the living embodiment of a mystic *danseuse* I once saw in Medina despite the prophet's prohibition of what he rightly conceived to be a sensual practice.

After dear Aubrey had completed with a few exquisite lines the drapery of his Salome, he filled in last of all the detail of the face and narrow forehead with the glorious hair, the luring, libidinous eyes pregnant of salacity, the slightly Semitic nostrils, so sensitive and so engaging, those lips that suggested the activity of a *tribade* [1] and the passion of an unending fellatio (by what art Beardsley imparted the suggestion of those esoteric delights I cannot say, but imparted they were!), the witchery whereof Herod is the victim revealed in every line of the face. Such was the spectacle that ravished my still unsated eyes: it is present before me today after half a century's painful experience of this mundane dust, this illusion of the senses, as I write these lines, like Dr. Samuel Johnson his famous preface, "amidst inconvenience and distraction, in sickness and in sorrow."

There exists a secular painting by a disciple of Wu Tao-tzü,[2] the greatest of T'ang religious painters, the Buonarotti of China, of the beloved consort of Ming Huang dancing before the emperor wearing the famous rainbow jacket. Aubrey had never heard of this picture, though he reverenced Chinese art; yet in his sketch of Salome's evolutions he follows close upon the traditions of that golden era.

To the dispassioned reader it will seem a far cry from Tolstoi to Aubrey Beardsley, but the connexion is duly effected by a

---

[1] Lesbian.
[2] Wu Daozi (680–c760), also known as Daoxuan.

certain luncheon at the Pines, Putney, the residence of Theodore Watts (later Watts-Dunton)[1] the novelist, in the autumn of 1896 after my return from Russia. It is well known that Algernon Charles Swinburne had been retrieved from his perennial state of drunken delirium, when he would wallow in utter nakedness upon the floor, sleeping off his crapulous nights in mellow oblivion, conveyed by that "good Samaritan" (for his own advertising ends) Watts to the 'shelter', of his middle-class home, saved indeed from the death-bringing 'fine champagne' and the copious hashish, but deprived of everything that makes life worth living in that banal environment of servitude to the meagre spirits that were Watts and his wife.

Edmund Gosse and Max Beerbohm have each described, from different points of view, that suburban *menage*, probably better than my pen could achieve. Well! to abridge this interpolation, Swinburne (with his nester Watts' gracious approval) had signified to Aubrey his willingness to sit for his portrait and asked me to join the quartet at luncheon, since (for Watts wrote the letter of invitation) "Mr. Swinburne had learned with interest of your stay at Yasnaya Polyana with the novelist[2] he most admires and would be glad (as shall we) to learn in detail of your impressions. Would you not come to lunch, together with Mr. Beardsley, who (Mr. Swinburne believes) is your close friend?"

Would I lunch with Swinburne? Would I not imbibe nectar and ambrosia with burning Sappho, or still more burning Catullus,

---

[1] Theodore Watts-Dunton (1832 –1914), English poet and poetry critic; friend and minder of Swinburne, whom he rescued from alcoholism and persuaded to continue writing.
[2] i.e. Count Tolstoy.

the lover of Lesbia! Aubrey was delighted: "Trelawny, you must excite Swinburne with your charming cosmopolitan conversation, while I am drawing him. I shall lie to him by saying that I can't make a sketch without a third party to not as Greek chorus!"

So Aubrey and I made the long excursion from Hyde Park to Putney S. W. in the hansom of that dear dead era and entered the dreary villa which housed the greatest poet of Victoria's reign. The Wattses were effusively insincere, but the great man was *morne*[1] even *abattu*,[2] inarticulate until we passed into the dining room. Here Swinburne's apparent depression seemed to be shaken off like an outworn shoe: I attributed the gratifying change to the presence of a pint bottle of Bass' extra pale ale adjoining his *couvert*,[3] evidently for his exclusive use. It was not cognac nor yet hashish, but perhaps brought to the divine poet a flushing solace from the ennui of Watts and Madame. We sat down, and Swinburne turned to Aubrey: "Oh: yes. Mr. Beardsley: I am one with you in your hatred of Wilde, though I am sorry for him now. I think *Salome une oeuvre magistrale."* [4] (Swinburne spoke French well but with the accent of "Stratford - Atte - Bowe notte the French of Paris" – Chaucer). "Oscar owes not the idea but the composition of *Salome* to Maurice Barrès who re-wrote nine-tenths of the play and corrected the mistakes in French," interrupted I. "Yes," said Swinburne, "as Doctor Johnson said of Milton's revisions of Lycidas: 'I make no doubt, sir, but it needed them!' I thought it absurd to make an English version of the play but am glad now, since you have illustrated it and now, Mr. Beardsley, you

---

[1] Bleak.
[2] Beaten down.
[3] Snuggery.
[4] A masterful work.

are reaping *la récolte*[1] in the vituperations of the Philistines toward you and all your works. I see you reply to them sometimes grid think you are wrong!"

Aubrey and Swinburne, who was sipping his ale like a liqueur with lustful relish, then engaged in *un tête-à-tête* which was lost to me, as the Watts started chattering in union and banality about Tolstoi. Aubrey had warned me, and now signalled to me across the table, to eschew Russia till the sitting for the portrait, as he wanted 'mes impressions de voyage' to be a sort of *pièce de résistance* for A.C.S.'s[2] benefit.

Theodore Watts, of course, was a novelist of repute and undoubtedly fancied himself to be on Tolstoi's place, a sort of brother practitioner: he began to pick holes in *Anna Karénina* and was distinctly gratified when I informed him that Tolstoi himself deplored the 'melodramatic' ending of Anne's suicide in front of Vronsky's train. At this stage, A.C.S. had drained his 'Bass' to the dregs and looked voluptuously at the empty bottle. "No more, old friend," said Theodore; "you know the rule of The Pines: you must wait till supper!"

Swinburne looked 'mustard' (as Aristophanes says) or rather daggers at his slave-driver, but acquiesced in gloomy taciturnity like a boy rebuked by 'The Head' at a preparatory school for lack of table manners. The collation terminated in an atmosphere of chilly sadness: Swinburne consented to my presence at the sitting for the portrait and the three of us left the Watts couple to their devices, adjourning to a small morning room. Aubrey, as was his wont, drew the curtains,

---

[1] The harvest.
[2] Algernon Charles Swinburne.

had a colza-oil lamp lit (electric light was not installed in those remote days) and signed to me to start a conversation which *épaterait*[1] (not in this case *les bourgeois* but) '*le divin poète qu'était*'[2] Swinburne.

I infer that my reader is familiar with A.C.S.' appearance: he was short of stature, very thin and graceful with lovely feminine hands and small harmonious feet: at sixty he was still the happy possessor of an aureola of abundant russet, auburn heir; eyes sharp and restless ('*yeux de police*'[3] as was once said of Leo XIII[4]), the most sensuous mouth in the world (as indeed one would expect from the author of *Les Noyades* or *Our Lady of Pain*), jaws emaciated and sunken (it being a fact that the Watts menage was not conducted on philanthropic lines, and Swinburne's £200 a year in discharge of bed and board scarcely obtained his money's worth, although it saved him from inevitable death through narcotic poisoning.

And so Beardsley prepared easel and materials, while I, just about to deliver myself of some probably banal remark, was saved the trouble by Swinburne: "Well, Mr. Backhouse, I have hardly had a word with you yet. Tell me, did Tolstoi express any very violent disapproval of me?" "No, Mr. Swinburne, not precisely; he is a keen admirer of *Atalanta in Calydon* and of *Songs before Sunrise*, but told me that your love poems were a most dangerous influence and were harming the Russian youth which devoured them as it does Verlaine whom Tolstoi condemns even more!"

---

[1] Would impress.
[2] The divine poet that was.
[3] Police eyes.
[4] Pope Leo XIII (1810–1903).

"Well, I don't see why Tolstoi condemns a poem such as my *Dolores*, which is really an educational 'tirade' against harlotry without any hidden suggestion of those 'unnatural sins' which he rightly or wrongly resents."

I could see in the dim religious light that Aubrey was satisfied with the natural trend of our talk: Swinburne was becoming exalted and he (Beardsley) was palpably warming to his subject. I observed that he had completed a perfect study of the wealth of hair and the low forehead; he was working this day in colour, an aquatintesque executed in line and faint wash.

At this moment I had a happy inspiration; leaving Tolstoi behind me, I spoke of the Tsar.

Swinburne's eyes flashed revolutionary fire; he might have been Mirabeau[1] thundering before the tribune: "The man who actually attends a ball the day after the Hodinsky Plain tragedy[2] is worse than Nero or Tamerlane,[3] mark my words: this Tsar *finira mal*.[4] Not as his grandsire[5] died, if judgment know of justice, slain by judgment he shall die;" a grim prophesy with fateful fulfilment twenty-two years later.

---

[1] Honoré Gabriel Riqueti, Count of Mirabeau (1749–1791), a leader of the early stages of the French Revolution.

[2] The Khodynka Tragedy was a Moscow crowd crush that in 1896 during the festivities following the coronation of Tsar Nicholas II, that resulted in 1,282 deaths and a huge number of injuries. Due to bad advice, and his own bad judgement, the Tsar and his wife attended a ball that evening at the French Embassy due to concern their absence would offend the hosts. This choice resulted in widespread criticism.

[3] Tamerlane, also known as Timur (1336 –1405), ruthless Turkic conqueror.

[4] Will end badly.

[5] i.e. Grandfather: Tsar Alexander II (1818–1881), who was assassinated.

Aubrey revelled in Swinburne's noble rage and drew his expression, that of a Dante dipping his pen in the hot ink wherewith he chastised the wicked, or, to go back further, like the Hebrew seer rebuking the erring King David, the adulterer, with incomparable art, a curve or so and a couple of lines, *voilà tout*.[1] Swinburne rose to contemplate the portrait: "Yes, said he, you have indeed a command of curve and line, but I do not care for these blotted masses of your background, though I know it is typical of your genius. Well, Mr. Beardsley, if you have finished for the moment, I am satisfied and will sign the work as a souvenir, thus: Something of resemblance: my candid opinion. Algernon Charles Swinburne, Putney, October 1896. To Aubrey Beardsley in remembrance."

Aubrey was delighted with Swinburne, with me, and with the world in general: he called my reference to the Tsar "a stroke of genius." I know not the destiny of this sketch but Aubrey asked for it Guineas 30. Swinburne remarked that he preferred it to Will Rothenstein's[2] portrait done a year or two before which once appertained to me. I remember that 'Will' (now Sir William) charged me £30. I do not know its present environment.

As Aubrey and I drove home, in our hansom, he told me of Swinburne's absorbing passion for a man of forty whom he named but the name conveyed nothing to me: it seemed that he had sought a meeting for homosexual purposes and, no doubt, for a debauch in his beloved hashish; but Watts had

---

[1] That is all.
[2] Sir William Rothenstein (1872–1945), painter, printmaker, draughtsman, lecturer, and writer on art.

forbidden him to leave The Pines: "If you go out, Swinburne, you shall never enter this house again."

It was a heart-rending servitude; and many years later shortly ere his death Asquith,[1] a fellow Balliol man, had offered to the poet a literary pension of £300 per annum, if he would emancipate himself from this tutelage of the *bourgeois gentilhomme* Watts; but A.C.S. declined the proposal on the ground of his political sentiments, "my freedom and my life republican." Swinburne had spoken to Aubrey and to me, as we took leave, of the Queen's *bon mot* regarding himself: "That dreadful Mr. Swinburne and that horrid republican Mr. Labouchère" (owner of *Truth*). Poor Queen! She, like all the Guelphs except perhaps Bertie Rex,[2] was delightfully destitute of humour, as when she records in her journal: "We like to visit Scotland, because see so many Scottish people there!"

Only a week before his death at Mentone, Aubrey was working on initials for Ben Jonson's *Volpone*: I saw them in the collection of Charles Freer at Detroit, Mich., U.S.A. before Washington housed them so worthily. There is no failing of genius, no faltering visible in those majestic headings and tail-pieces. His last letter to Smithers says that he had definitely left behind him all former methods; but it is idle to speculate what the new trend of his genius might have been. That his conversion and Holy Baptism were sincere, I doubt not, but they were largely due to the agony of fear which successive attacks of haemorrhage had imposed: he wrote to André: "My agony of mind is great at the slightest appearance of blood, for

---

[1] Herbert Henry Asquith, 1st Earl of Oxford and Asquith, (1852–1928), Liberal politician and Prime Minister from 1908 to 1916.
[2] King Edward VII.

one never knows if the first streaks are going to lead to something serious or not."

His mind became absorbed with spiritual things, since he never knew that any day might not prove to be his last. It was in February 1897 that he wrote from Bournemouth to Smithers and to Mr. John Pollitt[1] who owned the originals of the Lysistrata drawings (supposedly lewd, by intention perhaps but not in execution) that he was too tired to see them and that his thoughts were now turned toward his spiritual change.[2] After his First Communion all fear of death had left him; as Fr. Gray[3] writes: "had he lived, Aubrey Beardsley might have risen, whether through his art or otherwise, to a height from whence he could command the horizon he was created to soar . . . His soul, thus denuded of the accustomed resources of his being, discovered needs that unstable desires had obscured; he submitted, like Watteau his master, to the Catholic Church."

Well; it is certainly not for me to say otherwise; but, whenever I think of dear Aubrey, it is not as the devout convert to Holy Church but as the wistful, loving, sensuous citizen of the world who sought, ay and found, good everywhere.

Aubrey came to Paris in May 1897, one month after his Baptism, and we heard Holy Mass together at Saint Sulpice. He and I visited Oscar Wilde (just enlarged[4] from gaol) *au*

---

[1] *Jerome* Pollitt. See earlier biographical note.
[2] Probably meant to be 'emerged'. Ed.
[3] Rev. John Gray (1866 – 1934) English poet, partner of poet Marc-André Raffalovich and possible inspiration of Wilde's fictional Dorian Gray.
[4] Original typo. Probably meant to be: emerged.

sixième[1] of a second-rate hotel in the Quartier: we found him surrounded by "the green and yellow" wine (as he called it) i.e. the Chartreuse of his predilection, absinthe and fine champagne with baskets of hot-house peaches and grapes at his elbow. "As you see," said he, "I am dying expensively." His physical wreckage (the flotsam and jetsam of an erratic genius), bad as it was, distressed us less than his mental decay; it was clear from his talk with Aubrey, a sad mockery of bygone days and the brilliance of epigram that we remembered, that he was yearning after conversion, though it was not till November 1900, just before his death, that he was actually received into Holy Church by an Irish Father: although I have no right to judge him, I believe that it was a pose to impress the Philistines.

After my return from Egypt in November 1897, I saw Aubrey for the last time; he was about to spend the winter at Mentone and was in a sadly straitened plight owing to Leonard Smithers having announced inability to send to him the hundred guineas that he owed for his drawings. His friends accorded to him temporary assistance, but it is probable that his penury would have increased, had not that "beautiful angel death" come to his rescue, for work was becoming more and more difficult and physical exhaustion made him apathetic, except for his beloved rosary and his dear St. Alphonsus Liguori.[2] At this our last intimate talk he showed to me the exquisite 'Mademoiselle de Maupin' of which I have spoken; the tenderness of the face surpasses any other of his drawings and connoted an abundant promise for the future.

---

[1] On the sixth floor.
[2] St. Alphonsus Liguori (1696–1787), Italian Catholic bishop, a prolific spiritual writer, composer, artist, poet, lawyer, and theologian.

But it was not to be; he was of the *pauci quos aequus amavit Juppiter*, (one of the few beloved of Just Heaven). He charged me with his latest words to write to him from Peking about Chinese art and, if possible, to procure copies of the religious (laying stress on religious) paintings by the Michelangelo of the T'ang Dynasty of whom I have spoken, Wu Tao-tzü, perhaps the divinest artist of the World. *'Requiem aeternam dona:'*[1] Yet let rest only be labour in a sweeter guise.

So *'Dis aliter visum:'*[2] Aubrey died over forty-five years ago and I still draw my breath in pain, in the world but surely not of it; a strayed reveller whose fellow-banqueters have (all or nearly all) long since gone home. And so I must fill out my span in this present existence, awaiting the inevitable hour and contemplating with an outward dispassion (that I am far from fooling) the sorry spectacle of a great Power in the throes of wanton war and speeding deathward and to individual and collective ruin with "The dust of battle and death of Kings."

> "Is life a boon?
> If so, it shall befall
> That Death, whene'er He call,
> Must call too soon![3]

"*J'en doute*,"[4] as Martin says in *Candide*. Jesus of Nazareth tells us: "Well were it for that man, if he had never been born." And the Buddha, the world-honoured One:

---

[1] Eternal rest grant unto him.
[2] The gods have deemed otherwise.
[3] W.S. Gilbert. From *The Yeoman Of The Guard*.
[4] I doubt.

"So they fell, as all must fall,
Who follow self which is strife;
Since good of one comes through good of all,
And self-surrender for great and small,
For Love is the Law of Life!"

"'Twere better never to have lived at all," thought Byron.

WALTER PATER

It was an October morning and in the pale sun of chilly autumn I was walking in the mediaeval garden of Merton College, watching like Coquelin Aîné[1] in the last scene of *Cyrano de Bergerac* the doomed reluctant leaf falling; to mother earth to join its comrades laid beneath the parent tree, when the following note was handed to me:

B.N.C. (usual abbreviation in Oxford for Brasenose College). October 28, 1892.

My dear Trelawny,

I must call you this, for your name of Edmund is associated with a lost friend and has saddest memories. I do not love your surname, especially, with its hybrid spelling. Will you not come to luncheon; and after the walnuts and wine, if you and I are not too weary, we shall walk to "our scholar's loved hillside" (N.B. meaning "the scholar gypsy", a legend of 1650 A.D. in Matthew Arnold's poem). By the way, do you love Matthew Arnold? I hate his essays; and only care for 'Heinrich Heine' and 'In Rugby Chapel', of his verses. Charles Gore [2] (later Bishop) tells me that you are mystic and ritualistic: I like the latter quality but am not, yet, sure what the first epithet

---

[1] Benoît-Constant Coquelin (1841 –1909), known as Coquelin Aîné ('Coquelin the Elder'), French actor.
[2] Charles Gore (1853–1932), influential Bishop of Oxford, and chaplain to Queen Victoria and King Edward VII.

means; but Gore may, possibly, know. Shall not you come? Till luncheon, therefore, as on this day.

Walter Pater.

The punctuation was character in itself; he talked as he punctuated; and, for that reason, was not always easy to follow. So I to Brasenose, duly, as Pater would have said: his room should have been a haunt meet for a Saint Cyril or a Saint Bernard and suggested anthems in the cloister cell: there was a lovely Pieta, evidently fifteenth century, on the wall which was otherwise bereft of ornament, but the beautiful Charles II wainscot needed none. Pater was toying a jewelled crucifix as I entered: his pallor was unearthly and his eyes were lacklustre but in a measure lighted up as ho welcomed no without effusion as an expected guest. His books, many Elzevirs and Aldines,[1] Baskerville[2] prints of the classics, but so far as I saw, none of the master's own writings, were meticulously ranged by dates, for he adored order.

We down to a frugal luncheon set off with delectable Niersteiner, a very suitable accompaniment to the conversation on Greek love. Pater did not believe that Socrates was otherwise than 'steeped' (to use a parlance of the day for homosexuality): the passage in Plato (who would not misrepresent his master) where the sage catches sight of Charmides' beautiful genital organs and posterior through the accidental movement of his robe and is about to faint from emotion, shows clearly what Socrates desired (and, no doubt, duly obtained at a convenient season). "How absurd to expect

---

[1] Books from the celebrated Venetian Aldine and Dutch Elzevir presses of the 15th to 17th century.
[2] John Baskerville (1706–1775), printer and type-founder.

ascetic reticence, because we are dealing with a saint! John Addington Symonds' purple style, as you may suppose, is ill to my fancy, but I admire his defence of Buonarotti's active and unsated pederasty. It in brave in him to write so."

I asked Pater whether he thought that Michelangelo limited himself to active processes, and the reply was: "No. There could not but be reciprocity: nature demands it; it is the twin principle of light and darkness" (like the Yin and Yang of Chinese philosophy, though Pater was referring to the Manichean doctrine of opposing elements). The Philistines, Matthew Arnold at their head, though he claims to be a hater of profane crowd, shriek at the top of their voices anent the grossness of masculine intercopulation. Yet; where is the grossness? I suppose that these helots of art and sense mean the organ of generation, the phallus, and the anal cavity: the former is lovely and exquisite, especially the foreskin fair as a new bud in spring, the latter with seemly and sweet environment, the chaste curves, the erotic lines, has ever been the dear inspiration of sculpture and of painting. Take the Hermes at Olympia with its glorious phallus and delectable posterior! Then take the sexual parts of Aphrodite rising from the ocean! Are not they hideous in their poetry-less contour and obtrusive shape?"

"Like Socrates," went on the master, "when I see a beautiful undergraduate who is my *acroates* (listener at a lecture), I am even fain to hush myself in wonder as to the mystery which he conceals from my sight and which I shall perhaps never, never feast upon. Socrates in manifold directions is quite alien from me: his disorderliness and sloven habits are from me as poles apart. But one seldom admires him who is one's counterpart;

although, in my case, my hero Marcus Aurelius seems to be akin in his *esprit rangé*."[1]

"That is why I so dearly love the Roman ceremonial, the priest in glory enthroned, the lovely language of the office, the beautiful server's attitude in raising the tether's vestments during the periodical genuflexions, the people kneeling on the ground with awe, the moment when (as Homer says) "thereby was a wonder wrought," the sacred silence and the whispered *'Hoc est enim Corpus Meum,'*[2] whereon instantly the substance of the bread is gone forever and Jesus Christ, True God and True Man, rests between the priest's anointed fingers. Jesus has again had compassion upon the multitude."

"But, my dearest Trelawny",(note the superlative) "so, according to Charles Gore, that Anglican who in his heart hankereth after Rome, if only his theatrical fervours did connote a modicum of courage, you are ritualistically minded. Then what, in the Blessed Virgin's name, are you doing outside the Sanctuary of the Church? Not that I have a right to criticise your hesitancy; for I am still without the grace of Holy Baptism! Perhaps, your Hellenic shade of morals seems to you a deterring force; you err: they are a compelling incentive: they must needs urge you forwards."

"It is confession," faltered I, "that gives me to think and to pause like a benighted traveller at the parting of the ways. I do not covet the secular and time-honoured necessity to speak out all my multitudinous sins, the joys of the flesh and the sorrows that wear out the soul, this wellnigh incessant sexual

---

[1] Tidy mind.
[2] For this is my body.

146

activity, this carnality, this plenitude, which never lets me be. How, 'Maître,' shall I find it in me to proclaim, if the whisper of the confessional may justify the use of no big a word as 'proclaim' connotes, the endless series of homosexual practices? I shrink from the apposite, but embarrassing, questions of the priest, be he a Father Aloysius or a Father Hilarius, demanding erotic and very personal details of the *modus operandi*, the reactions of my *vis-à-vis*, the exact nature of the reciprocity to which you, *Maître*, but now referred, was there — or was there (as in my sad case) not – the *amari aliquid*[1] *après avoir bu le calice à la lie*, after draining the cup to the dregs, the sensation of futile spending and of ill-timed, misplaced lust. Such, then, is the cause of my long cowardly delay in completing the admonitions of Cardinal Newman[2] two and half years ago: some day, perhaps, it shall be other with me; and *quien sabe,'Maître*,[3] peraventure with you likewise."

"I seem to understand," said Pater; "but in your ease I should withhold such otiose particulars (like epithets of little meaning) from the confessor and can perceive scanty cause to satiate his unhealthy (ay! unhealthy) curiosity. You are under no bounden duty, no religious obligation, to etch forth, except in outline, your love-locked manoeuvre and you may fairly say to him: 'I traverse the gamut of emotion and translate it into concrete practice. *Voilà tout! Peccavi*:[4] Absolve me, Father, and award to me your severest penance and the chastisemant of

---

[1] Touch of bitterness.
[2] John Henry Newman (1801–1890), influential and controversial English theologian, scholar and poet; who was first an Anglican priest and later a Catholic priest and cardinal. His intense passions for his friends Hurrell Froude and Ambrose St. John explain much.
[3] Who knows, Master.
[4] That's all! I have sinned.

the discipline self-administered ('I suppose,' added he) for my *cupido and convoitise.*"[1]

"Speaking generally, it is good for us to confess; but particularly, so: by repetition, any and every argument loses its force; nay, it enhances the very evil that by confession you would fain remedy. I say fifty Ave Marias every day of my life: at high noon I repeat the Angelus, devout as Millet's[2] brother and rioter pausing from their toil in the fields! Do I believe? *Non, je ne suis pas croyant mais je ne suis pas incroyant non plus.*[3] It is better for us to believe that beyond these voices there is peace."

We were prolonging our walnut and liqueur period longer than was usual with an Oxford luncheon; and Pater said: "Shall you, Trelawny, after all these veridical revelations – which, in truth, I half guessed, without being Tiresias[4] or another of the "prophets old"; for, forgive me, dear Trelawny, your sexual content is written like the Codex Bezae[5] on your fair face" (I am citing the master's own epithet, sadly, I conceive, misapplied), "shall you, I repeat, feel yourself too greatly, enfeebled, exhausted in fact, to accompany me, on a short stroll, in this autumnal air, this melancholy of the falling year?"

"Surely, Master:" and we made our slow way toward "Happy Valley", for Pater and Max Beerbohm, unlike in other respects, possessed in common one feature, that of walking more

---

[1] Greed and covetousness.
[2] Jean-François Millet (1814 –1875) French artist. The reference is to his painting 'The Angelus', which depicts two peasants standing in a field in prayer.
[3] No, I'm not a believer, but I'm not an unbeliever either.
[4] A blind prophet in Greek mythology.
[5] The Codex Bezae Cantabrigensis: an ancient manuscript of the New Testament.

deliberately than *Le Grand Monarque*[1] himself, that master of dignity and deportment, whose *démarche majestueuse*[2] was so dear even to the heart of a Saint-Simon,[3] certainly not his unreserved admirer.

Leaving Hellenic loves for the moment, Pater discoursed to me, measuredly end dispassionately, on Pascal.[4] One of Turgenieff's[5] novels contains a character to whom the advice is given: "You must be fair to others:" he replies: "But I don't see why!" This answer is certainly straight-forward: the fact is that we all find, without admitting it, a difficulty in being fair to our enemies.

Take Pascal for example; how he maltreated the Jesuit Lalouère[6] because the latter dared to investigate the problems of curves and *le cycloide*[7] which he claimed as his own province. It would not suit Pascal to admit that a Jesuit could be a great mathematician. He was only interested in his own discoveries and is utterly indifferent to others' achievements. He writes a commonplace book out of material furnished by his friends on an ephemeral controversy between Port-Royal

---

[1] The Grand Monarch: Louis XIV.
[2] Majestic approach.
[3] Claude Henri de Rouvroy, Comte de Saint-Simon (1760 –1825), was a French political, economic and socialist theorist and businessman.
[4] Blaise Pascal (1623 –1662) French mathematician, physicist, inventor, philosopher, writer and Catholic theologian.
[5] Ivan Sergeyevich Turgenev (1818 –1883), Russian novelist, short story writer, poet, playwright, and translator.
[6] Antoine de Laloubère (1600–1664), Jesuit priest known for an incorrect solution of Pascal's problems on the cycloid, but was the first mathematician to study the properties of the helix.
[7] The cycloid: in geometry, the curve traced by a point on a circle as it rolls along a straight line without slipping.

and the Jesuits,[1] a note-book (*Les Pensées*) which his art has rendered immortal. He despises the arts, including that of writing; he holds beauty in horror as something unholy. Ill and unable to sleep, he scribbles sheets of notes as an apology for Christianity, and these notes after his death become the delight of freethinkers and sceptics, nay they are commended by his opponents, Voltaire [2] (who was certainly hostile), Bossuet,[3] Condorcet.[4]"

"He lived in filth and refused to allow anyone to sweep out his room: he blamed himself for enjoying the pleasures of the table and if any one expressed approval in his presence of a savoury dish, he called it salacity. He would not even permit his sister to say that she had met a beautiful woman for fear of engendering base sensual ideas. He could not bear to see a child embracing its mother and doubted of the most innocent friendships. So far from mourning over the death of a relation, he rejoiced over it if it were a Christian ending, fruitful of an entry to Purgatory."

"That Pascal was sincere," thought Pater, "I doubt not: he practised what he preached, but his teachings savour a little of

---

[1] A series of letters by Pascal known as *Les Provinciales* (The Provincial Letters), written in defence of Antoine Arnauld, an opponent of the Jesuits and defender of Jansenism, a Roman Catholic movement that held heretical doctrines on the nature of free will and predestination. Port-Royal Abbey in Paris was a stronghold of Jansenism.

[2] François-Marie Arouet (1694–1778), known by his nom de plume Voltaire; French Enlightenment writer, historian, and philosopher famous for his wit, his criticism of Christianity – especially the Roman Catholic Church – as well as his advocacy of freedom of speech, freedom of religion, and separation of Church and State.

[3] Jacques-Bénigne Lignel Bossuet (1627–1704), French bishop and theologian.

[4] Marie Jean Antoine Nicolas de Caritat, Marquis of Condorcet (1743 –1794), known as Nicolas de Condorcet; French philosopher and mathematician.

those given by the *dévot* to Orgon in *Tartufe!* That Moliere means to attack the Jesuits in that play, I do not believe; especially as he would have gravely offended Louis XIV with a word to their dispraise: it is more probable that it was the Jansenists of whom he was thinking." Pater continued: "Pascal loved the poor and lavished alms upon them as being part of Christ's body. It is true that he received them into his house but he loved poverty as the debauchee loves woman, because of the advantage that they brought to him: by loving the poor, he assured his own salvation. He loved them as a necessity which he welcomed as always with him, just as he loved vermin, boils and generally unclean environment."

"Pascal says more than once; 'Reason does not lead to God; only sentiment. The existence of God is an act of faith.' He reasoned on all subjects which were within the purview and domain of reason; but God is not subject thereto. Like a 'mystic' (to use the word of Gore which I quoted in my note to you) or a lover, he gave his heart to God, without knowing why, nor indeed even wishing to know."

"You have only to read Saint Theresa's meditations to follow my meaning. Had Pascal summoned his reason to cooperate with his faith, the latter would have perhaps collapsed like a house of cards. Mme. Périer, his sister who writes his life, a good-natured and discreet gossip, records the practice of Pascal, retired from the world, to resolve in a chill, bare chamber any and every visitor desirous of discussing religious topics. To the honest doubters he gave his advice and occasionally disputes ensued. Pascal hated controversies wherein reason was invoked against faith. In order to support such discussions, he wore an iron belt with nails pointed inward: so, whenever his opponent addressed an argument of reason, he pressed the points into his flesh, thus helping his neighbour without impairing the salvation of his soul. He did not doubt, but dreaded to be taken by surprise by some ingenious argument which might weaken his faith."

We returned from our walk in the gathering dusk, not without having stood entranced at the familiar view from the outlying high ground of the fair city with her dreaming spires: "She needs not June for beauty's heightening," the hackneyed quotation from Matthew Arnold's poem[1] that most pilgrims to 'Ozenford' have by heart.

Throughout the Advent term I attended Pater's lectures on Plato and Platonism: they were published after his death and, although I know not how much justification he has for dwelling on the *Siccum Lumen*, Dry Light of Sir Francis Bacon,[2] as a typically Platonic conception, the beauty of his slow, chaste *intonation traînante*[3] which was far removed from the Oxford drawl (so irritating to aliens) remains with me rather than the subject matter. Among the auditors were girl students from Newnham and Saint Margaret's colleges, and on the day when he lectured on Socratean love of the male form, the door was closed to the feminine element. It was in the days when "homosexuality" might not "be even so much as named among you, as becometh saints" (as Saint Paul says of fornication); but I think the women felt aggrieved by the loss of a treat.

---

[1] Thyrsis: written to commemorate his friend, the poet Arthur Hugh Clough.
[2] Francis Bacon, 1st Viscount St Alban (1561–1626), English philosopher and statesman who served as Attorney General and as Lord Chancellor of England. Like his brother Anthony, and despite his marriage, a homosexual.
[3] Trailing intonation.

Pater spoke with alarming frankness and raised blushes to my cheek, for in those remote times I suffered from *éreuthophobie*. The fact that the lecturer kept looking in my direction and almost seemed to be talking at me did not improve my composure; but the audience was sympathetic and homosexually minded. He was firmly convinced that Alcibiades' intimacy with the philosopher was mainly carnal and believed that the charges against him on the ground of corrupting the youth were due to the jealousy of other famous pathics to whom Socrates had refused his favours. The latter, of course, outlived Alcibiades by some seven years; but Pater believed that the brilliant child of fortune by his eloquence and persuasion might have turned the scale in favour of the sage by admitting the fact of reciprocal union, not at all something that the Athenians would object to 'per se', while denying any impiety or blasphemous intent on Socrates part toward the gods. "Forget not," said Pater, "Alcibiades' brilliant defence of Socrates many years before. If I were to say all I feel about the philosopher, you would all think me more drunk even than I am!"

It seems passing strange that Aristophanes in his satire of *The Clouds* on the "Cloud Dweller," *meteoros,*[1] that represented Socrates, withholds all allusion to pederastic cults and to Socratic predilection in this regard. Pater nearly brought the house down by his glowing peroration: "It is, in sober earnest, not a vice; it is the pastime, the *parergon,*[2] of great minds: if the object of marriage, as the English Prayer Book (with more carefulness than decency) informs us, is the procreation of children, than the purpose of reciprocal pederasty is to furnish

---

[1] In the air: the study of the astronomy
[2] A work that is supplementary to or a by-product of a larger work.

a timely vent for the natural passions, purgating [sic] them not indeed in the Aristotelian sense of pity and terror but by affording an easy solace in the ecstatic union of the masculine and feminine elements of which every male is composed and the same applies to female homosexual commerce. It is the spirit of Achilles' love for Patroclus, Xenophon's for his ideal brother in arms, Michelangelo and Shakespeare who open their hearts in sonnet sequence, nay I would even add of Jesus for John. What they, what Socrates, what Julius Caesar revelled in, shall we lightly condemn, in our haste, even if we do not imitate these supermen?"

That the Master always practised what he preached I would not contend. In a previous paper I have made allusion to his solitary homosexual encounter with myself: in theory it was a great consolation and boon to his gentle intellect; in practice it was a 'reach' which exceeded his grasp, a heaven we may aspire to but shall not enter. His theoretical carnal affluence was superabundant; his practical development meagre and negligible, not, very surely, owing to sexual excesses but to a functioning which fell below his requirement, *une source d'inadéquat débit*,[1] a fountain unsealed (it is true) but feeble of volume.

As, I suppose, pederasty was the preoccupation nearest to Pater's sympathies, even as it was, in a grosser sense, to those of John Addington Symonds, like Pater too soon removed from the world of men, I have dwelt on this "facet" of a complex nature and shall now pass on to his hero-worship, concentrated, as is known from his writings, on Marcus

---

[1] A source of inadequate flow.

Aurelius[1] and the Epicureans,[2] those masterpieces of chaste, nervous English that the world will not willingly let die.[3]

Be it my congenial task, in language which falls far short of Pater's compass and achievement, to speak of another hero-worship which he affected for the emperor Julian,[4] the so-called Apostate, to whom Holy Church gladly attributes the mythical *bon mot*: "Thou hast conquered, o pale Galilean." As is known, Christianity had triumphed, but how is it going to accommodate this new cult to ancient ideas? How is the Church to apply its relations to the world of letters, thus marking a definite 'Latinising' of the Galileans? It is germane to add here that Pater had a distinct penchant for *le Manichéisme*[5] and admired St. Augustine of Hippo for having

---

[1] Marcus Aurelius Antoninus (121–180), Roman emperor from 161 to 180 and Stoic philosopher. Last of the rulers known as the 'Five Good Emperors'.

[2] Epicureanism is a system of philosophy founded around 307 BC based upon the teachings of the ancient Greek philosopher Epicurus. Epicureanism was originally a challenge to Platonism. Later its main opponent became Stoicism. Epicurus believed that the greatest good was to seek modest, sustainable pleasure in the form of a state of *ataraxia* (tranquillity and freedom from fear) and *aponia* (the absence of bodily pain) through knowledge of the workings of the world and limiting desires.

[3] Pater's philosophical novel *Marius the Epicurean* (1885), set in the Rome of the Antonines, examined a young Roman who pursues an ideal of the aesthetic life – a life based on sensation – tempered by asceticism. Leaving behind the religion of his childhood, sampling one philosophy after another, becoming secretary to Emperor Marcus Aurelius, Marius tests his author's theory of the stimulating effect of the pursuit of sensation and insight as an ideal in itself.

[4] Flavius Claudius Julianus (331 – 26 June 363) Roman emperor from 361 to 363, and philosopher and author, who rejected Christianity in favour of Neoplatonic Hellenism.

[5] Manichaeism was a dualistic religious system with Christian, Gnostic, and pagan elements, founded in Persia in the 3rd century by Manes (c. 216– c. 276). It was based on a supposed primeval conflict between light and darkness, played out within human beings and in the world. It spread widely in the Roman Empire and in Asia, and survived in eastern Turkestan (Xinjiang) until the 13th century.

been at one time a member of the sect. The African master of rhetoric that was Augustine delighted in taking an opposite side in a controversy from innate love of paradox, a true disciple of his compatriot Terence, Augustine who was perhaps one of the giant intellects of the world for all times.

Pater's admiration for Constantine[1] is decidedly small, but he praised Valentinian I[2] who assured religious peace, that zealous, ignorant Christian who was happiest in the society of two tame she-bears. He had no love for the Arians but persecuted none on religious grounds, admitting pagans and Christians to the highest offices. It is remarkable that such a degree of unity had been achieved in the fourth century of our era: to the service of the state both pagans and Christians consecrated their devotion; there was a definite tolerance between opponents who showed that homogeneity of religious belief is not necessary to form a strong and united nation. Valentinian was no totalitarian and proved (what would the Führer say) that a diversity of cults was no cause of weakening to the body politic and the national sentiment. The controversy between Saint Ambrose, the holy bishop of Milan,[3] and Symmachus[4] the great pagan scholar is well known. Valentinian had removed the statue of Victory from the Senate, thus preventing the Pagan senators who were not in a minority from burning incense before the altar of the goddess. They demanded its replacement, but Ambrose

---

[1] Flavius Valerius Constantinus (c. 272 – 22 May 337), also known as Constantine the Great; Roman emperor from 306 to 337.
[2] Flavius Valentinianus (321 –375), Roman emperor from 364 to 375.
[3] Aurelius Ambrosius (c. 340 – 397), venerated as Saint Ambrose, Bishop of Milan; theologian, and one of the most influential ecclesiastical figures of the 4th century.
[4] Quintus Aurelius Symmachus 'Eusebius' 9 c. 345 – 402) Roman statesman, orator, and man of letters. Aurelius Ambrosius was his cousin.

156

objected on the ground of religious tolerance, since it was unfair to expect Christian senators to be accomplices at an act of pagan worship; even as in our day your free thinker resents the presence of a Christian emblem outside the churches.

How then was pagan culture adapted to the needs of triumphant Christianity? At the inception Christian culture was almost non-existent: the gospels with their exquisite savour were not composed in a style that Seneca[1] would have approved; the barbarous phraseology of a Luke or a Matthew was calculated to disgust a patrician who had imbibed the masterpieces of antiquity with his mother's milk. It is only within the last century or so that the New Testament was held to be a literary monument of value; in the Middle Ages none had admitted it. The Christians had been denominated a new race, born yesterday, without nationality or traditions, banded against every civil and religious institution, persecuted, branded with infamy and proud of the detestation they inspired. But when even the lawyers and rhetoricians had become Christian and the highest in the land accepted the cult, the latter possessed no schools of its own and had perforce to send its youth to the pagan seminaries where they learned of the loves of the gods. Failure to study letters would have disqualified them for civil appointment; so the Christian youth sat under the Pagan pedagogue and learned mythology, the giant wars, the loves of Catullus,[2] "his glory, his beauty and his shame."

---

[1] Lucius Annaeus Seneca the Younger (c. 4 BC – AD 65), usually known as Seneca; Roman Stoic philosopher, statesman, dramatist, and in one work, satirist.
[2] Gaius Valerius Catullus (c. 84BC – c. 54 BC), poet of the late Roman Republic.

Grammar, rhetoric, poetry, these were the things to which Roman society attached weight. The Romans of the decadence were in reality less depraved than we imagine and cherished a sort of filial piety for the intellectual treasures that had been bequeathed to them but which they lacked the wit to add to. Like the Chinese literate of the old examination system, they thought that the worthiest of all occupations was the ability to turn out sonorous phrases and to compose elegant essays. In the fourth century a good stylist and rhetorician might even aspire to the throne: the Church which was now so powerful made no effort to create a new system of education based upon her doctrines, and the Christian graduates continued, like the pagans, to imitate Cicero[1] and Virgil. The Church was conquered by the school: it was a real victory for letters and ensured the survival of a portion of classical literature. And the day came when the Renaissance brought the revenge of the Muses, ay even within the Vatican where Pagan art and sculpture definitely prevailed. The beauty of the ancient world was reborn in the revival of the arts.

Julian lost his uncle, Constantine, when a boy, escaping with his brother Gallus from the massacre of his family. His boyhood as spent in Caesarea, where Constantine confined him without making up his mind whether he was to live or die. Gallus became insane: Julian, when he left prison, was active, chaste and intelligent, so that Constantine sanctioned his studying at Athens and Byzantium, awaiting his destiny which was the imperial title. The Empress Eusebia loved him and persuaded Constantine to confer upon him the title of Caesar and the government of Gaul.

---

[1] Marcus Tullius Cicero (106BC – 43 BC), Roman statesman, lawyer, scholar, philosopher.

Julian was indifferent to his personal appearance: his beard was never trimmed, because he thought that an unkempt beard savoured the philosopher. He let his hair grow like birds' feathers; his nails were black and his hands stained, for he wished to appear gauche and rude of manners. He called himself a clown and a savage, a barbarian from Thrace. But Eusebia loved him and presented him with a collection of poetic and philosophic works.

Julian, who belied Catherine be Médicis *obiter dictum*: "*Nous autres qui sommee rois ou reines ne possédons qu'assez rarement la qualité de reconnaissance*," "a crowned head is seldom grateful," never forgot Eusebia's generosity and in the glowing panegyric which he composed to her memory wrote: "Eusebia's gift of books enabled me to satisfy my unquenched thirst for study, so that my sojourn in distant Gaul and Germany represented for me a scholar's course in humane letters. As I turned over with unceasing research the volumes of my love, I was ever mindful of her to whom I owed the gift. When I take the field in a campaign, I always include among my impedimenta of travel several books of the collection" (like Napoléon).

Pater thought that there was sexual affinity between Julian and Eusebia: there are women, said he, who relish males of uncared for appearance, just as a certain "esthete" of Oxford (I regret to say) enjoys his sexuality greatest, when his collaborator is of the gutter and malodorous as Diogenes.

The young Julian, scholar and philosopher, showed at first to little advantage as a legionary with helmet (*galea*), shield (*rectum*) and cuirass (*lorica*), in military shoes (*caliga*), with a short dagger or '*pugio*' suspended to his left side and the '*pilum*' or dart to his right. He had the scholar's painful stoop, marched with the downcast eyes of a school-boy at his desk, could not keep time and during his drill murmured in discontent: "This '*lorica*' (cuirass) is as uncomfortable as a saddle on an ox's back;" "Plato mine, how I suffer!"

The ideal sojourn for Julian was the Academy with Mount Lycabettus in the vicinity and the violet tints of the hills of Attica. But he laboured over his training and became a hardy captain, showing himself in his German campaigns a strategist equal to Trojan. Thrice he crossed the Rhine, delivered 20,000 prisoners of war, reduced several fortresses and became master of the country. In his progresses he never abandoned his simplicity; in his headquarters at Lutetia (Paris) he spent his days in austere meditation, studying the Neo-Platonic doctrine. He fasted before the altars praying to the gods, who granted to him visions of a Roman empire no longer Christian. His soldiers proclaimed him Augustus in the Thermes whose ruins stand today; he scornfully refused the woman's diadem they offered him for [a] crown but accepted a trooper's collar as a token of sovereignty.

Constantine's death made Julian sole ruler of the empire. Soon after his accession he marched eastward and was hailed at Argentoratum (Strasbourg) by an aged blind woman: "That man shall restore the temples of the gods!" Julian was still nominally Christian and had, as a youth, read the gospel in the church of Caesarea; but the blind woman was acclaimed by the Pagans as a messenger of the gods, a sort of Athena appearing to the Greeks before Troy. Julian's reign of a few months saw the accomplishment of her prophecy; for Christianity had

160

been the religion of the murderers of his house and he hated the Galilean.

At Julian's accession it is probable that the Pagans were in a majority of the population: in Europe Christianity had scarcely penetrated the countryside and the Pagus or village still worshipped the ancient gods; Asia was mainly Christian and Africa mainly Pagan.

Julian re-established the altars of the gods without thought of political expediency; his nights were spent in vigil and prayer: he would rise from his coarse couch of matting to write and meditate, he was an *exalté*, an *illuminé* inspired by thoughts like those: "As a child I loved the rays of the sun; by day I fixed my thought toward Titan and night I never wearied of studying the stare. I became unconscious of my surroundings and heard not those who spoke to me."

What he restored was Hellenism rather than Paganism in its sense of idolatry: it was Neo-Platonism with its Alexandrine trinity and the philosopher's supreme deity, the sun-god, the initiation into mysteries, the immortality of heroes and sages. Julian lived like a saint and an ascetic: Ammianus Marcellinus[1] records that after his wife Helen's death he never again had carnal intercourse: "he was more easily a stranger to sensual pleasure, seeing that he seldom slept and deliberately starved himself, whether in his palace or in the field." He regarded it indecent for females to perform the evolution of the dance and differed from his fellow Neo-Platonists in his horror of pederastic delights. He lived in the dirt and squalor of a

---

[1] Ammianus Marcellinus (c. 330–c. 391/400) Roman historian and soldier.

Christian monk which contrasted with the delicacy and poesy of the Hellenism he loved.

"Might not," asked Pater pensively, "the modern world have been better if Hellenism had prevailed over the cross? Alas! his work perished with Julian himself and the pious hopes of Libanius [1] turned to dust and ashes: "Today we live again under a god-ruler; the air is purified by the smoke of the sacrifice and the altar fires are kindled anew."

Was Julian's attempt so insensate as the world believes? The incessant disputes among the Christian churches were of ill omen for a society which perceived the need of one universal religion; during his reign of a few months the emperor's pilgrimages to the temples aroused such frantic enthusiasm that Julian was obliged to issue a decree forbidding all such manifestations as impious toward the rods, whose servant he was. A Christian bishop, Pegasus of Ilion, became a convert to Hellenism, the march of the world seemed to begin afresh. Julian's enemies accused him of persecuting the Galileans; Christian propaganda has never been conspicuous for fairness, and "I often wonder (said Pater) whether even Nero [2] has not been maligned by the church, just as Tiberius [3] certainly was by the generation which succeeded him."

In a rescript Julian ordained that no violence be perpetrated toward Galileans and no force be exercised to compel their

---

[1] Libanius (c. 314 – 392 or 393), Greek teacher of rhetoric of the Sophist school. During the rise of Christian hegemony in the later Roman Empire, he remained unconverted.

[2] Nero Claudius Caesar Augustus Germanicus (37–68AD), originally named Lucius Domitius Ahenobarbus, fifth emperor of Rome; reigned 54 –68 AD.

[3] Tiberius Caesar Augustus (42 BC –37AD), second Roman emperor, reigning from 14 to 37AD.

worship in the temples. "Man must be persuaded by reason and not by stripes and punishments. I enjoin those who profess the true faith to refrain from doing to the Galileans bodily hurt: we must pity those deluded folk but have no right to hate them for their blind stubborn *obtenebratio* (befuddledness) of intellect."

For persecution Julian substituted sarcasm and irony, being past-master of subtle humour. No one enjoys being laughed at and the victims of his wit accused him of intolerance, forgetting that he might have put them to death instead of mocking their errors in a satire after the style of Lucian,[1] in every word a sting! Julian showed himself a humourist in recalling from exile the Arian bishops whom Constantine had banished, "because these Christians are worse than wild beasts when they engage in religious controversy and their recall will weaken the church!"

He deprived the Christians of the right of teaching rhetoric and the classics. Let them leave the duty of interpreting Homer and Plato to the Hellenists; they can betake themselves to the churches and explain Luke or Matthew. He seriously contemplated rebuilding the Temple of Jerusalem to show that Jesus was a lying prophet; it was a project worthy of *Le Roi Soleil*;[2] but death overtook him when in full measure of victory during his Persian campaign.

He had conquered Armenia and Mesopotamia, crossed the Tigris and taken Ctesiphon when a bow drawn at a venture mortally wounded him in the liver. His testament is perhaps,

---

[1] Lucian of Samosata (c. 125 – after 180), Syrian satirist and rhetorician.
[2] The Sun King: Louis XIV.

thought Pater, the most remarkable document that antiquity has preserved for us. "My friends and comrades, nature requireth from me the return of her loan; as a debtor I am happy to repay that which I owe to her. Unlike the majority of men, I feel neither regret nor remorse at the hour of death. Philosophy has taught to me that the soul is only happy after emancipation from the trammels of the flesh and that it is an occasion for rejoicing rather than of mourning when the noble part of our nature is separated from that which degrades and humiliates it. The gods have often accorded death as the highest reward of virtue; and I accept it so a favour, since Heaven designs to spare to me difficulties to which I might have yielded or perhaps have caused as to commit an unworthy action. Having lived without crime I die without remorse. Both as regards the time of my enforced reclusion in a remote region away from the Court and since my elevation to the imperial throne I have regarded my dignity as an emanation of the power of God and can fain to believe that I have preserved it unsullied and unstained; for I have governed with mildness my peoples and have never engaged without good cause in war. If I have failed, 'tis because success depends on the will of the gods. The sole end of a righteous government in the happiness of its subjects; therefore I have detested arbitrary rule which saps the morals of a people and corrupts the state. Peace I have ever loved; but when my country called me to take up arms, I obeyed as a son obeys his mother. I have not flinched from danger but have faced it with a light heart. I will not conceal from you the ancient prophecy that I was destined to die a violent death. For this cause I thank eternal God for not bringing about my death at the hands of conspirators nor from the sufferings of prolonged illness and the cruelty of a tyrant. I adore God's goodness in calling me from this world by a glorious death in the midst of a glorious enterprise. To the wise man it is equally an act of cowardice to desire death when it is his duty to live, as to regret life when the moment of death has arrived."

"This, testament," declared Pater, "is worthy to be placed along-side Socrates' discourse in the *Phaeda* on the immortality of the soul: nothing in my ideal hero, Marcus Aurelius, surpasses its eloquence and unimpassioned sincerity. Julian's habits were, as you may suppose, alien from my predilection and tastes, but I salute in him the noblest type of a consistent purpose and unflinching achievement that is known to me. He failed: and is, for that cause, condemned by the world and naturally by the church which has persistently maligned him, as it maligns Pontius Pilate in the Creed, Pontius who could not have saved Jesus if he would; and in fact he gave to the Jewish people the chance of saving him.

As Pater spoke of his love of neatness, for he was always attired (*il mettait avec un goût exquis*[1]) as if for a Church Parade held each Sunday near that dreadful statue of Achilles[2] in honour of Arthur, Duke of Wellington, nude except for the saving fig leaf over his genitals, where *le beau monde* loved to see and be seen after their Protestant devotions in a happier era. I could not forget a recent parallel, in a sort of impish glee, as I contrasted Pater's philosophy of life with that of the Emperor Julian.

A bill had been introduced in the House of Commons for the amelioration of agricultural conditions: the Honourable

---

[1] He wore with exquisite taste.
[2] In Hyde Park, London.

Bobbie Spencer, later Viscount Althorp and Earl Spencer,[1] a patrician of the patricians, the best dressed man in the House, beautifully groomed, in a perfectly cut morning-coat and cashmere trousers, high collared (like poor Prince Eddie, Duke of Clarence[2] often known as 'Collars and Cuffs') with 'four in hand' black cravate and pearl-shaped tie-pin, patent leather boots, rose to address the expectant senate: "Sir," (addressing according to custom the Speaker) "I am not an agricultural labourer" . . . the rest was drowned in roars of laughter but the incident was recalled to me by Pater's disclaimer of sympathy with Julian's monkish tastes and unclean hands and nails.

Pater loved the Jesuits and their rigorous system of training, whereby the novice is forced to undertake some work to him utterly uncongenial. "Were you or I to join the order, Trelawny, the superior would make you apply yourself to carpentry and me to cookery!" He quoted the motto of Loyola:[3]

> "So thro' life, death, thro' sorrow and thro' sinning,
> He shall suffice me, for no bath sufficed,
> Christ is the End for Christ was the Beginning,
> Christ the Beginning for the End is Christ."

As a child I had always been fascinated by Titian's portrait of Saint Ignatius in late middle life of which my family possessed the original, there being, a copy at Windsor Castle; the emaciated, saintly face, the marvellous lustre of the eyes which seemed to rebuke one's every gesture, so attracted my childish mind that I would sit for hours together

---

[1] Charles Robert 'Bobby' Spencer, 6th Earl Spencer (1857–1922).
[2] Prince Albert Victor, Duke of Clarence and Avondale, aka 'Prince Eddy' (1864–1892).
[3] St. Ignatius Loyola. Spanish priest and theologian.

contemplating the saint's visage, while my wicked parents bickered like cat end dog in another room. Literally, a case of the world forgetting, by the world forgot: perhaps the sadness of my youth was all to the good as a preparation for a better destiny, a fuller sojourn on this planet.

Pater thought the treatment of Ignatius by history one of the latter's greatest torts: he was the gentlest of men, utterly devoid of ambition or self-aggrandisement, but he is thought of as a Machiavelli. His disciples had called themselves Iniguista after his former name Inigo, but he insisted upon their taking the appellation "Companions of Jesus." Loyola, chosen by vote as head of the new order, refused, bade his company pray and vote again, with the same result. He would say with Augustine: *Ubi amatur, non laboratur, aut si laboratur labor amatur.* "Where love is, there is no toil, or if toil there be, the toil is loved."

In drawing up the Constitution of the Order (which incidentally rejects the use of the "discipline" in the Order), the first sentence ran: "More vital than any written law is the interior law of charity." His subjects were to love poverty like a mother, to love and to desire humiliations, to exercise the *quidam universalis amor*[1] without reward or fruit of their labour, loving being its own reward. Ignatius died without a parting word, without even receiving the last Sacraments, quietly and unconcerned, as if his death were a matter of routine that should trouble none.

Speaking of physiognomy, Pater told me (as I mentioned) that I had my sinister predilections written in the face: none who

---

[1] A certain universal love.

saw the master but must needs associate him not mayhap with pedication, but at least with estheticism of the epicurean type to whom Wilde and his works were anathema.

Dr. Axel Munthe[1] recounts in one of his books how Le Docteur Cheroot of Paris claimed that he could claimed that he could diagnose a patient's ills and habits from his or her visage, just as sexual malformation might be a clue to a malady of the nervous system. I am sure that I attracted Pater but, while he sympathised with my exotic tastes, he attributed them to a sort of physiological deformity; in reality he only differed from me in a less robust sensuality due to his weaker physique.

To his gentle soul excess *à la Wilde* was abhorrent; the idea of indecent rendezvous for avowed lascivious purposes with illiterate and filthy male harlots was not so much disgusting as simply incomprehensible; but could he have lived, as one might have hoped, for he died at 55, for another fifteen years, I should have been able to recount to him the tale of erotic adventures in Europe and Cathay and feel confident that there would have been nothing in my narrative at all alien to his dispositions *d'artiste et de poète.*

My passion was a white flame, not a mephitic miasma: it burned me out but 'twas a vestal fire. Pater gave to me a beautifully bound Elzevir of the twin Platonic dialogue, *Critias and Timaeus,*[2] with the dedication: "To Trelawny, a lover of beauty. *Prospice!* (Look toward). Happy he who knows that

---

[1] Axel Martin Fredrik Munthe (1857 –1949), Swedish-born medical doctor and psychiatrist, best known as the author of *The Story of San Michele*, an autobiographical account of his life and work.
[2] By Plato.

this life is heaven," with a quotation from his favourite poet, Euripides:

"In the meadow sitting, he plucked with rejoicing heart the spoil of the flowers, gathering them one by one."

Pater, who had a scholarly knowledge of *La Divina Commedia*, read a good deal of Dante with me, though his favourite passages were some of the most *abscons*[1] and obscure (to me) of the *Paradiso*. I remember, nevertheless, that his best beloved quotation was Manfred's famous exclamation telling of his death and of the desecration of his place of sepulture with the reference to the green bough of hope that refreshes even the worst and the most depraved of men. *S'il m'en souvient,*[2] it is this passage to which *le grand lettré que fut M. Paléologue, ancien Ambassadeur de France suprès de l'empereur de Russié,*[3] makes allusion *à propos* of Rasputin's[4] death and suggests that it would be as "balm in Gilead" for the stricken soul of Alexandra Feodorovna,[5] if only he dared to forward it to Tsarskoye!

---

[1] Difficult to understand.

[2] If I remember.

[3] The great scholar, M. Paléologue, former French ambassador to the Emperor of Russia.

[4] Grigori Yefimovich Rasputin (1869–1916), Russian mystic and self-proclaimed holy man who befriended the family of Nicholas II, last emperor of Russia, and gained considerable influence. Assassinated.

[5] Alexandra Feodorovna (1872–1918), wife and Tsarina consort of Tsar Nicholas II of Russia

Pater greatly loved the French poets *du Moyen Age,*[1] not so much *la chanson de Roland* as Charles d'Orléans[2] and Villon of whom I speak in my paper on Paul Verlaine: as a dog lover he adored the former's lines:

> *"Pres lit, Briquet aux pendantes oreilles!*
> *Tu scez que c'est de deduit de gibier. . .*
> *Tu ne fais pas miracles mais merveilles. . .*
> *Pres là Briquet aux pendantes oreilles!"*

(Come hither, spaniel of the drooping ears:
Thou knowest 'tis a resort of game:
Thou art more than a wonder worker.)

Equally did he affect those exquisite verses of Orléans to le duc de Bourbon,[3] a prisoner after Azincourt who died in captivity in 1434, unable to pay the formidable ransom (130,000 *écus d'or*) demanded by the English Crown:

> *"Mon gracieux cousin, duc de Bourbon,*
> *Je vous requier, quant vous aurez loisir,*
> *Que me faites par balade ou chanson*
> *De votre estat ancunement sentir* (that you send to me
> some news of your state); *Car quant a moy sachiez que,*
> *sans mentir,*
> *Je sens mon coeur renouveller de joie*

---

[1] Of the Middle Ages.

[2] Charles, Duke of Orléans (1394–1465), son of Louis I, Duke of Orléans; held prisoner by the English for 25 years after the Battle of Agincourt, but released in 1440.

[3] Jean de Bourbon, Duke of Bourbon and Auvergne; eldest son of Louis II and Anne of Auvergne (1381–1434); captured at the Battle of Agincourt and died a prisoner in London.

En esperant le bon temps a venir
Par bonne paix que brief Dieu nous envoys."[1]

My school-fellow, Lionel Johnson,[2] a charming poet in the classic mould, alas! the victim of chronic alcoholism (as his touching verses *The Dark Angel* show), a devout convert to the church, attracted Pater in a different way from myself, for Johnson was austere and unsexed. Pater approved of his lines:

> "Whom grim Lucretius of the mighty line
> Has awed, but not bowed down,"

also the poem on Charles I's statue at the site of his execution, for Pater was a Jacobite and defender of the martyr king:

> "Alone with night he rides,
> There by his own Whitehall:
> No Parliament divides,
> Nor armed bands appal.
> Which the more full of fate:
> The stars or those sad eyes?
> Which the more desolate;
> Thy face or those dark skies?"

---

[1] "My gracious cousin, Duke of Bourbon,
I ask you, when you have leisure,
What do I do by ballad or song
That you send me some news of your state;
That I can know that, without lying,
I feel my heart renewing with joy
Hopefully the good time to come
Through the good peace that God briefly sent us. "
[2] Lionel Pigot Johnson (1867– 1902), English poet, essayist, and critic.

On the last evening of his life in the summer of 1894, I dined with Pater: like Julius Caesar on the eve of the Ides of March at a banquet given by Lepidus, when the dictator, asked what manner of death he should choose, replied: "A sudden one;" so did Pater, who complained of shortness of breath, remark on the absurdity of the English liturgy praying against a sudden death, the best rift of the gods.

On the following morning he walked, as usual, to his lecture room and fell down dead at the door-step, as I have narrated else-where. It was a beautiful death and I thought of Browning's[1] lines "Our Master, calm and dead borne on our shoulders" in *A Grammarian's Funeral*, addressed, I believe, to Thomas Linacre.[2]

In him I lost a kindred spirit, probably my superior in intellect, certainly the greatest of English prose stylists, and with equal certainty the kindest, most unselfish, most chivalrous of men who was in his age, but not of it, one who detested the sordid philistinism of the Victorian era and the drab self-satisfaction of the British middle-class, scarce other than children playing at the edge of an abyss, into which today they have fallen.

> "By their great memories the gods are known:
> The gods remember everlastingly:
> They strike;
> Remorselessly and ever like for like."

---

[1] Robert Browning (1812–1889) English poet and playwright.
[2] Thomas Linacre or Lynaker (c. 1460–1524) English humanist scholar and physician.

'Tis verily the doom of *la bourgeoisie* in a tired world and the apotheosis, let us trust, of something higher, the fair beginning of a time.

> "Fifty years have gone round
> Since thou arosest to tread
> In the summer morning the road
> Of death, at a call unforeseen,
> Sudden . . . . .
> Oh! gentle soul, by what shore
> Tarriest thou now?"

(Arnold, mutatis mutandis)

A TANGLED SKEIN

For you would have felt my soul in a kiss,
And known that once if I loved you well;
And I would have given my soul for this,
To burn for ever in burning Hell!
Seven sorrows the priests give their Virgin;
But thy sins which are seventy times seven
Seven ages shall take thee to purge in,
And then they will haunt thee in Heaven!

"Covet earnestly the best gifts, said Saul of Tarsus, but behold! I show unto you a more excellent way. The greatest of these is charity."

Saul (later Paul) was a man of one idea which nothing could shake: Christ's:

> "I am Christ's, and let the name suffice you.
> Ay, for me too he greatly hath sufficed.
> Lo, with no winning words I would entice you.
> Paul has no honour and no friend but Christ."

At the same time he was adaptable and became all things to all men. My life has been an adaptation to my environment in pursuit of no particular idea, 'sans' creed and devoid of dogma. I have gained (as I believe) the regard of people in twenty different lands by acceptance of their values, quite apart from my own preconceptions which, however, rarely existed, being all things to all men.

Voltaire once called *un préjugé "une opinion sans jugement"*:[1] I have always felt that others were the best judges of their own affairs. Is not one cause of the comparative failure of a certain power as a colonising nation the fact that it never in history once attempted to enter in the spirit of the governed races?

I should think that the Confucian principle of Forbearance or *Shu* represented the same idea: to the sage this character

---

[1] A prejudice: an opinion without judgement.

summed up the spirit of social intercourse, just as to the charming young Rabbi of Nazareth the love of God and the love of one's neighbour constituted his philosophy of life.

The acceptance of others' points of view is not a British characteristic; that I achieved so large a measure of success in dealing with many contrasted personalities may be partly due to Celtic blood. I am no leader of lost causes, no Lawrence of Arabia, no Gordon of Khartoum, but any reader of my memoirs can see that by rallying myself to others' opinions I won very considerable influence and merged myself in my environment without losing the distinctive traits of my temperament.

It was, I fancy, Chateaubriand[1] (or was it Sainte-Beuve[2]) who said of *une grande amoureuse*[3] of his day that she was good to talk to about ideas. Never, in my multitudinous commerce with Manchus of highest rank, except only in the case of Kuang Hsü to whom I was obviously antipathetic on account of my intimacy with Tz'u Hsi, did I encounter a rebuff. I had the unquestioned 'entree' to perhaps fifty palaces or houses of the great; never was I treated as an alien, always as one of the family. Critics would assert that it could only be at the expense of sincerity, perhaps even by belittling our Caucasian civilisation, that doors were opened to me, so that I never had cause to *faire antichambre ni compter les clous de la porte.*[4] Yet, it was not by *dénigrement* and *disparagement* of my own country that men and women were fain to receive me with

---

[1] François-René, Vicomte de Chateaubriand (1768 –1848), French writer, politician, diplomat and historian who had a notable influence on French literature of the nineteenth century.
[2] Charles Augustin Sainte-Beuve (1804–1869), French literary critic.
[3] A great lover.
[4] Wait for an audience or count the nails of the door.

open arms: I would not deny that after closer acquaintance I often expressed my detestation of our western materialism and of British hypocrisy, but I won access in the first instance by an agreeableness of manner and by my genuine wish to be (not to pose, as) an enquirer, one who wished to learn in the spirit that the greatest sage of China welcomed.

Again, my peculiar standard of morals with the zest for strange adventures stimulating the libidinous side of my nature, which surely, as I am bound to admit, developed itself in titanic sensual excesses, had in the inception nought to do with the appeal I made to young and old. Carnal relations may have, ay and did, come later as the amity developed; but it was not mainly reciprocal plenitude of carnality that attracted sweet Cassia Flower, the Old Buddha, Lien-ying,[1] Junglu,[2] so many fair eunuchs, my dearest Pao-ch'en,[3] Prince Kung[4] and his love-sick *fidus Achates*, ay even the bath attendants at the Hammam and the *comparses*[5] of the theatres, the Manchu soldiery on palace duty, the empress' court ladies, the Yogi and the abbot, the medium of White Cloud Temple and the Bonzes[6] of the Western Hills.

No! Looking back on the vicissitudes of over fifty years and recalling the sorrows of a life which has known, and is still knowing, sombre days, awaiting the inevitable hour when darkness falls, I can see that it was magnetism and sympathy

---

[1] Li Lien-ying, Chief Eunuch, who appears in *Décadence Mandchoue*.
[2] Junglu, Grand Secretary of the Infantry Command in *Décadence Mandchoue*.
[3] Chan Pao-ch'en: an official whom Backhouse claimed as a long-term lover in *Décadence Mandchoue*.
[4] Prince Kung (1833–98), a high-ranking Chinese statesman.
[5] Stooges.
[6] Religious teachers.

that so often carried everything before it, the feeling that here was an alien, a foreign 'devil', whose sole wish was to absorb the best, ay and the worst, elements of a society hitherto beyond his ken. The erotic gambols, the amorous manoeuvres as of a salacious ram or a buck-rabbit came later in plethoric abundance; but it was not as a client entering a bordel to see, and to be seen in, some orgy of unbridled concupiscence that my personality was accented without let or hindrance, practically without introduction or passport.

When still a young man, I gained admission to the Hall of Chaste Pleasures, an ambiguous resort, through a card of Prince Ch'ing. Whether Duke Tsai Lan would have allowed my cooperation without this powerful introduction as a spectator in his bout of frenzied love and relentless flagellation at dearest Cassia's hands I do not pretend to guess: it is probable that he would have denominated me *un sot en trois lettres*[1] or saddled me with *le mot de Cambronne, Merde;*[2] but those were early days and my presence at the male brothel might then have savoured of curiosity or superiority. The time came, however, when I was readily accepted in the multitudinous haunts whither fancy led me, as being, what in fact I was, a zestful enquirer to whom *nihil humanum a me alienum fuit.*[3]

Human affairs are said to be governed by two elements, personal magnetism and good fortune (that goddess whom Juvenal so mercilessly flays in his famous peroration to the tenth Satire, generally considered as his masterpiece, and imitated by Dr. Johnson in *The Vanity of Human Wishes* to

---

[1] Very foolish (literally: a three letter fool).
[2] Shit! Supposedly said by French General Pierre Cambronne at Waterloo when called to surrender.
[3] I am human. I consider nothing human alien to me. (Proverb)

point a moral and adorn a tale. Although in my humble opinion, as in that of the humanist Prof. Ramsay,[1] the fourth satire with its powerful attack on womankind *genus immutabile semper*[2] surpasses it both in eloquence and acerbity), that goddess whom mortals foolishly worship and thereby conduce to their own ruin.

Certainly, fortune has showered few favours upon me but the quality of magnetism remains and apparently may remain to the end. Mayhap,[3] the fickle goddess may intend to make amends to me for "the slings and arrows of outrageous fortune" so amply accorded to me in this life by the grant of special favours in the next. Shall I, Catholic, perchance find a place round and about the Yellow Springs[4] and foregather there with the Empress and so many more dear associates in blissful communion?

My heart has no knowledge; my faith no presentiment. Shall I be witness of a new celestial polity, a dispensation based on justice, *redeunt saturnia regna*,[5] where life is duty and love is law? Shall I see her again, the clear-cut imperial features so delicate in their ivory and olive, the almond eyes, the glorious raven hair?

Shall I have sweet commerce again with her and know from her love? If it may not be, then I must eke out my span, for better or worse, a miserable captive of war, a man without a

---

[1] George Gilbert Ramsay (1839–1921), British classical scholar and translator of Juvenal.
[2] Always unchanging.
[3] Perhaps.
[4] In Chinese and Japanese mythology, the underworld.
[5] Honoured rules return.

fear, without a hope (as Goethe's[1] *Faust* declares himself), in this perplexing world and for the life beyond the grave I can but pray a dreamless sleep. But, in the words of Plato which he places in the mouth of Socrates when reasoning on the possible immortality of the soul in the *Phaedo*,

"Great is the prize and the hope is great."

The Irish Father who on November 25, 1900 received Oscar Wilde into Holy Church thought fit, rather in contravention of the 'secret' of the confessional to publish *urbi et orbi*,[2] that his new penitent had expressed a poignant sorrow at the lateness of his conversion; for the true Faith, *la vera fede*, would have 'curbed' his degeneracy and imposed to his *décadence* or *dégringolade*, a salutary check. Are these deathbed conversions of as much value as the Church would have us believe? 'Unto this last' is a comforting doctrine. *Tu latronem exaudisti*[3] and today the penitent robber is a saint in Paradise in close proximity to Almighty God. Who shall say?

Not otherwise did that exalted, pre-eminent genius, Aubrey Beardsley, write to me from Mentone on March 10, 1898, a week before he died: "Jesus is Your Lord and Saviour; mine equally so. My dearest Trelawny, I am dying. Pray for my soul in Purgatory. I have repented and by all that is holy implore you to seek repentance too: it is never too late, for the door is still open to the worst. I promised to leave to you my obscene

---

[1] Johann Wolfgang von Goethe (1749–1832) German poet, playwright, novelist, scientist, statesman, theatre director, and critic.
[2] To the City [of Rome] and to the World: denotes a papal address and apostolic blessing.
[3] Through the dying thief forgiven. From the Latin hymn *Dies irae* sung during the Catholic funeral mass.

drawing *The Flagellation* which I dedicated to you. May Jesus and the Blessed Virgin forgive you and me! I have burned it, as it was obscene and unholy. Christ's sheltering arms of love alike are cast round better and round worse. Forgive me. Love, deepest love, as always. Aubrey, in my death agony. Hotel Cosmopolitain, Menton." (Although we crossed the frontier of limited, but erotic, contacts, let me say here once for all that Aubrey and I never had carnal intercourse, but he was interested in an abstract sense concerning my idiosyncrasy, realising the appeal to the senses without concrete trial of its joys.)

It was a consummate drawing in aquatintesque executed in line and faint wash: a comely youth with long black hair and the expression of a Rafaele Sarto[1] overpowered by priapean lusts is half recumbent on a settee, his face midway between pain and bliss, turned toward the *fouailleur,*[2] who is himself wholly nude and presenting to the world and to his God an orgasm of cyclopean dimension, wielding *une poignée de verges,*[3] his hand raised in relentless sensual force to belabour the naked *fesses*[4] (*le mele*, the "apples") of the recipient serene in the possession of a capacious hair-encircled *proctodaeum* which is adumbrated by two delicious curves, all a mystery and a wild desire. The patient's equally advanced state of erection is visible (almost palpable) between his half open thighs amid a profusion of perineal curly ringlets.

---

[1] Possibly a mistranscription for Raffaello Sanzio da Urbino – the painter Raphael.
[2] Libertine.
[3] A swatch of birches bound together.
[4] Buttocks.

Wonderful was the strength of those clean firm lines, the bold mass of blotted shadow, the great white spaces, the rhythm of the whole composition which carried with it a suggestion of a Greek vase, a primitive of Giotto[1] or a print of Hokusai.[2] Never a curve, never a line that failed to present an impression of inimitable quality and of original idiom. Aubrey thought of dubbing his drawing '*A Revel of Masoch*' or '*Sade et ses ébats. Dédicace à mon cher ami, Trelawny Backhouse.*'[3]

He who should survive the perusal of my *Décadence Mandchoue* may not impossibly be driven to a conclusion that, if the Manchu regime were decadent, I was still more so and I would not attempt to deny nor to palliate the soft impeachment. The explanation may be found not only in an ample dose of original sin, but in the environment of my early years which I am now about to describe.

It was my fate to be the child of two utterly bad people, a father as false as Iscariot and as salacious as the great god Pan, a mother half Jezebel and half Maenad, a *Mégère des plus effrontées*,[4] subject to violent paroxysms of rage, probably more or less *détraquée* or *tapée*.[5] Both these accursed persons, now (I trust) roaming in the world of shades, forlorn, disconsolate ghosts during a thousand Kalpas[6] of Buddhist eternity, made me the special object of their sadistic cruelty.

---

[1] Giotto di Bondone (c. 1267–1337), Italian painter who reintroduced realism.
[2] Katsushika Hokusai (1760 - 1849), Japanese artist, ukiyo-e painter and printmaker.
[3] Sade and his antics. Dedicated to my dear friend Trelawny Backhouse.
[4] A cheeky shrew.
[5] Unhinged.
[6] A Kalpa is 40 million and 20,000 years. EB

Numberless as the sands of the seashore were the *fessées*[1] that I underwent at their figuratively gore-stained hands; although candour forces me to admit that, like Rousseau [2] in his *Confessions*, I acquired a definite sensuous gratification out of each chastisement administered on general principles for actions of which I was uncapable.

As a child of six, I recall one Sunday morning when my wicked and vindictive *bonne*[3] told my mother that I had 'stolen' a presentation brooch from her (the nurse's) room, the fact being that she had pawned the ornament. And my sire to chastise my buttocks without adducing explanation or cause, while my mother diverted her cruel, torture loving eyes with this choice spectacle, like Messalina [4] revelling in the gladiatorial combats, except that in this case 'twas a child of six, the victim of an unchaste, corrupt, lascivious Neronian monster of thirty years and his wicked sinister lust-haunted wife.

The Murdstones were angels in the home of poor David Copperfield in comparison to *ces drôles que furent Jonathan Backhouse et Florence Trelawny, son épouse.*[5] Her rages were veritable cataclysms; I recall on one occasion at a London terminal, after I had accidentally become separated from her

---

[1] Spankings.
[2] Jean-Jacques Rousseau (1712–1778), Genevan philosopher, writer, and composer. His political philosophy influenced the progress of the Enlightenment throughout Europe, as well as aspects of the French Revolution and the development of modern political, economic, and educational thought.
[3] Maid.
[4] Valeria Messalina (c. 17/20–48), third wife of the Roman emperor Claudius, famed for her murderous cruelty and promiscuity.
[5] To those queers that were Jonathan Backhouse and Florence Trelawny, his wife.

in the crowd, how she shrieked like an antic Bacchanal on Mount Ida on my rejoining her: "You wicked boy, you wicked boy!!" and [causing] *un homme du peuple*[1] to exclaim very audibly: "Too much brandy, old girl: you've got a face on you to scare the crows."

She 'nagged' me night and day through my childish years, and I was of definite use to my father whose sexual activities led him in the direction of the daughter of a neighbouring clergyman, because my imaginary apocryphal misdemeanours served as a convenient cloak to his adulteries, and in the 'happy' couple's endless faultfinding of a hapless child was found a subject which could obliterate tactless references to his lust-driven roaming after strange flesh.

"Children begin by loving their parents; as they grow older, they judge them; seldom, if ever, do they forgive them," as Wilde wrote in *A Woman of No Importance*. Well, in my case, there was never love, always implacable enmity, the study of revenge, immortal hate, and the desire to trample on their graves, a hope that, in a measure, was fulfilled when I cursed in my sire's company at the tomb of my dam her abhorred memory in Chinese, Japanese, Mongol, Manchu, Russian, Pali, German, French, Italian, Spanish, Danish and English, not without a few opprobrious and highly indecent epithets in many other tongues, all the chosen coin of the gutter moulded forth for the benefit of her hated ghost and his stricken ears. He was partly paralysed and unable to extricate himself from my linguistic activities; whilst I watched with unspeakable, unperturbed relish the hot tears welling from his treacherous,

---

[1] A man of the people.

hyena-like, cunning eyes, that could bear to look on torture but that dared not look on war.

"A woman's life is built up of curves of emotion; it is on lines of intellect that a man's life progresses."[1] I think that the Old Buddha did not err when she told me that the Yin element was predominant in my complex nature, despite the fact that I owned (abounding in that sense) to the orgasms of a male even as a Bull Moose *en rut*: perhaps for this cause I have always made a definite appeal to the feminine sex; although I admit that some of the latter were homosexual, *'t'ung helm ai'*.

Aged nine, I was packed off to the Ascot preparatory school of that arch-flogger Sneyd Kynnersley, *ce cardiaque à la maigreur squelettique*[2] and was *sous sa férule*[3] for over three years. He had lavish ideas, installed electric light at great cost when it was almost unknown even in public edifices, before the Queen adopted it at Windsor or Buckingham Palace. He would take the whole school on distant *randonnées*[4] all over England at his own expense: I remember one expedition to Sidmouth, 200 miles distant, where we all bathed and ate strawberries and cream, returning to Ascot at 4a.m. the next day! Then he would take a chosen few to London for theatrical performances and visits to the museums; and during the annual society carnival of Ascot races he invariably marched the whole school of fifty boys to the course, where we witnessed the royal procession (Victoria's obstinate widowhood precluded her presence) from Windsor and admired Alexandra, Princess of Wales, in her radiant and

---

[1] Wilde. E.B.
[2] This heart of skeletal thinness.
[3] Under his rule.
[4] Hikes.

perennial youth. Kynnersley was a rabid Tory and had little use for me as a great nephew of the arch-Whig, C. J. Fox.[1]

His chastisements, as Graf von Kessler,[2] *mon camarade d'école* [3] records in his memoirs, were unforgettable experiences, as our bleeding buttocks testified, bearing witness to his sadistic tendencies, but I deny him not a certain generosity. I was a most sentimental child and recall how Kynnersley and the whole class laughed at me when I read the line from the *Aeneid* where Aeneas sees in a dream the ghost of Hector, *quantum mutatus ab illo Hectore. . .* , who says to him: *"Si Pergama dextra defendi hac possent etiam defensa fuissent."* "Could this right hand have defended Troy, defended 'twould have been." I shed floods of tears in vicarious sympathy for *"Lacrimae rerum"*, tears over the fall of great fortunes. And now Sneyd Kynnersley has been dead these fifty-seven years: I hope he is able to enjoy his flogging activities in Paradise or in Hell.

When Paul Verlaine joined the staff (February 1886), I passed many happy days under his stimulating teaching and acquired a knowledge of the French spirit, *ce panache, cette fleur de chevalerie qu'est la France.*[4] I have only one cause to bless the memory of my most repellent detestable sire, and that is his unexpected permission to pass the *vacances, les jours pascals*, in Paris with Verlaine: I learnt in Panama something that textbooks could not convey, that cosmopolitan outlook, that large-minded habit of life which England in her petty-narrow

---

1 Charles James Fox (1749–1806), British Whig statesman.
2 Harry Clemens Ulrich, Count von Kessler (1868–1937) German diarist and diplomat.
3 My school comrade.
4 This panache, this flower of chivalry which is France.

insularity has always lacked, ay and always will. More's the Pity. Merry and Amen!!

My time at Ascot brought me into contact with Winston Churchill who, like me, was unhappy in a school which catered for the average unimaginative Briton: he told me in 1883 that he was a "very living conservative" and intended one day to be prime-minister. Maurice Baring, who spoke French well, deliberately adopted an English pronunciation to escape the jeers of his school-comrades for affectation. My brother Sir Roger Backhouse, G.C.B., G.C.V.O.,[1] who attained the highest place in H.B.M.'s[2] Navy as First Lord, certainly owed nothing to St. Georges', which was a nursery of stereotyped intellects. Roger was always very rude to me: as a boy of nine, he controverted some remark of mine with a: "Did you dream that, Edme?" 'Twas a great man, but grim and aloof. "Uncapable of pity: void and empty of any dram of mercy."[3]

Six years at Winchester College were little other than a carnival of unbridled lust blended with glad laborious days of training in the humanities. I do not vouch for the statistic but fancy that between 1886 and 1892 I enjoyed carnal intimacy with at least thirty (perhaps more) boys, ascendant and descendant. Had we been found out, expulsion would have been sure and certain. I tremble to think of the sort of nightmare existence my Medea-like mother now grilling in the hottest corner of Nethermost Hell would have inflicted upon me, had the penalty for 'soi-disant' moral flagitiousness been incurred. However, I escaped scot-free, though in my time

---

[1] Admiral of the Fleet Sir Roger Roland Charles Backhouse (1878–1939).
[2] His Britannic Majesty's.
[3] The Merchant of Venice. EB

perhaps a score of boys were expelled for *pedicatio* and for *coitus inter crura* offences (apart from actual penetration), for both of which corporal chastisement was deemed over-light. In fact, those Winchester birchings amounted to very little but appealed to my taste, *à mon goût d'esthète*;[1] the bigger boys were allowed to cane the juniors over the shoulders, not, as one might imagine, across the breech, unmercifully and usually abused the inhuman privilege which the school-statutes had authorised for five centuries; "lest one good custom should corrupt the world."

I obtained a high scholarship at Merton College, Oxon, and was known as Postmaster, a word which is a corruption of Portionis Magister and has (naturally) nought to do with the postal service. My 'outside college' tutor was Walter Pater of Brasenose and I fell completely under his spell. An Italian Father of Siena once assured me that I could not imagine the assaults of lubricity and salacious impulses that beset him, *en moyenne*,[2] regularly once a month and he had to give vent to them by masturbation or by *pedicatio*. In fact, he asked me to accept his *pedicatio* or at least to masturbate him; I declined. I should have styled Pater a sensuous ascetic who needed timeous[3] outlets: his homosexual affinities are well known and my readers may not be astonished to hear that our temperaments met on common and congenial ground. His was a measured type of sensuality very different from mine. Moderation was his motto (*sophrosune* or sober-mindedness) and he would go without sexual activities for months at a time,

---

[1] To my aesthetic taste.
[2] On average.
[3] Sufficiently early.

190

the while he discoursed of and lectured upon "The Dry Light, *siccum lumen,* let Plato teach us to love that, also, duly."

Punctuated with two apparently otiose commas, some verse translations I had made from the Hippolytus of Euripides greatly charmed him ("yes; they are dear lines," said he); and his reward was what for him constituted a bout of love and lust; an attempt of ineffectual penetration, albeit by my higher standards it was scarce other than *un coup d'essai,*[1] in no sense *un coup de maître.*[2] His beautifully measured voice and even rhythm, slightly marred by the affected *traînant*[3] accent of Oxford, are still in my ears; the pale ascetic features, the heavy moustache concealing a sensitive and poetic mouth, the eyes *cernés*[4] and heavy, the painful gait of a *cardiaque*[5] who knew his days were abbreviated, all of these things made to me an irresistible appeal. He fell down dead in the summer of 1894 just as he was entering the dining room where he was tabled to lecture to a few pupils: there he lay without any of the ungainliness of death, as if he had contentedly passed to some greater work, some better ordered polity.

In *The New Republic,* W. H. Mallock[6] presents a portrait of Pater under the transparent disguise of Mr. Rose which, to my

---

[1] An attempt.
[2] A master stroke.
[3] Drawling.
[4] Dark ringed.
[5] Heart patient.
[6] William Hurrell Mallock (1849–1923). Mallock believed the new curriculum of Classical secularism was undermining the Christian faith of English youth, and that they were being further corrupted by the aestheticism of those like Walter Pater. In 1876, he anonymously published a series of satirical fictions in the London magazine *Belgravia*, which mocked leading figures at Oxford. These were developed into a novel, *The New Republic, or, Culture, Faith, And Philosophy In An English Country House,*

mind, cannot be surpassed. The great master of Balliol, Benjamin Jowett, [1] is equally drawn to the life as Doctor Jenkinson; Pater will receive a fuller study when I write further of his hero-worship of Euripides, also of the Emperor Julian, so-called apostate, whom he placed on a pedestal as high as, nay higher than, his adored Marcus Aurelius. Sir Max Beerbohm seems to me to model his beautiful prose on Walter Pater's faultless style, artifice which has become nature, "art that's turned his nature," as Browning says in "One word more," that poem of devotion to his wife.

Jowett has been described by abler pens than mine, by men of his college who knew him more intimately. But I remember an essay which I wrote by his direction: "Why was the drama never popular in Rome?" It was quite slight, and when I went to his study to read to him the paper, I anticipated the sarcastic comments whereof he was master, or possibly the implied rebuke of no comment at all. He sat there blinking like a wise cat before the fire, whilst I did my best by good elocution to lend colour to the subject. He heard me to the end and his reaction was: "quite so", from the Master a very unusual compliment.

Mr. Gladstone, just become prime-minister for the fourth and last time, came to Oxford during my first term to lecture on medieval universities, and I had the honour of being invited to a *soirée* at Christ Church given in his honour by Dean Paget.[2] It

which was a was a *succès-de-scandale*. In it, Pater was parodied as the effete 'Mr. Rose'.

[1] Benjamin Jowett (1817–1893) influential Oxford tutor, administrative reformer, and translator (and bowdleriser) of Plato.

[2] Francis Paget (1851–1911), English theologian, author and the 33rd Bishop of Oxford.

seemed that he had heard of my kinsmanship with Charles James Fox, and in the short conversation I had with him, he asked me about family letters by the great statesman in our possession, especially in regard to an understanding with Napoleon and his early correspondence on the Irish question. "Who can doubt," said Mr. Gladstone, "that Fox was right and Pitt wrong as concerning a settlement in Ireland?" As to Napoleon, had Fox lived, I doubt not but that he, as head of the government, in spite of George III's patriotic but insensate obstinacy, would have achieved a lasting arrangement with the emperor; and the two nations in alliance would thus have changed the face of history." Mr. Gladstone was interested, or so I thought, to hear that I was studying Japanese as an extra-academic subject: it was before the Japan-Chinese war, but Gladstone's predictions to me about Japan's future expansion have been fulfilled almost to the letter.

Verlaine came to stay with me in 1892, and it was only with considerable difficulty that I was able to minister to his needs in 'absinthe,' as that delectable *boisson*[1] was nowhere to be had in antiquated Oxford, but Signor Romano[2] (the Roman as we all called him), well-known later as the genial proprietor of a great restaurant on the Strand, obtained for me a case of *Verte,* and dear Lélian was gloriously *arsouille*[3] during the rest of his visit. I remember his taking me to hear mass at the Catholic Church, and after a pious devotional interlude his amorous gambols with a good-looking under-graduate, for which purpose he borrowed my bedroom and the sadly crumpled, dislocated drapery of my virgin (!!) couch after the

---

[1] Drink.
[2] (Nicolino) Alfonso Romano (?–1901). Head waiter of the Café Royal, who founded the famous restaurant Romanos.
[3] Drunk.

happy consummation abounded as evidence of the transaction plain, as used to be a mile-stone in pre-war times. English boys certainly attracted him, and I never heard of him say a word against Albion, alone among my many French friends in those days of mutual *mésintelligence*, Egypt, Siam, Newfoundland, French shore fisheries, etc.

In the following year 1893 he came again to the university as the guest of the artist Will Rothenstein, now Sir William Rothenstein and delivered several *conferences*. In fact, he liked the environment so well that he in a measure outstayed his welcome. Rothenstein's portrait of Verlaine never appealed to me so much as the sketch made of him in hospital at the end of his life which ennobled and transfigured his features not by flattery but by the artist's spiritual vision. I must consecrate a further study to Lélian and content myself now with a short reference to one who was indeed one of the most dominating influences of my early life and in some respects as a beacon amid the shadows of a melancholy adolescence. "They are indeed our beacon lights seen as we go."[1]

As might be expected from the divine 'insouciance' of genius, we had to provide him with funds for his return to Paris. Max Beerbohm and I were at the same college: I recall his saying to me that I was no subject for his admirable caricatures, as I possessed no outstanding feature, even though the ensemble might (ay! and did) appeal to a good many people. Never shall I forget his genial urbanity and wit, his large tolerance and acceptance of ideas which were alien from his predilection.

---

[1] Vaughan. E.B. Henry Vaughan (1621–1695), Welsh metaphysical poet, author and translator.

Once he told me with keenest pleasure that Oscar Wilde had spoken of him, Max, as the most brilliant of the young decadents of the nineties.

Despite his deep admiration for Wilde as a playwright, that comet in the theatrical firmament, as he called him in an article for the *Saturday Review*, I do not believe that he had great liking for him as a man. Max, Oscar, Bozie and I often dined together at that time, at Kettelars in Soho, at the Berkeley in Piccadilly or the Savoy whence he was later excluded owing to a homosexual incident in his bedroom. Max was always witty, as was another Merton ex-undergraduate now dead, Reggie Turner;[1] but I never remember any remark of Oscar that impressed itself with the exception of the petulance of injured vanity, for he had the disease of self-adulation and might have sat for Dickens' portrait of Harold Skimpole, that overgrown child who, however, in money matters was singularly adept in securing the lion share, despite a pretended indifference to such mundane considerations. Bozie edited *The Spirit Lamp* in my Oxford days: one anonymous article, *The Priest and the Acolyte*, which was attributed wrongly to Oscar, spoke very frankly of extra-ecclesiastical liaisons, one sentence running "And the man stood naked before God" and presumably before the acolyte *par dessus le marché.*[2]

---

[1] Reginald 'Reggie' Turner (1869 –1938), English author, an aesthete and a member of the circle of Oscar Wilde.
[2] As well.

In the long vacation of 1893, I travelled on the same steamer to Canada with Henry Irving[1] and Ellen Terry,[2] she was then still at the height of her charm and I knew that I attracted her. Many were the intimate chats that we enjoyed on the deck of the *Numidian* and we succeeded in making Irving frantically jealous. From what she said to me, it was easy to see that there was a rift within the lute between the two great protagonists of English drama, although their actual separation did not occur for another seven or more years.

As she writes of Irving in her memoirs, so she spoke of him to me as the incarnation of selfishness who would not tolerate, nor speak well of a rival. She admired his art but despised him as a man, even telling me that she might have married him but for his egoism and self-adoration. When they presented *Hamlet*, she informed me that for the part of Ophelia it had been her wish to be in black, instead of the traditional white, but that 'Henry' had vetoed her request because the black of the Danish prince's costume would *jouer* ill with the particular shade that she desired for Ophelia.

When the company gave a 'command' performance of *The Merchant of Venice* at Windsor, Ellen said that in the Trial scene she had, as usual, paused to look appealingly to Shylock before beginning "The quality of Mercy" speech, but that Victoria had imagined she was at a loss for the words, had tapped with her stick, and graciously given her *la réplique*: "The quality of Mercy" . . . so loudly that Ellen, never strong in remembering, without the prompter's aid, the book of the

---

[1] Sir Henry Irving (1838–1905), born John Henry Brodribb; celebrated English stage actor-manager.
[2] Dame Alice Ellen Terry (1847–1928), renowned English actress.

words, became, to use a theatrical term, fluffy and forgot the familiar lines.

For some years Ellen corresponded with me, and her letters bear comparison with the very best English literature and, in fact, one of her *bons mots*, "Before talking of eccentricity first find the circle," was quoted in the House of Commons by the *premier ministre* of the day. She was not consistent in love, as indeed her whole career would suggest with its fateful chances and changes, and after some years she abandoned me like an outworn fan in autumn, but not because of my particular idiosyncrasy: it was rather owing to the fact that she conceived the (neither small nor negligible) resources of my brain to be exhausted, as far as she was concerned. Poor woman, she erred, sadly!

But for a brief season I believe that she was definitely in love with me in a material sense; to her I owe much valuable education on the art of histrionics which stood me later in good stead. She preferred comedy parts such as Beatrice in *Much Ado about Nothing*, Portia of course and Nance Oldfield; but to me it always seemed that she excelled in pathos and that not even queen Sarah herself (though Duse might) could have equalled her in the final scene (*d'ailleurs* quite untrue to history) where Henrietta de France (at the time safe at the Louvre) bids farewell to Charles as he is leaving for Whitehall and for the scaffold on that 30 January 1648 (1649). As Lady Macbeth, she was herself, the paragon of charming womanhood, but was very far from Shakespeare's august creation. Never shall I forget her consummate pathos in:

"What shall Cordelia do? Love and be silent?"[1] Truly hers was a face made for the luring and the love of man.

I was in no sense conspicuous at the University, but did not devote my whole energies to sexual developments nor do I know that the latter were really my main source of interest. When in London during vacations I became intimate with Henry James, Edmund Gosse who always impressed me (as he did Mrs. Asquith[2]) with his pettiness and readiness to take umbrage even in the case of lifelong friends, George Moore,[3] Conrad[4] (whose English I found very difficult to understand despite his rather foreign but wonderful mastery of our tongue); Maarten Martens,[5] the Dutch novelist, whose *God's Fool* always impressed me as a revealing study, during his visits to London; Beardsley, Harland[6] the novelist, a versatile Parisian and the least typical American I ever knew, John Davidson, poet and dramatist whose tragic suicide in the Cornish Sea greatly moved me, le Gallienne,[7] Dowson[8] and other members of the 'Bodley Head' galaxy.

Naturally I became intimate with John Lane, the astute Devonshire publisher, who produced in tiny editions so many works that their authors imagined immortal. His shrewd,

---

[1] King Lear, Act I. E.B.
[2] Margot Asquith. See earlier note.
[3] George Augustus Moore (1852–1933), Irish novelist, short-story writer, poet, art critic, memoirist and dramatist.
[4] Joseph Conrad, born Józef Teodor Konrad Korzeniowski (1857–1924), Polish-British author.
[5] Jozua Marius Willem van der Poorten Schwartz, pen name Maarten Maartens (1858–1915), Dutch writer who wrote in English.
[6] Henry Harland. See earlier note.
[7] Richard Le Gallienne (1866 –1947), English author and poet.
[8] Ernest Christopher Dowson (1867–1900), English poet, novelist, short-story writer, often associated with the Decadent movement.

cunning eyes *à fleur de tête*[1] marked me out as a possible prey, since I was supposed to be wealthy, and in fact he tried to induce me to take at my expense the suite of rooms at the Albany[2] of which he ultimately made his publishing office. He accepted my unstinted hospitality times without number and repaid me by relentless calumny and *dénigrement*. Then he decided to produce *The Yellow Book* (in spring of 1894) my name figured in the prospectus of contributors; and a *soi-disant littératour* of Cambridge made a cheap witticism out of my *prénom et nom de famine*[3] which happened to head the list of contributors by dubbing me 'A Lear-eye Bacchus,' a typical undergraduate gibe. I was in good company, for my dear Aubrey became 'Daubrey Weirdsley' and Max Beerbohm 'Bare Bum,' a sobriquet as vulgar as insolent, for I suppose that it was intended to suggest proclivities in regard to the male or female (*quién sabe*)[4] posterior, in which Max was assuredly disinterested (certainly so as regards the *Arschloche*[5] of masculine type).

I wrote for *The Yellow Book* a study which later I asked leave to withdraw as being considered in dubious taste by parties to whom I was bound to give way. It concerned an Englishman of old family, Mr. Noel,[6] a relative of Lord Byron and of the Earl of Gainsborough, who possessed an estate on the island of

---

[1] Bulging eyes.
[2] A famous apartment complex in Piccadilly.
[3] First name and surname.
[4] Who knows. (A statement).
[5] Arsehole.
[6] Frank Noel.

Eubaea (Evvoia) [1] not far from the Euripus [2] with its mysterious tides and Chalois familiar in the Tale of Troy.

He had kindly received me as his guest during one August, having met me accidentally in Athena, and showed to me most generous hospitality, distressed by the fact that I incurred a serious fall one pitch dark night from an unprotected balcony, since I had rashly moved my chair, unwarned by Noel of the absence of parapet. Mr. Noel was, as I found out later, ostracised by the foreign community and in the best Greek circles owing to his supposed complicity (in the year 1870) in the ransoming of two wealthy Yorkshiremen, Lord Muncaster[3] and Mr. H. [sic] Vyner[4] (brother-in-law of Lord Ripon – later Marquess), who had been captured by brigands, being really tenants of Noel.

The two gentlemen had been seized in the mainland near the plains of Marathon and a ransom of (I think) a million drachmas (at that time say £35,000) was demanded. Lots were cast between the two prisoners for the release of the winner in order to arrange for the ransom. Both men were wealthy, but, as Muncaster thought he could obtain the money on collateral security more easily than Vyner who would have had to break certain family entails, the latter chivalrously waived his priority, partly on the ground that Muncaster was a married man. Apparently the latter raised the money, or at least the greater portion, but failed to appear at the appointed

---

[1] Euboea.
[2] Strait between the island and the main land. E.B.

[3] Josslyn Francis Pennington, 5th Baron Muncaster (1834 –1917) British soldier and Conservative Party politician.
[4] Frederick Grantham Vyner (1847–1870. Beloved by Lord Rosebery.

rendezvous and informed the authorities. The brigands cut off one of Vyner's ears and announced that he would be put to death, unless the ransom was paid within a *délai*[1] of ten days. Muncaster again failed of his promise and Vyner lost his life. It was openly said that Mr. Noel was privy to the plot and would have received half the proceeds of the ransom. The tragedy made a great sensation in England and the Prince of Wales wrote personally to Lord Ripon, then a member of Mr. Gladstone's government, to express his august sympathy and displeasure at Muncaster's treachery.[2]

As I say, all those works were to me a sealed book, but after my return from the *villégiature chez M. Noel*,[3] I attended a garden party at Tattoi, their summer *plaisance*, given by the King and Queen of the Hellenes. When I was presented *au charmant monarque que fut feu le Roi Georges*,[4] he smiled most genially (if a trifle ironically) and said in fluent English: "Oh! yes, Mr. Backhouse, I have heard a lot about you. Did you come across any brigands in my kingdom during your wanderings? You stayed with Noel in Evvoia (Eubaea), quite an ideal spot to encounter them!"

In fact, when Mr. Noel and I repaired to the British Legation prior to our journey to Evvoia, so as to inform Mr. Edwin Egerton (later Sir Edwin), the Minister, of my movements (for I had come to Greece with a special introduction from the Foreign Office) and to bespeak his good offices in case of our

---

[1] Time limit.
[2] It was reported that due to the national disgrace of the affair, the Greek Government sought to shift the blame on to Noel. See also: *Letters of Mr Frank Noel respecting the Murder by Brigands of the Captives of Maraton*, Williams and Norgate, London 1871.
[3] Vacation at Mr. Noel's.
[4] To the charming monarch that was the late King George.

meeting brigands, Mr. Egerton, a typical British diplomat, yawned in a discreet, but bored way, remarking: "You are the best judge of brigands, surely, Mr. Noel!" I suppose that as I was a callow youth, the sarcasm escaped me but it greatly irritated poor Noel, and I do not wonder thereat.

Well, after my reception at Tattoi, I wrote to Mr. Noel about the matter and assured him of my gratitude for his hospitality; he sent to me a charming reply, explaining that he had been falsely accused and authorising me to present the facts in the guise of a romance, *un roman à clef*, stupidly adding that he should sue King George I of Greece for slander! I wrote the paper, submitting it to Noel who approved it without remark – it was accepted by Harland (to whom at the moment I was acting as sub-editor) and was to be published in Number I of *The Yellow Book* along with Max Beerbohm's well-known essay on Cosmetics, Henry James' *The Lion* and the drawings by Aubrey which "... like an eagle in a dove-cote, Flutter'd your Volscians in Corioli; Alone I did it."[1]

As, however, my family had certain connections with the great house of Vyner and in view of Lord Ripon's high place in the government, I submitted the paper to Lady Ripon, the sister, and to Mr. R. C. Vyner, the brother, of the murdered man. They approved of the spirit of my article, and Lady Ripon quoted the scriptural: "Vengeance is Mine: I will repay", which Tolstoi uses as the motto to Anna Karenina; but both of them, and particularly Lady Ripon who was a woman of the greatest piety, asked that I should, "as a favour to them," withdraw the paper, "as it was better not to revive buried and discreditable (to Muncaster) memories."

---

[1] Coriolanus, last scene. E.B.

Henry James had read my *coup d'essai* not without approval *sous réserve*: he wrote to me:

"Dear Mr. Backhouse,

Je vous en fais mon compliment. [1] You have written a psychological study of which the subject would appeal to Paul Bourget.[2] Might I hint to you, suggest would be the better word, that you still lack technique? It will cost to you much time and labour to acquire; but you will allow me to say, without flattery, that I believe you will succeed. Why not ask Geo. Moore to read over your paper and to make a few luciferous suggestions? Cordially, Henry James. March 21, 94."

Until five years ago, I still possessed this almost maiden effort and re-read it one summer's day of 1937: it impressed me, despite certain crudities and, as Henry James thought, lack of technique, as a study, not without value, of a neurotic self-ridden man. And I looked back upon my work in the spirit of one who had endeavoured well. It was vivid and, I think, convincing: anyhow it satisfied Noel who much regretted that what he unjustly called a "ridiculous family prejudice" had vetoed publication. John Lane was furious with me for listening to Lady Ripon and her brother, threatening to sue me for breach of contract. As, however, I had some law and was informed by Mr. Geo. Lewis (late Sir George Lewis Bt.)[3] that he had no case whatsoever, I told him in no measured term that I was quite indisposed (*peu disposé à me soumettre à votre*

---

[1] I congratulate you.
[2] Paul Charles Joseph Bourget (1852–1935), French novelist and critic.
[3] Sir George Henry Lewis, 1st Baronet (1833–1911), the famous lawyer in England.

disgracieux chantage)[1] to submit to his base 'blackmail'. He knew not a word of French, so I am afraid that the sarcasm fell on deaf ears, for none but he saw my reply, only Aubrey who approved it.

Muncaster only died a few years back, receiving an obituary notice of *The Times* which recalled the incident in veiled, but far from flattering terms. He had been practically ostracised in Yorkshire for half a century. Lord Muncaster, *entouré du mépris de tours*[2] would probably have started a process for libel had the article appeared, but no British jury was likely to award to him other than contemptuous damages.

I sent my article to George Moore and saw him later at the Authors Club: he discoursed to me with eloquence and fluency, praising the subject but criticising the treatment. "The public will only read romances which without being commonplace fall within the bounds of the possible, as they consider that which is outside their conception is alien to their tastes." (*Les grands esprits se rencontrent*[3] for Anatole France makes *un propos identique*[4] in *La Belle au bois dormant.*) "Your paper is a record of fact, but as a *nouvelle* it will not do: you should rewrite it as an historical record. Jane Austen once criticised her niece's novel because it related an incident of a man who had broken his arm and who took a long stroll the same day; this had actually occurred in the case of the authoress' father, but Jane declared that it was too much (even though a fact) for the public to swallow."

---

[1] Little disposed to submit to your disgraceful blackmail.
[2] Surrounded by contempt.
[3] Great minds think alike.
[4] An identical statement.

I admired Moore's lion head and pontifical assurance, his delivery *urbi et orbi*: [1] yet despite his mellifluous flow of language, I did not always rise to his exalted level of thought, which seemed to me like a phrase of little meaning, though the words are strong: sound and fury signifying nothing.

Duse[2] came to London that summer and presented *La Dame aux Camélias* and *L'Arlésienne*: in the last act of the former play where the heroine is dying of tuberculosis, I thought her definitely superior to Sarah. Thanks to Ellen Terry, she received me at the theatre in the company of a *garçonne*, in male evening dress, wearing a monocle, hair closely wrapped, a malacca gold-headed cane in her hand and a *gibus*.[3] She was very jealous of my presence and I was told that this sentimental attachment was shortening Eleanora Duse's days. This was palpably not the case, as the diva had multitudinous male *affaires du coeur* [4] in succession to this Lesbian attachment, but I fancy at the end of her life she discovered another inseparable homosexual affinity who made her life miserable by tyranny and supervision at Florence after the breach with Gabriel d'Annunzio.

At that time I started a short career as a prodigal plunger in the turf and won over £1,000 in a great Ascot handicap. By the introduction of Haddon Chambers,[5] an Australian playwright who had found success in London, I became acquainted with a

---

[1] To the city and the world: as in a papal address.
[2] Eleonora Giulia Amalia Duse 1858–1924), commonly known as Eleonara Duse; renowned Italian actress.
[3] Opera hat - name of inventor, an old name for folding: hats. E.B.
[4] Affairs of the heart.
[5] Charles Haddon Spurgeon Chambers (1860 –1921), Australian-born dramatist who relocated to England. Twice married.

Jewish diamond broker, *un coquin fieffé*[1] named Leveson, an Australian known as 'Captain' Kennion,[2] a brother of the then Bishop of Bath and Wells, and two low class racing habitues. These gentlemen imagined me to be very wealthy and looked upon me as a heaven-sent windfall, *une bonne aubaine*. Their idea was to invite my company to the carnival known as Goodwood races, to do fictitious betting commission for me in the ring and to suck from me my last penny. It is possible that I might have been their victim, as Kennion was essentially plausible: however, on arriving at the beautiful circular course in the Duke of Richmond's park at the top of a long hill, I ran into the Right Hon. James Lowther M.P., [3] a fellow Yorkshireman who had been Chief Secretary for Ireland and was a great figure in the racing world, owner of thoroughbreds and a shining light of the Jockey Club, that *crème de la crème* of British aristocracy.

---

[1] An unmitigated rogue.

[2] Thomas Robert Kennion (1851–1917), only brother of the Rt. Rev. George Wyndham Kennion, Anglican Bishop of Bath and Wells. He was born in England. (Perhaps Backhouse's mistake over nationality was due to his brother having also been Bishop of Adelaide.) He served in the West York Milita, became a drill instructor in South Africa for the Cape Mounted Police, joined the Metropolitan Police, and was appointed Chief Constable of Wigan in 1880. He resigned just three years later (whether of his own volition is unknown), and then became with his wife, Emily Charlotte, a theatrical manager. In 1888 they were bankrupted, but this was annulled. He died in South Africa, suggesting they possibly separated (Emily had lost one of her legs in an accident, and would die following the removal of the other.) Despite Kennion being termed "courteous, obliging, and kind to all" on his departure as Chief-Constable, a later series of newspaper reports, including one involving the passing of a dud cheque, does suggest a dual character. [Appointment Of A New Chief Constable Of Wigan, *Wigan Observer and District Advertiser*, 14 August 1880, p5; Presentation To The Late Chief Constable, *Wigan Observer and District Advertiser*, 21 March 1884, p5; A Dishonoured Cheque, *Exeter And Plymouth Gazette*, 10 February 1902, p2; A Theatrical Venture, *The Daily Telegraph*, 6 October 1903, p5; The Music Box, *The Stage*, 17 August 1922, p13; FamilySearch.org.]

[3] James Lowther (1840–1904) Conservative politician and sportsman.

Most graciously, in the midst of his pre-occupations (he had just been conversing with Albert Edward, Prince of Wales, and the notorious Mrs. Langtry,[1] 'Bertie's' cast off favourite was waiting to speak with him) he called me to him: "Fake a stomach-ache, look the part as you, being an actor, can do, and go back to London at once. You are in the hands of the worst sharpers in town: they will skin you till you pawn your shirt." And so I rather ingeniously assumed the postures of one smitten on the stage with a sudden pain and by Lowther's kindness was removed from the course to a jolting ambulance waggon.

The nearest railway station at Chichester was some miles away; but I survived the ambulance *cahotage*[2] (like *la fortune qui me cahote toujours*)[3] and retraced my steps to London town, miraculously and suddenly cured of my unlooked for indisposition. Twas a knightly gesture of a front-bench politician and former member of the government to come to my rescue in an *impasse* in which I should have known better than to involve myself, neck and crop, *jusqu'au cou!*[4]

In the intervals of numerous love affairs on which I will not dwell as they were only the curtain raisers to an endless series of prodigal excesses elsewhere narrated, I became a *habitué* of the Farm Street[5] Jesuit Church, where once Walter Pater had loved to *assister* with his harmonious presence, if not as

---

[1] Emilie Charlotte Langtry, née Le Breton, later,Lady de Bathe (1853–1929), English Society beauty, actress, producer, and sometime mistress of the Prince of Wales.
[2] Jolting.
[3] The fortune that has always jolted me.
[4] Up to the neck.
[5] In Mayfair.

worshipper, then as aesthete who loved the rich ritual and the incense wafted heaven-ward. Father Bernard[1] took me over the Catechism and I very nearly followed the admonition of Cardinal Newman in 1890 to receive Holy Baptism: yet to the good father's grievous disappointment I failed at the last and recall his reproachful: "You shall not come to Me, but I will come to you", a prophesy duly fulfilled in my old age 48 years thereafter. *Le giron de l'Eglise: quel indicible bonhour! Quelle benediction de Dieu![2]*

Dr. Charles Gore, later Bishop of Oxford, also took me under his wing at Pusey House: I think he lacked the courage to imitate Newman's example and remember his speaking of the essential primacy of Rome, the need for reunion and his phrase: "The Basilica of Saint Peter must for ever blazon its message *urbi et orbi*: it is eternal as Rome herself." Gore was fond of young men in a slightly sensuous way which might have given an impression of lewdness, as he embraced his disciples in the street; albeit in fact he was purity itself and rebuked my relations with Verlaine, suspecting, I fancy, that there was more in them than met the eye. He certainly liked my candour and called me *'anima naturaliter Christiana,'*[3] a compliment which, as the reader knows, I in no way deserved then nor deserve now.

---

[1] Rev. Bernard Vaughan. See earlier note.
[2] The bosom of the Church: what unspeakable goodness! What a blessing of God!
[3] Naturally Christian.

As a contrast to those ritualistic and erotic, activities, I sat at the feet of Herbert Spencer[1] at the Athenaeum[2] and he spoke of my flair for languages, remarking that he deemed it of a low order among intellectual endowments and a reversion to primitive man. It had never occurred to me that the denizens of the stone age (or what would today be called Peking man) were linguists, and felt rather flattered at the thought.

Spencer's vast intellect was strangely pedestrian: poetry and imagination were relentlessly shut out. His talks with me at the Athenaeum always attracted a number of interested auditors, much to his annoyance, though most people of his eminence would have been flattered; but, of course, there was a considerable episcopal and clerical element at the Athenaeum to whom he was anathema. He said that he would gladly have proposed me as a member but his unpopularity in the religious world would have ensured my being blackballed, *tnatum religio potuit suadere malorum.*[3] Clouston, a great alienist[4] of Edinburgh, told me my brain was purely mimetic without creative power.

Meantime, Wilde's reckless publicity in flaunting his predilection, more particularly with *la canaille,*[5] lackeys, grooms and professional blackmailers, was drawing him nearer to the abyss: incidents repeated themselves when he left behind ocular proofs of his orgies in hotel bedrooms:

---

[1] Herbert Spencer (1820–1903) English philosopher, sociologist, biologist, and anthropologist; famous for his hypothesis of social Darwinism whereby superior physical force shapes history.
[2] The Athenaeum club in in Pall Mall: founded in 1824 for gentlemen with intellectual interests.
[3] Lucretius. E.B. "To such heights of evil are men driven by religion."
[4] Psychiatrist.
[5] Riff-raff.

horrible proofs of a most painstaking *pedicatio* were found on the sheets and meticulously preserved by the management to be produced in due course at the third *procès*[1] with the medical analysis of human semen, human excrements *et de la vaseline*: like Messalina (except for the homosexuality) he performed mock marriage in the Hotel Bristol with a catamite in female attire from the gutter and the results of their union were concrete and visible (as formerly at the Savoy Hotel) on the drapery of the nuptial couch. At the time he was drawing £200 weekly from his two plays, *An Ideal Husband* and *The Importance of Being Earnest*: but his *folie des grandeurs* prevented his benefiting from his large income. It is certain that no action would have been taken by the Treasury, had he not himself brought the matter into the limelight by his insensate action against Queensberry. *Quos vult perdere prius dementat Juppiter.*[2]

In 1895 I started a new liaison of a type which may surprise my readers: *la belle Otéro*,[3] *le danseuse* was then at the height of her fame but *un insulaire*[4] named C. W. L. Bulpett[5] was paying to her huge subsidies out of borrowed money (he was heir to a wealthy banker and the usurers were glad to lend him

---

[1] Trial.

[2] Those whom Jupiter wishes to destroy he first deprives of reason.

[3] Carolina 'La Belle' Otero (1868–1965), spanish courtesan, dancer and actress.

[4] An islander: i.e. not someone from the Continent.

[5] Charles William Lloyd Bulpett (1852–1939), English barrister, big game hunter, mountain climber (including of the Matterhorn), boxer, fencer, wrestler, and cricketer. As a young man he swam the Thames in a frock coat, top hat and cane for a wager of £100. He befriended Baron and Baroness Blixen; authored *A Picnic Party in East Africa,* and died in Nairobi. Otero allegedly denuded him of £100,000.

[https://oldafricamagazine.com/charles-bulpett/]

money at 60%), demanding in return a monopoly, surely an unreasonable request in such an environment.

At all events, *elle to mit à la porte*[1] and I succeeded him without the slightest expectation of interfering in her manifold love-engagements, so long as she allowed to me a certain priority and preferential share. So I took for her a *chic appartement* at l'Hotel Westminster, Rue de is Paix, my choice being due to the management's intimate knowledge of my family which enabled me to obtain practically unlimited credit (not in the Comte de Monte Christo sense but by ordinary standards) for Otéro's needs which were on a grand scale. Mme. Bernhardt laughed at my infatuation: *"Tu vas t'en mordre les doigts tôt ou tard; tu regretteras bien sûrement ton collage, qui nest guère digne d'un homme de ton acabit et est des plus stupides. C'est à dèsopiler la rate, à la vérité; voilà tout: je m'esclaffe à ton compte, mon cheri."*[2]

Fate, nevertheless, treated me in this connection with undeserved favour; like that ancient of the Mongolian Boundary Pass, who saw in the loss of an admired horse a blessing in disguise, so did my 'amours' with Otero reap for me an unexpected harvest, *une récolte que je ne méritais guère.*[3] It was thus wise. During that arctic January of 1895, when Panama shivered and *grelottait la fièvre, en présence des ravages de cette fatale grippe,*[4] Otéro became indisposed (apparently *d'une crise nerveuse*)[5] and I, in obedience to my

---

[1] She showed him the door.
[2] "You'll bite your fingers sooner or later, you'll certainly regret your liaison, which is hardly worthy of a man of your style and is most stupid. That's all: I laugh on your account, my dear. "
[3] A harvest that I did not deserve.
[4] Shivering with fever, in the ravages of this fatal flu.
[5] A nervous crisis.

idol's tearful wish, escorted her to Monte Carlo and *la Côte d'Azur* for a sojourn among the flowers of the *Midi*. She was the observed of all observers, while men (and women) probably wondered *"que diable allais-je faire dans cette galère,"* [1] to misquote Molière. I knew not whether I had the words *ressortissant Britannique* [2] inscribed upon *ce visage déformé, cette trogne d'outre:* [3] if so, they may have exclaimed: *"Mais pour un insulaire, avouez que voilà un insulaire".* [4]

One evening Otéro, whose frankness I admired, casually notified me of a *rendez-vous d'amour* with a grand duke (Boris, [5] I believe), and suggested that *"j'aurais la bonté de foutre le camp pour la moment, afin de la mettre à même de recevoir cette Altesse-là des plus precieuses dans le salon à nous ou plutôt à moi"*!! [6] She was certainly *culottés à un haut degré*, but *comme d'habitude* [7] I yielded to her *lubie* [8] and betook myself to the Casino. *Eh! bien! j'avais de la veine ce soir-là* [9] and found myself the gainer of Fr.30,000, more than ample to defray the far from negligible outlay that Monte Carlo connotes, especially with a famous *demi-mondaine qui me menait par le bec.* [10]

---

[1] What the devil was I going to do in this gallery.
[2] British national.
[3] This deformed face, this face from beyond.
[4] But as an islander, admit that here you're an outsider.
[5] Grand Duke Boris Vladimirovich of Russia (1877–1943), son of Grand Duke Vladimir Alexandrovich of Russia, a first cousin of Tsar Nicholas II. A notorious playboy.
[6] "I would be kind enough to get the hell out for the moment, in order to put her in a position to receive this most precious Highness in this living room of ours, or rather mine"!!
[7] Cheeky to a high degree but as usual...
[8] Caprice.
[9] Ah well! I was lucky that night.
[10] High class prostitute who lead me by the nose.

Whom should I meet at the tables than Sam Lewis, [1] the notorious Israelite usurer of Cork Street Piccadilly, the same who left his fortune of one and a half million sterling to the London Hospital, *à la Rockefeller*, wishing to redeem a career that had battened on the pabulum furnished by the embarrassed aristocracy, Marquis of Ailesbury, [2] Lord Haldon [3] and the rest including Albert Edward, Prince of Wales, who was honoured by special rates, by abundant (and I believe genuine, for he had a kind heart) charitable dispositions at the last.

He was a little man (bold as Julius Caesar, that generous friend of Jews in Rome's Suburra, that "noblest man that ever lived in the tide of times"), aged about sixty, with an attractive *bonhomie*: certainly he liked me personally and had often accommodated my immediate sieve-like needs with loans for a 'monkey' (£500) and more at 60% *usure*. He was an enthusiastic gambler but, I believe, made a point of limiting his stakes to Fr.25,000 ('or' of course), £1,000 in what we used then to call sovereigns, or ever we cried 'Ichabod', the glory is departed!

He had been, to my nescience, an interested spectator of my 'chance', probably not devoid of jealousy, seeing that *il était allé aux cerises* [4] and had lost, so he said (and doubt it not), Fr.24,000 in one unlucky coup after another. He called out to

---

[1] Samuel Lewis (1837–1901); the most famous and fashionable London money-lender of his day; philanthropist.
[2] George William Thomas Brudenell-Bruce, 4th Marquess of Ailesbury (1863–1894), a chronic gambler and wastral.
[3] Lawrence Hesketh Palk, 2nd Baron Haldon (1846–1904); a chronic gambler, bankrupted 1891. [Iain Fraser, *The Palk Family Of Haldon House And Torquay*, Sylverwood Publishing, Newton Abbot 2008, pp67-76.
[4] He had bad luck.

me in Cockney English across the tables: "Old Boy" (his favourite mode of salutation), "you have won more than is good for you: I know your naughty tastes. Look here! come to my rescue and lend me say Fr.25,000. I am going to have a good old gamble, and you can go home to 'la belle Otéro' if she has finished with Boris!" (How he knew, I have no idea, but 'Sam' was omniscient in affairs of the heart). And I *de répondre*: "All right, Sam (he was one of those one instinctively addressed by his *nom de baptême*), take these 25 Crédit Lyonnais *billets* of 1,000 apiece and *bonne chance*. I'll not charge you 60% interest, you old devil: you shall have it for love. *Bonsoir*: I'm going back to my fickle flame." "Thanks, old boy: I shan't forget *et tu auras de mes nouvelles demain matin*.[1] So I made my way hotelwards, found Otéro unsated with love and bed (as Homer remarks) and ready for a fresh bout with me. The British temperament (or Semitic, as Herr Hitler might agree) is badly understood on the Continent; as a nation, we are indeed shut off from the whole human race outside the tiny inland, as in the time of Virgil, the Mantuan seer.

I knew my man and assured her that he would repay to me the accommodation, at the latest, even if he lost again, as soon as funds could be remitted to Monaco from London. Well Otéro had had enough of *coitus par les voies naturelles*,[2] and insisted upon repeated acts of *pedicatio, feuille de rose, des manoeuvres buccales et labiales, l'avalement de ce dont on bûche, et tout is reste*.[3]

---

[1] And you will hear from me tomorrow morning.
[2] Coitus by natural routes.
[3] Anal intercourse, anilingus, cunnilingus, semen swallowing, and everything else.

Tired out next morning, I received a visit from Sam: he had won over a million francs the previous evening, I had brought to him luck, he would never forget it. As an earnest [missing word] of his future favours and willingness to allow to me all required accommodation not exceeding (say) £5,000 on 'expectations' at 'reduced' rates (probably 40%), he had brought back to me my Fr.25,000 plus what he called *un témoignage de reconnaissance des plus profondes*[1] in the shape of Fr.100:000, say £4000 sterling, being a commission of 10% on his winnings.

I felt embarrassed in the presence of such princely generosity but could not hurt his feelings (for he was terribly touchy, like many Jews) by refusal: even so he continued to think of me as his creditor and always remained my friend in weal and in woe. Dear Sam, *sit tibi terra levis*,[2] he died in 1900,[3] and his wife, a fat Jewess, almost immediately cajoled herself into *secondes noces*[4] with a worthless army officer who ill-treated her and mocked her vulgarity, while feeding on her money, for Sam left to her a liberal jointure for life.

The return to Paname coincided with the end of my vacation, but the outbreak of influenza had necessitated the postponement of the last term at Oxford. Otéro and I remained on friendly terms, but found "mettle more attractive"[5] in the following spring and graciously dispensed me, much to Sarah's delight, from following further in her train.

---

[1] A testimony of deepest gratitude.
[2] May the earth rest lightly on you.
[3] January 1901.
[4] Second marriage.
[5] Shakespeare, *Hamlet.* E.B.

And now I must, for candour, record briefly an event, which still to name, my memory quakes and fears. I fell in love with a girl named Doris,[1] member of a very ancient Yorkshire house, a daughter of the gods divinely tall and most divinely fair. She promised to marry me and could perchance have changed the whole face of my life. It may be that other *penchants* would have been discarded like an outworn shoe, and that I should have led an existence sheltered, wealthy and easy in the hospitable county of York. It was not to be: *Dis aliter visum!*[2]

The date had been set for our bridal day and all was going merry as a marriage bell. Presents past counting were showered upon us, cheques, clocks, tiepins for me, a diamond tiara for her, a splendid hunter from her father, for she was a superb equestrian, plate, *coutellerie*,[3] napery and heaven knows what else. Four days before the wedding, I received a note from Doris: "My dear Boy, I cannot marry you, because I am infatuated by Fred S., must needs marry him privately tomorrow. Good-bye. Keep the locket I gave you, to Edmund from Doris Always, always, ("Always" sometimes does not last long!). Good-bye: Doris."

When I read this effusion, my first thought was: "What a bore! All the presents must be returned to the senders!" I was stunned for the nonce but this wound was deep. The happy couple came back from *le lune de meil*[4] to the Yorkshire home of Fred S. The day following their return, they went out hunting: her hunter was in the first flight, made a false step and broke Doris' neck. I attended the funeral as an outsider

---

[1] Unidentified.
[2] The gods deemed otherwise.
[3] Cutlery.
[4] The honeymoon.

grieving greatly and Fred S. came up to thank me for what he called a kind gesture and for the red roses (her favourite flower) which I had sent as a *couronne*.[1] Thus ended my romance. Twas a case of the *'Pauci quos sequus amavit Juppiter'*, "Just heaven is sparing of his favours to mortals."

During the *vacances pascales* I was in Paris and learned to know Monsieur Got[2] of *La Comédie Francaise*, an urbane gentleman who gave to me many theatrical lessons which have remained vividly with me. I admired his reserve, his absence of gesture, his studied avoidance of emphasis: for my benefit he took a scene from *Le Juif Polonais*,[3] where Mattathias, stricken by haunting remorse from his crime of fifteen years ago, says to Christian Bème, the intended of his daughter, who in discussing the as-yet undetected crime and the undiscovered *corpus delicti*,[4] remarks that an error was made by the authorities in not arresting the proprietors of lime kilns: "Why! Christian, I had a lime kiln at that time" (laughing whole-heartedly and in full appreciation of the joke in perfect imitation of an innocent man's delight at the coincidence). And Christian to reply; "You, Burgomaster, you!" and to roar with laughter. Now, as Irving presented the scene, it was palpable to the audience that he was the guilty man: his reply amounted to a conscious stricken admission.

As M. Got rehearsed it to me, none would have imagined him guilty with his frank easy manner, his natural laugh, his

---

[1] Wreath.

[2] François Jules Edmond Got (1822–1901), French actor and librettist.

[3] *The Polish Jew*: an 1867 stage play by authors Émile Erckmann and Alexandre Chatrian. It was later adapted as an opera. Hearing sleigh bells at his daughter's wedding, a Jewish innkeeper is reminded of a past murder he committed.

[4] Body of the crime.

bearing and dominance were absolutely disarming. He repeated the lesson several times and finally expressed himself satisfied. When he gave the final scene, where the wretched Burgomaster, demon haunted, dreams of his trial and sentence to death for murder; it is the wedding day of Bème and Julia, the daughter. Mattathias' door is looked: Bème breaks it open and rushes in to discover the Burgomaster rising distraught from his bed and exclaiming *'d'une voix coupée at presque inartioulée'*: *"Ôte-moi la corde du cou!"*[1] and falls dead. Tis only then that Bème realises that he is marrying with the family of a confessed murderer. In the London presentation of Irving, the Burgomaster's guilt was apparent from the beginning.

Mme. Bernhardt most graciously acted a scene from *Cléopâtre* with me, for the moment, as Antoine. I felt like exclaiming to my goddess: "I am grown sick of unreal passions! Make the world thine Actium, me thine Antony!" It was the scene wherein Sardou presents the amorous Lagide consummating by her flight at Actium the defeat and disgrace of her lover, *pour le garder tout à elle.*[2] Anatole France, however, *croyait plutôt qu'elle s'était sauvée, saisie d'une pour folle;*[3] if he is right, he differs in toto from Sarah's conception. Antoine perceives the purple-sailed barge, the Antoniade, fleeing from the line of battle; he pursues her, abandoning the fight by a cowardice which in his case, the hero of Pharsalia and of Philippi becomes an sot of courage. As Oscar Wilde says: "There are terrible temptations which it requires strength to yield to. Only fools say that weakness succumbs to temptation."

---

[1] In a broken and almost inarticulate voice "Take off my neck rope!"
[2] To keep it all to herself.
[3] Believed rather that she had fled, seized by madness.

Antoine accoste l'Antoniade; il y monte et sa sásseoir seul à la proue, la tête dans ses mains.[1]

Such was the scene that Sarah permitted me to act with her: she was very critical without withholding a need of praise. It was the technique which I lacked and thanks to her magnetic personality acquired beyond my expectation. She actually proffered to me a place as companion in her company during a future *tournée,*[2] and as interpreter in English and Spanish to the press and the public ignorant of French.

I don't suppose that she could ever have offered to me parts of importance, even if my histrionic ability had excelled, owing to my French accent, though incomparably better than now in a degenerate eld[3] not being sufficiently *perfectionné*. Still, it was a gratifying memory, something that one would not willingly let die, "while this machine is to him," to quote Hamlet's letter to Ophelia.

Mallarmé, whose *séjours*[4] at the Rue de Rome were somewhat spasmodic, was in Paris that Easter: generosity itself, he suggested our sending an eleemosynary [5] offering to poor Lélian not in our name, but in that of a group of contemporaries without naming them, but with the legends

---

[1] Antoine accosted the Antoniade; he climbed up and sat alone at the prow, his head in his hands.
[2] Tour.
[3] *Eld = old age (antique). E.B.
[4] Stays.
[5] Charitable.

"*Homage au génie*".[1] Mirbeau,[2] Loti[3] and we two managed to arrange the transaction with the Crédit Lyonnais, and a bank messenger convoyed the draft to Lélian who was *infiniment touché* and attributed the gift to Daudet and Zola (of all people in a distinctly improbable combination!).

Verlaine's attribution of this dole, *ce denier d'aumone*, to Zola, the last man to send anonymous presents, started a talk with Stéphane[4] on the Médan school; as is well known, Mallarmé was actively opposed to Zolaism or his particular type of naturalism, and ridiculed the pretentious heralding of *Le Rêve* and the publishers' announcement that M. Zola had actually on this occasion written a pure book quite proper *pour la jeune fille*.[5]

He did not condemn *Nana* so much as *L'Assommoir*, *La Joie de vivre* or *La Terre* which was, as it was to Tolstoi, to him a thing accursed. Stéphane admired the tribedistic[6] section of the novel[7] with Satine and said it coincided with Nana's present tastes! *"Tiens,"* said he, *"veux-tu faire la connaissance de Nana? Elle ne fut jamais atteinte de cette petite verole ni en est morte non plus comme Zola dit. Elle est toujours on vie, mais it to faudra faire un petit pèlerinage à Melun. Voici mon Bristol; va la trouver; ça t'intéressera; c'est un type unique."*[8]

---

1 Homage to genius.
2 Octave Mirbeau (1848 –1917) was a French novelist, art critic, travel writer, pamphleteer, journalist, and playwright.
3 Pierre Loti, pseudonym of Louis Marie-Julien Viaud (1850–1923), French naval officer and novelist, known for his exotic novels and short stories.
4 i.e. Stéphane Mallarmé.
5 For a girl.
6 Lesbian.
7 *Nana.*
8 "Here," said he, "Do you want to meet Nana?" She was never affected by this smallpox nor died of it as Zola said. She is still alive, but it is necessary

And so I to the Gare de Lyon, and the *parcours à cette villa féerique qu'arrose la Seine*.[1] Madame Durieux's house with its tiny well-kept garden suggested Gaston and real (not Zolaesque) *joie de vivre*. She, Nana, as I very nearly called her, received me with great cordiality. "Why didn't Stéphane come too? I suppose you want to hear my opinion of Zola's outrageous libel on me? Well, *je l'appelle un fripon et un sot des plus maudits: voilà tout"*.[2] Then she told me how the incident in the theatre when the Prince of Wales (disguised as Prince d'Ecosse by Zola) visits her then (accidentally) in a state of stark nudity in her dressing room actually occurred; she had been appearing as Aphrodite rising from the sea (naturally unclad) and Albert Edward took her by surprise, without allowing her a moment to put a wrap round her.

His conversation inviting her to London, *"où nous vous donnerons un si bon accueil que jamais, jamais vous ne retournerez à Paris"*, is textually reproduced by Zola; equally the remark of the impresario: *"Ces messieurs savent très Bien comment une femme est faite: ne vous dérangez pas: on ne peut pas vous manger."* And the Prince *de répondre finement: "Mais ce n'est pas certain!"* a witticism which Nana told him to be *tout à fait Parisien!*[3]

---

to make a small pilgrimage to Melun. This is my calling card; go and find her; it will interest you. She's a unique type."

[1] Route to this magical villa watered by the Seine.

[2] "I call him a rogue and a most cursed fool: that's all."

[3] "Where we will give you such a warm welcome that never, never will you return to Paris", is textually reproduced by Zola; Equally the remark of the impresario: "These gentlemen know very well how a woman is made: do not disturb yourself: we cannot eat you." And the Prince remarks finely': "But it is not certain!" A witticism which Nana told him to be 'quite Parisian!

Mme. Durieux was about (I should judge) 38: her beautiful golden hair to which Zola refers struck me as innocent of dyes. She admitted the accuracy of the report of the Grand Prix carnival and her jest: *"Qui va me monter?"*[1] in reference to the horse 'Nana' which was among the entries. As to Satine, she in no way denied the *liaison* which, I imagine, had many successors. "I am sick of man[sic] where love is concerned," said she to me, *"toujours des cochonneries."*[2] She sent many messages to Stéphane and Octave (Mirbeau), and I left feeling that Zola had, no doubt for the purpose of his *Rougon Macquart* series, *dénaturé,*[3] a famous *demi-mondaine* who was far removed from the soulless, heartless, not even alluring, bawd, the source of corruption and the poisoning of society whom he depicts *avec tant de maîtrise at avec tent d'hostilitié.*[4]

Both Stéphane and Mirbeau asked me if Nana had introduced me to her tribade[5] friend: she should have, said Octave, for you and she, *mutatis mutandis,*[6] have kindred tastes! I told Mirbeau how *Les Confessions d'une Femme de Chambre* had delighted me, especially the scene of the consumptive dying during the act of copulation and 'la devote' kissing the indecent relic, no other than the erect 'tool' of an unchaste gargoyle which a holy priest had amputated in the clerestory of his church. I quoted to his pleasuring "Die of a rose in aromatic pain."

---

[1] "Who's going to ride me?"
[2] "Always junk."
[3] Altered the nature of.
[4] With so much mastery and hostility.
[5] Lesbian.
[6] The necessary changes having been made.

He asked me what I thought of *Le Jardin des Supplices*: at that time China connoted to me very little and I told him that I was prepared to take his most unnatural travesty at its face value. It is, of course, an utterly impossible picture labelled 'China' for the sake of an inverisimilitude "to split the ears of the groundlings" [1] in other words the vulgar crowd, *profanum vulgue*. [2] *"Ex Africa semper aliquid novi."* [3]

Loti was in Paris just then in one of his most Anglophobe moods: one evening in the 'quarter' he became, *entre deux vertes*, unusually eloquent with *des boutades* [4] on the subject of English aggression in Egypt, Siam, eta. Seeing me, wincing perhaps a little, in a corner, he called out: *"Tiens, mon ami: tu n'as rien a faire avec tout cela: tu es cosmopolite. Mais admets tout de même que c'est toujours la Perfide Albion!: N'ai-je pas raison? Dis!"* Et moi de m'esclaffer: *"Touter ces choses là ne m'intéressent guère."* [5] In 1900 I met Loti [6] in Peking and he recalled his jest and my (as he called it) *esprit d'à propos.* [7]

After completing my Oxford course I went to Japan and only returned to Paris in January 1896, there to hear of dear Lélian's peaceful death (though Mallarmé informed me he had been sadly neglected by his mistress and *bonne à tout faire Euminie Krantz qui faisait danser le panier et l'accablait*

---

1 Hamlet III. 2. 12.   EB
2 Common masses.
3 Out of Africa, always something new.
4 Quips.
5 "Here, my friend: You have nothing to do with all this: you are cosmopolitan." But admit that it is always the perfidious Albion!: Am I not right? Say! " And I laugh, "To listen to these things does not interest me. "
6 Pierre Loti: French novelist and naval officer.
7 Appropriate spirit.

d'injures),[1] leaving almost immediately for Russia where I had many introductions and in fact had *liens de parenti*[2] with the British Ambassador.[3] I became very intimate, too intimate, with a nephew (Alyosha) of Prince Lobanoff[4] who introduced me to the Russian bath, the chastisement of the Vyenek with its peculiar appeal to one of my degenerate type; as, however, several manoeuvres differ not the world over, I refrain from expatiating on a subject which I have not neglected elsewhere in my narrative. I spent all that summer in Russia, staying at Yasnaya Polyana with Tolstoi to whom I was sympathetic, although had he known of my secret predilections, I do not doubt but that he would never have received me at all.

It was an exhilarating month in his company: he was full of *The Kreutzer Sonata* which he had recently written and regretted his authorship of what is perhaps the greatest novel of the world, *Voina e Mir, War and Peace.* I had been a privileged guest at the coronation[5] in the Uspenski Sobor[6] and thought that the long ceremony would have gained by better stage management.

The tragedy of the Hodinsky Plain where three thousand peasants were crushed to death in the struggle for imperial souvenirs had occurred on the day before an audience

---

[1] Maid of everything Euminie Krantz who made the basket dance and overwhelmed him with insults.
[2] Parentage links.
[3] Sir Nicholas Roderick O'Conor (1843–1908), Anglo-Irish diplomat; British Ambassador to Russia 1895–1898).
[4] Prince Aleksey Borisovich Lobanov-Rostovsky (1824–1896), Foreign Minister and Chancellor of the Russian Empire.
[5] Of Tsar Nicholas II: crowned 26 May 1896.
[6] Dormition Cathedral, Moscow.

accorded to me by the Grand Duchess Serge, [1] Princess Elizabeth, the elder sister of the Tsaritsa, later to become a *religieuse* who died by an atrocious death. She received me more than graciously and to me appeared more beautiful even than her sister. The Hodinsky tragedy had profoundly shocked her: she too was superstitious (often more so than Alix[2]) and a believer in omens. "What a judgment from God on the regime," said she; "what a presage of woe for the new reign! Merciful God, grant to us repentance for our sins."

She told me that Their Majesties had not allowed the French ambassador to cancel his *soirée* (as he wished) in their honour, speaking most bitterly of the Tsar's immediate entourage which should have known better than "to feast in the house of death" (her own words). Suddenly speaking in French (she had honoured me by at first conversing in German, in which I was then very fluent, in compliment to her native tongue and in a sense to my own origins. "Blood is thicker than water, *quand même*," she continued: *"Elle finira mal: Mon Dieu, j'ai d'affreux pressentiments à leur égard: moi, j'ai si peu d'influence sur elle, mais tout de même je vais faire tout mon possible, et peut-être le bon Dieu va exaucer mes humbles prières."*[3]

---

[1] Grand Duchess Elizabeth Feodorovna of Russia ; born Princess Elizabeth of Hesse and by the Rhine (1864–1918); sister of Empress Alexandra Feodorovna of Russia, and wife of Grand Duke Serge. Although he was homosexual, the marriage was happy. Following his assassination in 1905, Elizabeth became a nun. During the Revolution she was murdered with a group of others by being beaten and thrown down a mineshaft, into which grenades were tossed.

[2] Empress Alexandra.

[3] Still, "She continued:" "It will end badly: My God, I have dreadful forebodings regarding them: I have so little influence on her, but still I will do everything I can, and perhaps the good Lord shall grant my humble prayers."

As is well known, Alexandra Feodorowna never listened to her sister's advice and even at the end, when the position was almost hopeless and Elizabeth journeyed to Tsarskoye to make a last desperate effort to bring Alix to her senses regarding public feeling and to undeceive her as regards the forged letters of loyalty and enthusiasm which poured in daily by Rasputin's fatal contriving, she was met by the rejoinder to her: *"Alors j'aurais mieux fait de ne pas venir ici"*[1] with a *"Oui"*, and a similar rude monosyllabic affirmative to her: *"Alors! Je ferais mieux de rentrer à Moscou à l'instant?"*[2] *"Oui."* (Why the two sisters talked in French, I know not, as English was Alix's usual language, and naturally German her mother tongue. But I believe that the above conversation is accurately quoted: it probably indicates estrangement and coolness.)

Before the close of the audience, Grand Duke Serge[3] entered his wife's boudoir: he has been condemned for ill-treatment of Elizabeth, unbridled lust and cruelty, accused also as being a pervert, a sufferer from *ramollissement du cerveau,*[4] (which, if true, was hardly a crime). He was, of course, *l'ami intime* of His Majesty reposing in God, Edward VII; but I believe Victoria herself rather affected him [*sic*] and did not think him ill-suited to her favourite grandchild.

As far as my casual acquaintance despite the infinite gulf between the erstwhile *Tsarstvuiuschtchi Dom* (Reigning House) of Romanoff and the pariah pervert *qu'est l'auteur de*

---

[1] "So I would have done better not to come here."
[2] "So I better go back to Moscow immediately."
[3] Grand Duke Sergei Alexandrovich of Russia (1857–1905) fifth son of Tsar Alexander II of Russia, an unpopular Governor-General of Moscow.
[4] Softening of the brain.

cette autobiographie au moins véridique, [1] I found Serge courteous, pro-British or rather pro-European (so far as that sentiment appealed to me, for in Russia 'Europe' meant outside Muscovy, as she never regarded herself part of the European system), polished, *un homme du monde, avec infiniment de tact,* [2] even cordial. He blamed himself as responsible for the Hodinsky disaster, in his capacity as *gouverneur de is place de Moscou* but I believe that the Commission of Inquiry (as might be expected) whitewashed him and reproached the lack of homogeneous control.

I have written elsewhere of 'Nikki's'[3] cordial reception and of his fascinating charm: he must have praised me beyond my deserts to his mother Marie Feodorovna[4] (Dagmar Marie or Minnie whom Victoria so loved and admired), as I received a summons from H.I.M. to the Anitchkin Palace and she honoured me with a long audience, saying amongst other things that I was *"loin d'être typiquement Britannique"*,[5] as indeed she remarked to others, as I shall later describe.

She bade me take an opportunity to visit the Princess Yurevskaya (Dolgorouki), [6] the wife *en secondes noces* [7] of

---

[1] That is the author of this autobiography, at least truthful.
[2] A man of the world, infinitely tactful.
[3] Tsar Nicholas II.
[4] Maria Feodorovna, Empress of Russia; born Princess Dagmar of Denmark (1847–1928); wife and consort of Tsar Alexander III (reigned 1881–1894); sister of Queen Alexandra of Great Britain.
[5] Far from being typically British.
[6] Princess Yurievskaya, born Princess Catherine Dolgorukova (1847–1922); long-time mistress, and later morganatic wife of Tsar Alexander II of Russia. They had four children. Following his death she was granted a generous pension and lived in Paris and on the Riviera.
[7] In a second wedding. It occurred in secret, following the death of his first wife.

Alexander II[1] and to say she (Marie) had sent me. "I always loved her, though I may not always have approved of the Tsar, my father-in-law, when he provided for her apartments in the close vicinity of the Tsaritsa,[2] who was dying of a mortal ill but also of a broken heart. She had said to Marie on one occasion: *"Comme femme je peux tout pardonner, mais en tent qu'elle blesse ma dignité d'impératrice, les choses ne devraient pas être comme ça."*[3]

The Empress Dowager (how strange the two words seem to me as applied to another than my great mistress Tz'u Hsi) added that after Alexander's assassination, before he passed away, Princess Yurevskaya was kneeling in prayer beside the operating table and that, when she (Marie) and her husband entered, they both motioned to her to remain till the end, as indeed was her right. Malicious writers had spoken of an indecent scene of recrimination *au chevet* [4] of the dying Tsar (who, however, was unconscious). It is a dastardly lie, said Marie: *"au contraire, nous la comblâmes d'égards"*,[5] and it was by my request that she (poor dear heart!) remained in Petersburg for the fortnight-long funeral ceremonies, kneeling daily at *le lit de parade*[6] and removing the veil that etiquette imposed, to kiss her dear dead husband's calm, majestic features.

---

[1] Tsar Alexander II (1818 –1881) of Russia. Assassinated by a bomb, and taken back to the Winter Palace where he died.
[2] Maria Alexandrovna, Empress of Russia; Princess Marie of Hesse and by Rhine (1824–1880); wife of Tsar Alexander II. She suffered from tuberculosis, which eventually killed her.
[3] "As a woman I can forgive everything, but in the attempt to hurt my dignity as an empress, things should not be like this."
[4] At the bedside.
[5] "On the contrary, we overwhelmed her with consideration."
[6] The parade bed.

Marie Feodorovna has been maligned as the reactionary influence during Alexander III's thirteen years reign; perhaps her well known friendship for Pobyedonostseff, [1] *le plus obstiné des réactionnaires*, [2] may be the cause, but to me it seemed that she was all gentleness and charm, with a greater intellect than her sister Queen Alexandra, but with the same grace and the same fascinating smile. It was abundantly clear that she hated Germany and more particularly Wilhelm II, although for the Empress Augusta [3] with her pro-French sentiments she expressed a deep affection. Of Victoria she said: "a great queen, a despot who would have been a second Elizabeth in another age, but her bigoted admiration for her favourite daughter's [4] adopted country does not excuse her persistent anti-Russian policy, nor her cruelty towards Denmark after the Prussian aggression of 1864, to say nothing of her coldness towards the senior British princess, Alexandra, although of late years she has shown other dispositions, as my father, King Christian, [5] himself admits."

It may be thought that these family topics were a somewhat indecent revelation to a stranger Briton, but I imagine that frankness was Marie's chiefest quality, and naturally I should not repeat what was said *en confidence*, were it not that others, less meticulously scrupulous, have published largely

---

[1] Konstantin Petrovich Pobedonostsev (1827–1907), Russian jurist, statesman, and adviser to three Tsars.

[2] The most stubborn of the reactionaries.

[3] Augusta Victoria of Schleswig-Holstein, Empress of Germany (1858 – 1921); first wife and consort of Wilhelm II.

[4] i.e. Victoria Adelaide Mary Louisa, Empress of Germany and Princess Royal (1840–1901); eldest daughter of Queen Victoria; wife of Frederick III of Germany; mother of Wilhelm II, and mother-in-law of Empress Augusta.

[5] King Christian IX of Denmark (1818–1906); reigned 1863 to 1906.

apocryphal glorifications of the great queen's sweetness of temper and tactful harmony, qualities which she conspicuously lacked. Marie told me that 'Nikky' (speedily correcting her familiarity with "the emperor") had been greatly pleased with Nicolai Alexandrowitch Tolstoi's recommendation of my unworthy self and had found me *"dénué de tous les préjugés que l'on associe ordinairement au tempérament britannique, 'pig headed' et obstinément incapable d'entendre plus d'un son de cloche"*.[1]

I would fain mention here, though outside of its chronological sequence, that in obedience to the Empress Marie's behest I duly in the course of a gambling visit to Monaco, waited upon Princess Yurevskaya at Nice. Her charm passes all understanding; she was still in deep mourning, for him who was the light of her existence and called herself *un revenant*[2] for whom all life was done. But she was pleased with her stepdaughter-in-law's gracious message and assured me that both Marie and 'Sasha' had always been kindly disposed toward her.

The latter, Alexander III, had indeed been executor of her husband's testament as regards the payment of annual subsidies to her two sons, one of whom I met and he impressed me with his resemblance, on a smaller scale, to the late emperor, his stepbrother Teper usopshey V Bozie,[3] now sleeping in God, *der Hochselige Kaiser*,[4] Alexander III. The

---

[1] "Deprived of all the prejudices that are ordinarily associated with the British temperament,' pig headed ' and stubbornly unable to hear more than the sound of a bell."
[2] A ghost.
[3] Now deceased in [obscure].
[4] The High-Blessed Emperor.

princess's face was sympathetic rather than beautiful, but a photograph of the later seventies that she showed me, presented abounding evidence of a typical Slavonic *piquant magnétisme*.[1] She told me that her love for 'her dead' was her religion and that she read over once again Alexander II's love letters every day of her life, especially those written as always in French during the campaign for the Bulgar cause against the Sultan[2] from the seat of war, with the well-known gibe at Disraeli's expense *"ce c--- de Beaconsfield, l'ennemi invétéré et implacable de la Russie"*.[3]

She survived in her august widowhood till the third decade of the present century, and I believe that the Grand Duke Nicoli,[4] the Russian Commander in Chief of the Great War from his exile on the Riviera frequently paid homage to her gracious personality. I have ever cherished reverence to the House of Romanoff on account of Alexander I's[5] friendliness to my family: my visit to the princess was scarce other than the evocation of a phantom from the past, though at that time I did not perceive the writing on the wall nor realize that the Dynasty was doomed, thinking in my blindness that "threatened men live long", even as I should have said of the Manchu Dynasty.

To return to Marie Feodorovna, H.M. *me congédia*[6] most graciously, assuring me that she should write to her sister the Princess of Wales about me, in the hope that H.R.H. would

---

[1] Piquant magnetism.
[2] The Russo-Turkish War of 1877–1878.
[3] "This c---of Beaconsfield, the inveterate and relentless enemy of Russia".
[4] Grand Duke Nicholas Nikolaevich of Russia (1856–1929), Russian general.
[5] Tsar Alexander I of Russia (1777–1825).
[6] Dismissed me.

exercise her influence with Lord Salisbury[1] for me to remain in Russia. As will presently transpire, it was only later that I learned of her kind reference to me in a letter to her constant correspondent, *l'impératrice Eugénie*. Canon Harvey[*sic*], [2] rector of Sandringham and friend of the Prince and Princess, with whom I stayed some months later, learned from Alix that her sister had indeed mentioned me in a letter in which she had apparently given to my name the original German spelling.

I should like to have recorded a delightful intimacy with Countess P. whose name is imprinted in my heart of hearts, but I believe that she happily still lives and I am unable to submit for her approval what it had been in my mind to write. Happily the memory abides and in the darkness I shall not forget; albeit I dare not flatter myself that to her exquisite self my personality could have been in any sense *impressionnante*[3] though she may have deemed me *aufrichtig*[4] and affectionate.

I arrived in London during the imperial couple's visit to Balmoral [5] and knew that the Tsaritsa asked for an appointment in Russia in my favour. Lord Salisbury gave to me a special nomination which would have culminated in the sense that Alexandra Feodorovna graciously desired. But my heart was in the Orient so that I (and others) thought that my temperament was better adapted to Chinese psychology than to Slavonia. And I doubt whether we erred, apart from sexual questions which, as Dr. Johnson says, have really little

---

[1] Robert Arthur Talbot Gascoyne-Cecil, 3rd Marquess of Salisbury (1830–1903); then Conservative Prime Minister of Great Britain.
[2] Rev. Canon Frederick Alfred John Hervey (1846–1910).
[3] Impressive.
[4] Sincere.
[5] In the autumn of 1896.

influence upon life as a whole (though they had some upon the Old Buddha), but are only the *zakuski*[1] before the repast or the walnuts and wine for dessert, that Robert Brinsley Sheridan (Sherry)[2] so affected, that prince of good fellows and *de bons vivants qui tombs dans la misère*[3] at the last.

As a great preacher once said: "This mirage, this illusion of the senses, this union of souls and bodies, my friends, what is it all but a dream that fades at daybreak, a shadow that departeth, a swallow's temporary abode on a moving tent."

Sir Archibald Philip Primrose, Knight of the Garter, Knight of the Thistle, Privy Councillor, a Baronet of Scotland, Earl of Rosebery, Earl of Midlothian, Viscount Delany, Baron Mentmore, greatly influenced my life and mental structure between the years 1892 and 1898. His mother had married *en secondes noces* His Grace the Duke of Cleveland[4] of historic Raby Castle, once the seat of Earl Warwick,[5] 'the Kingmaker' during the Wars of the Roses; head of the great Vane house (the dukedom now extinct), one of whose members, Sir Harry Vane the younger[6], lost his head after the Restoration of Charles II who, by Clarendon's[7] advice, feared to let him live.

---

[1] Refreshments.

[2] Richard Brinsley Butler Sheridan (1751–1816),Irish satirist, politician, playwright, poet, and long-term owner of the London Theatre Royal, Drury Lane.

[3] Those who live well who fall into misery.

[4] Harry George Powlett, 4th and last Duke of Cleveland (1803–1891).

[5] Richard Neville, 16th Earl of Warwick (1428–1471), English nobleman, administrator, and military commander.

[6] Sir Henry Vane (1613 –1662), English politician, statesman, and colonial governor. Beheaded for high treason on Tower Hill.

[7] Edward Hyde, 1st Earl of Clarendon (1609–1674), English statesman, lawyer, diplomat and historian who served as chief advisor to Charles I during the First English Civil War, and Lord Chancellor to Charles II from 1660 to 1667.

Raby was close to my home and both Duke (who died in extreme old age about 1890) and Duchess were intimates of my family: it was through her (in 1892 living at Battle Abbey the site of 'English Harold's'[1] death at Hastings in 1066 when Saxon England perished with its heroic King and Norman tyranny oppressed the land), that I first met Lord Rosebery, just after Mr. Gladstone had formed his fourth and last ministry in august 1892, attributing to his faithful Scots henchman the Foreign Secretaryship, greatly to the satisfaction of Queen Victoria. Praise from an enemy always sets one thinking; but the Iron Chancellor, [2] perhaps the greatest man of the 19th century after Napoléon, never flattered nor entertained an *arrière-pensée*[3] and Bismarck had a real admiration for Lord Rosebery as a statesman who knew what he wanted and knew when to give way; not like Lord Salisbury ungraciously, but with a spirit of conciliation and with a courteous tact which attracts: "you lend colour to the phrase of 'gauntlet in the velvet glove', as that protagonist of heroic mould and stature expressed it, the last five words being written in English by him.

Lord Rosebery, devoid of any prominent feature, was the despair of caricaturists who could work their will on Mr. Gladstone, Mr. Arthur Balfour, Sir Wm. Harcourt,[4] or Lord

---

[1] King Harold II (c. 1022 –1066).
[2] Prince Otto von Bismarck, Duke of Lauenburg, Count of Bismarck-Schönhausen, (1815–1898). German statesman, diplomat, nobleman, and writer. He masterminded the unification of Germany in 1871 and served as its first chancellor until 1890, in which capacity he dominated European affairs for two decades.
[3] Ulterior motive.
[4] Sir William George Granville Venables Vernon Harcourt (1827–1904) was a British lawyer, journalist and Liberal statesman.

Salisbury with his ample countenance and protruding paunch; the former was short of stature but rather above the average in girth: clean shaven and round faced he gave to me the impression of juvenility (save for his care-ridden look he was almost baby-faced), though aged forty-five when first I saw him. His eyes were large and somewhat *à fleur de tête*:[1] they were heavily *battus* (*cernés*), lined with black circles, eloquent of vigilant nights and perhaps of excessive potations; but redolent of a subtle wit and an ironical, if mild and slightly bored, humour. I think that the 'man in the street', not knowing his identity, would have set him down as a country squire, hailing from the north 'countree', a lover of sport and the various activities of that much calumniated class, now, I imagine, as extinct in Britain as is the dodo on the Isle de Reunion, its latest haunt, where the aborigines were said to cook its eggs in the local geysers.

I am no reader of physiognomy and cannot (for the life of me) affirm whether Lord Rosebery's rather small chin connoted weakness of will, or his upper lip a lack of decision and concentration (wise-acre apophthegms[2] to adapt themselves to popular judgments). Personally I never found him wanting in any of these qualities, though I often saw him bored and 'fed-up' with his vast wealth and the world *où l'on s'ennuie*.[3] His master at Eton, William Cory,[4] had said of him as a boy of sixteen that he coveted *sine pulvere palmam*, the highest place

---

[1] Bulging.
[2] Aphorisms.
[3] Where one is bored.
[4] William Johnson, later William Cory (1823–1892), English schoolmaster and author. Considered the greatest Eton master of his day, he had favourites, and was dismissed. Although a homosexual pederast (possibly platonic), his attractive wife Rosa, née Guille, thirty-six years his junior, with whom he had a son, had pursued him into marriage.

without the drudging hard work thereto attached. It was an easy forecast; but to me Lord Rosebery seemed indifferent to honours, though he won plenty, He has been written down 'a splendid failure', which, on the face of it, is as untrue as most popular *obiter dicta*. That he enjoyed life, as (say) the Old Buddha did, I doubt; it was to him a banquet without relish or savour, served with irritating lack of despatch or dignity.

I have hesitated to speak of him, save indirectly, owing to my name having been mentioned after Lord Drumlanrig's tragic death in 1894 in connection with Lord Rosebery (who had in March of that year succeeded Mr. Gladstone as Prime Minister). The person responsible for sundry semi-slanderous (and certainly malevolent) statements was 'Lulu' Harcourt,[1] later first Viscount Harcourt, who, with all his faults, was undoubtedly a good son and was employed by Sir William Harcourt, the colleague and implacable enemy of Lord Rosebery, as an intermediary in many embarrassing situations in the year and a quarter of the latter's premiership 'Lulu', on the principle of 'Birds of a feather', was the last man who had the right to bring accusations of pederasty against Lord Rosebery; for the plenitude of his homosexuality was (as I know well and many others of that generation) the paramount influence of his life; but disappointment *vis-à-vis* Lord Rosebery's preferences hampered his dispassionate judgment, and jealousy of Drumlanrig, if not of myself, directed the trend of his witty but sometimes mendacious

---

[1] Lewis 'Lulu/Loulou' Vernon Harcourt, 1st Viscount Harcourt, born Reginald Vernon Harcourt (1863–1922); British Liberal M.P.; Secretary of State for the Colonies from 1910 to 1915. Married heiress Mary Ethel Burns, and had issue. Suicided in the wake of a scandal involving the hen teenage Edward James (1907–1984), to whom he had exposed himself.

revelations, though I deny not that they reposed on a solid foundation of fact.

Lulu died, a comparatively young man, in 1916: Lord Rosebery's death occurred in May 1929. The latter had bound me to solemn secrecy regarding our intimacy; but *autres temps autres moeurs*,[1] and what could not have been said in the Victorian era is admissible in the present day and should not be regarded as a posthumous attack on a bright name which 'hallows song'; especially as my dear and honoured chief had expressly added the rider to his injunction: "Believe me, for your sake, far more than for mine, I make to you this request, earnestly and measuredly. For myself I care nought." To the present generation Lord Rosebery is not even *magni nominis umbra*;[2] except perhaps still remembered in sporting circles as twice winner of the Derby, a sure passport, far more than a victory in war, to popular esteem.

In my day the man in the street regarded him as a *bon vivant*, a *connaisseur* of the vintages which he greatly affected, a great racing man and an unsated lover of his own sex. His marriage with a Rothschild had brought to him over a million sterling; he had been a devoted husband and Lady Rosebery's death in 1890 had been, to quote Louis XIV's *bon mot* on the decease of his Spanish Consort, *le seul chagrin qu'elle m'eût jamais causé.*[3]

He told me that after his bereavement in 1890 he was staying in his Neapolitan villa and when visiting the Blue Grotto at Capri became attracted, *à l'instar de Tibère*,[4] to an Italian

---

[1] Other times, other customs.
[2] The shadow of a great name.
[3] The only grief she would ever have caused me.
[4] Like Tiberius.

ephebus[1] who was disporting himself in utter nakedness at that historical post sacred to love and lust. He then for the first time revelled in the beauty of the masculine posterior which was to become his dominant passion, perhaps not even yielding pleas to his bookloving propensities which were literally his second nature.

My introduction to Lord Rosebery took place in November 1892; the College authorities at Oxford gave to me leave of absence for four nights for the purpose of keeping my term ('eating my dinners', as the expression goes) at the Inner Temple as a law student. I was asked to a small *soirée* in his magnificent Berkeley Square mansion with its grand ballroom: among the guests were the Oxford scientist, the genial and very eccentric Prof. Roy [*sic*] Lankester, F.R.S.,[2] John Addington Symonds who wrote of Michelangelo's male love and of Greek pederasty, homosexual to the finger tips, Lord Randolph Churchill[3] and Arthur Humphries,[*sic*] the genial Piccadilly publisher,[4] George Alexander[5] the great actor (it was a Sunday, when the London theatres have *relâche*[6]), Lord Drumlanrig,[7] then known as Viscount Douglas of Hawick, Bozie Douglas' eldest brother, and Lord Rosebery's

---

[1] Youth.
[2] Sir (Edwin) Ray Lankester (1847–1929) zoologist. It was said of him that no one did more in his time to popularise science.
[3] Lord Randolph Henry Spencer-Churchill (1849–1895), British statesman. Father of Sir Winston Churchill.
[4] Arthur Lee Humphreys (1865–1946), co-owner of Hatchard's bookshop in Piccadilly, publisher under his own name, and local historian.
[5] Sir George Alexander (1858–1918), born George Alexander Gibb Samson, English stage actor, theatre producer and manager.
[6] Respite.
[7] Francis Archibald Douglas, Viscount Drumlanrig (1867–1894), later, 1st Baron Kelhead; eldest son of the 9th Marquess of Queensberry, and brother Lord Alfred Douglas, lover of Oscar Wilde.

confidential secretary, not yet created (to the infinite chagrin of his father the Marquess of Queensberry) a peer of the United Kingdom in his own right (Queensberry as a Scottish peer not being entitled to a seat in the House of Lords).

Lord Rosebery's urbane humour and subtle wit attracted me as it did everyone else: I recall that he was pleased at my quotation of a jest uttered by a courtier on the fall of the Third Empire: *"après tout nous nous sommes diablement bien amusés"*[1]; and he turned to Randolph with a: "Just what you said, Randy, after you turned out the Liberals in 1885: It's all over; but it's not been bad fun." I don't recall Lord Randolph's reply but remember how ill he looked though he had still to years to live.

Lord Douglas took me aside and asked me many pointed questions regarding my Winchester days and my intimacies with his brother. I neither dissembled nor cloaked the facts and Douglas listened with interest. He was extremely and ideally handsome, an Adonis or a Ganymede of charming manners and a pleasing habit (like Bozie) of blushing if one's *propos*[2] became *risqués*: Douglas begged me to dine with him in town after the Oxford term.

I did not know what impression I had made on Lord Rosebery; so was gratified to receive a note from Douglas renewing his invitation and adding that "the Chief" had found me interesting *"avec la beauté du diable"* [3] (rather a strange

---

[1] After all, we had a lot of fun.
[2] Conversation.
[3] With the beauty of the Devil.

expression to apply to a male!). The Duchess of Cleveland[1] also told my mother that Lord Rosebery had taken a fancy to me and would invite me again during the vacation, and he desired closer acquaintance. Well! He obtained more than acquaintance in a very short time; and I am proud to think that he found me worthy of it. It was a triumph of my youth, a feather in my adolescent cap.

My intimacy with Douglas rapidly developed: we had tastes in common and allowed them to expand to the fullest amplitude. It was just about then that 'Lulu' began his campaign of suggestion regarding Lord Rosebery and his secretary: the motive was political in order to strengthen Sir William Harcourt's possibilities of reversion to the premiership. Many scandalous anonymous letters reached Douglas and, I believe, Lord Rosebery himself, including a cartoon inscribed "The new Tiberius" which was unblushingly obscene.

I never met Mr. A.J. Balfour, later Earl of Balfour, K.G., but frequently saw him at the New Club, Edinburgh, a most exclusive resort, and was always impressed by the great gulf fixed between Lord Rosebery's easy, natural bearing toward his fellow members and Balfour's self-conscious mannerism in avoiding the scrutiny of the curious by screening his face with a handkerchief as he entered the public rooms of the club, thereby attracting all the more attention. It was an ingrained

---

[1] Catherine Lucy Wilhelmina Powlett, Duchess of Cleveland, née Stanhope (1819 –1901), English historian, including as author of *The Battle Abbey Roll with some Account of the Norman Lineages*, and genealogist; mother of the 5th Earl of Rosebery. Married firstly, Archibald Primrose, Lord Dalmeny (1809-1851), eldest son of Archibald Primrose, 4th Earl of Rosebery; and secondly, Harry George Powlett, 4th and last Duke of Cleveland (1803–1891).

self-conscious shyness, of which I, humble mortal!, suffer myself.

It is difficult for me to attempt the recapture of Lord Rosebery's charm of diction: phrases like "ploughing the sands of the sea-shore", "my lonely furrow", "the predominant partner", "they will never come back to us as we knew them, but in another sense they are with us today" (when unveiling a war memorial in Edinburgh) ring as true today as when they were spoken.

When I next saw Lord Rosebery in London, he showed to me the letter of Prince Bismarck, dated April 1890, thanking him for the original of the cartoon published in a London weekly (Punch), "Dropping the pilot", after the prince's dismissal by Wilhelm II. The Prince wrote in German to express his appreciation of a Scotsman's sympathy and his conviction that Lord Rosebery would, when the opportunity offered of his party being in power, develop friendly relations between Germany and his country. The figure of the Prince descending the gangway is finely portrayed, but the drawing of the emperor taking over the wheel and steering the ship of state is less satisfactory and does not resemble Wilhelm II in the least. Lord Rosebery suffered from persistent insomnia, and the wine cup in which he freely indulged failed to bring the gift of sleep.

I thought of the hackneyed line in *Henry IV* "Uneasy lies the head that wears a crown"; but in his case release from the cares of office did not bring peaceful nights, and to the end of his life the long trouble never left him. As I was still an undergraduate, the lengthy vacations, much of which had to be spent in study of the humanities, provided me, thanks to

Lord Rosebery's kindness, recurring intervals for profiting, now and again, from the charm of his personality and the magic of his brilliant table talk; he was a citizen of the world in the highest sense, modest, always ready to defer to the opinion of lesser men, delighted to cull information, for example even cross-examining me as to the accented syllable in slavonic words and the place of the pronoun in Magyar conjugations.

Douglas was not a great scholar, and Lord Rosebery, who had a good deal of private correspondence with the French ambassador, used to send for me at unlikely hours for the drafting at his dictation of intimate notes to His Excellency, for in no circumstance would he employ English, being faithful to the tradition that French is the only language for a *grand seigneur* when writing to friends of other nationality.

Out of their chronological order, it behoves me to name here two such letters of moment that it fell to me to put into French. The first was on Sunday, June 24, 1894 (the day after Mrs. Simpson's husband, David, once King Edward VIII, was born, unless my memory of a historic event trippeth by one day): news had arrived from Lyon of the murder of President Carnot[1] while *en carrosse*[2] like Henri IV, in an official progress.

In those days telephones were the exception; I was staying it the Buckingham Palace Hotel, where I received a hastily scribbled: "Come at once, R." On arrival at Berkeley square, I took my chief's directions and wrote: *"Monsieur*

---

[1] Marie François Sadi Carnot (1837–1894) French statesman, who served as the President of France from 1887 until his assassination in 1894 – stabbed by an Italian anarchist.
[2] By coach.

l'Ambassadeur! Tout en ayant la mort dans l'âme je m'empresse d'exprimer à Votre Excellence les sentiments de la plus profonde horreur avec laquelle je viens d'apprendre l'affreuse nouvelle du lâche assassinat du Président de la République. Je tiens à faire connaître à Votre Excellence l'assurance de ma plus vive sympathie à l'occasion de cette cruelle perte que la France vient de subir. Le Grande Bretagne tout entière, en prenant part au deuil de la Nation Amie s'incline devant la dépouille mortelle de l'illustre homme d'Etat que fut feu le Président de la République et rend hommage à sa vie de désintéressement exalté et de sublime patriotisme. Au beau nom de famille que portait M. le Président Carnot, a-t-il su apporter de nouveaux lauriers freîchement cueillis qui ne périront assurément jamais et qui constitueront un monument indestructible de la glorieuee histoire de France." [1]

The second letter, I think, in April 1895 at the Peace Treaty of Shimonoseki, and the *démarche*[2] of the Three Powers, France, Germany and Russia, respecting the Kuantung Peninsula. *"Monsieur l'ambassadeur, En tant que premier ministre de sa Majesté je regrette d'avoir à porter à la connaisance de Votre Excellence que le Gouvernement de la Majesté se trouve dans*

---

[1] "Mr. Ambassador! While having death in my soul I hasten to express to Your Excellency the feelings of the deepest horror with which I have just learnt the dreadful news of the cowardly assassination of the President of the Republic. I would like to share with Your Excellency the assurance of my deepest sympathy on the occasion of this cruel loss that France has just undergone. The whole of Great Britain joins in the mourning of the friendly Nation, bowing to the mortal remains of the illustrious statesman who was the late President of the Republic and pays homage to his life of exalted selflessness and sublime patriotism. To the fine family name that Mr Carnot bore he was able to bring fresh laurels, which will certainly never perish, and which would constitute an indestructible monument to the glorious history of France.

[2] Approach.

l'impossibilité de s'associer à la note collective au Japon de la part des Trois Puissances touchant la cession par la Chine de la péninsule du Kuantung. La Comte de Kimberley est en train de préparer un exposé détaillé de ce qui fait qua le Gouvernement britannieue dont je suis à la tête ne ce trouve pas en mesure d'y participer; mais je tiens à saisir l'occasion, à titre purement officieux, bien entendu, de rendre compte à Votre Excellence de notre décision, que je vous prie, Monsieur l'Ambassadeur, de bien vouloir ne pas divulguer, en attendant la dépêche formelle du secrétaire d'Eaat, lord Kimberly, à ce sujet."[1]

I would add here that during my visit to Japan Lord Rosebery's refusal to join the Three Powers' protest in regard to the cession of the territory on the mainland obtained for him and for Great Britain a very real, if fleeting, popularity. On my return in January 1896, Lord Rosebery, now in opposition, was greatly heartened by the effect (which he fondly believed permanent) of his gesture in acceptance of the principle: "To the victors the spoils."

I spent some days in September 1893 as Lord Rosebery's guest at Dalmeny: never shall I forget how my bedsheets had not been aired by a careless housemaid and were as damp as the 'easterly hair' (mist) of the Edinburgh region. Fortunately

---

[1] "Mr. Ambassador, As Prime Minister of His Majesty, I regret to inform Your Excellency that Her Majesty's Government is unable to associate itself with the collective memorandum in Japan of the part of the Three Powers relating to the transfer by China of the Kuantung Peninsula. The Earl of Kimberley is preparing a detailed account of why the British Government, of which I am the head, does not find itself able to participate. But I would like to take this opportunity, of course, to inform Your Excellency of our decision, which I request you, Ambassador, not to disclose, pending the formal despatch of the Secretary of State, Lord Kimberly, on this subject. "

for my chances of rheumatic fever, I did not sleep in them but arrayed myself in a dressing-gown's protection.

It was a habit of Lord Rosebery, when his guests were retiring for the night, to invite one of them to accompany him on a lengthy midnight drive before he adjourned to his own solitary couch. He took me on these nocturnal excursions on a number of occasions, chatting most gaily and with sparkling zest all the way, despite the Midlothian fogs and mists from the North Sea.

Years later, when my brother-in-law Sir John Findlay[1] was admitted to his intimacy, Lord Rosebery frequently selected him as his companion, although in his case there was no question or thought of homosexual relations, Findlay returning in the carriage to Dalmeny while Lord Rosebery betook himself to his lonely vigil in Barn Bogle.[2]

I have not spoken here of Lord Rosebery's two houses at Epsom, Mentmore and the Durdans, the latter owning an exquisite miniature library which contained many mementoes of Pitt, and sumptuous bindings executed for the Court of France in the reigns of Louis XIV and Louis XV as well as for *Mesdames*, the aunts of Louis XVI. Lord Rosebery was a master of style: his two books, on Pitt, and Napoleon, the Last Phase, dealing with Sainte-Hélène, are *chefs-d'oeuvre* of easy

---

[1] Sir John Ritchie Finlay, 1st Baronet (1866–1930); principal partner in Messrs. John Ritchie and Co., proprietors and publishers of *The Scotsman* and its associated newspapers. Married Harriet Jane Backhouse (later Dame Harriet), and had issue.
[2] Barnbougle Castle, a tower house within the Dalmney estate on the Firth of Forth.

wit and beautiful prose, the latter work not pleasant reading for an English admirer of the emperor!

My second and third nights were spent with Lord Rosebery in this detached and solitary house some distance from Dalmeny, Barn Bogle, where he retired o'nights in the futile effort to woo sleep or, as in my ease and that of Douglas, to substitute Eros for Morpheus, wherein he achieved a full success.

On the evening of my arrival at Dalmeny he took me into his beautiful library and showed to me his Napoleonic literature with broad-sheets and caricatures, letters to Marie Louise from the emperor Francis and the Pope Pius VII. Amongst the trophies in his study were two Eton birch-rods decked in the light blue colours of the school reminiscent of his boyhood's floggings. It has been said of him that he enjoyed reciprocal flagellation like Swinburne, to excite his passions (already sufficiently far-reaching); but he never suggested the proceeding in his intercourse with me. My readers will agree that, when a young man is privileged to have sexual intercourse with a prime-minister, any proposal regarding the *modus operandi* must emanate from the latter, and as far as I was concerned, it was the case of being *le locataire* (the tenant as a Frenchman wittily puts it) and passivity was the invariable order of the day, but passivity has its own expedients, as the passive voice has its tenses and moods (*ses modes et ses temps*).

The vigils that I shared with him at Barn Bogle connoted on his part the consumption of a bottle and a half of port wine during the night; on neither occasion of my first visit to Dalmeny did he close his eyes: but in the intervals of erotic activities he talked with brilliance and epigram! I wish that I could recall specimens of his lively wit and his comments on leading men and woman of the day, beginning with the Queen whose banality delighted him, while he recognised certain great qualities if only she could overcome the hidebound prejudices so characteristic: of the Guelphs and of a descendant of George III. To his enemies, such as Harcourt or Sir Charles (later Lord) Russell, [1] he was extraordinarily tolerant: there was a good-humoured acceptance of others' values which is rare in statesmen or politicians, something in which, for example, Mr. Gladstone was entirely lacking.

Like the Arabs and the Ottomans (today called Turks) Lord Rosebery was fortunate in his ability to perform a lingering and protracted copulation equally agreeable to both parties; it was his custom to prolong the action of sex for some twenty minutes if not more; retaining his large, thickset organ stationary and fixed in the patient's rectum and, I suppose, similarly inserted (mutatis mutandis) in case of intersexual commerce. I paid to him many visits in his Midlothian home; but forbear to repeat otiose details. *Ab uno disce omnes!*[2] Let the reader guess the course that the strange idiosyncrasies of sex take, if the matter attracts him (or her). Prime Ministers are much as other people, and I have done to the subject of copulative ecstasies full justice elsewhere in my narrative.

I have mentioned that on Mr. Gladstone's resignation in March 1894 when the queen 'sent for' Lord Rosebery as his successor, the latter obtained Her Majesty's consent to his secretary, Lord Douglas, being created a peer of the United Kingdom,

---

[1] Charles Arthur Russell, Baron Russell of Killowen (1832–1900), Anglo-Irish statesman and Lord Chief Justice of England.
[2] From one, learn all – i.e. from one instance the whole may be inferred.

Baron Drumlanrig (his previous viscounty being a courtesy title), whereby he had the right to a meet in the Upper House and as thus more easily available for his chief during parliamentary debates. His father, Marquess of Queensberry, a great prize-fighter but a vulgar cad, a *roturier*[1] in everything except his noble birth, was indignant at his eldest son's promotion to the 'Painted Chamber' of the Lords; 'Lulu' had suggested to him that the relations between prime-minister and secretary were scarcely platonic (as common parlance, unfair to Plato's pederastic tastes, puts it), and by setting private detectives to work Lord Queensberry obtained very damaging evidence of a carnal bout after a supper party at Bourne End on the River Thames.

Queensberry wrote to the prime-minister threatening exposure in a letter to the republican owner of *Truth,* Mr. Henry Labouchère,[2] Lord Rosebery's inveterate enemy, unless he resigned office and severed relations with Drumlanrig. Apparently the evidence on which he relied was that of two maid servants at the inn and the concrete proofs afforded (as in the Wilde case) by the condition of the drapery of the bed on which the two lovers had passed their night. Drumlanrig took his life by shooting; but the inquest found (*splendide mendax*[3] and by a generous fraud) that it was due to death by misadventure owing to his gun having exploded when he was crossing a stile.

This tragedy which was a noble sacrifice on the altar of his chief's fair fame nearly broke Lord Rosebery's heart, and to me

---

[1] Commoner.
[2] Henry Du Pré Labouchère (1831–1912).
[3] Nobly false : untruthful for a good cause.

who had enjoyed a close reciprocal union with Drumlanrig was a source of poignant grief. He was a real loss to the political world, cultured, charming and generous to friend and foe. There is no doubt but that his refusal to countenance 'Lulu' Harcourt's sensual overtures (to which I am ashamed to admit having yielded), had inspired the latter with the hatred of disappointed passion; and *il y était pour quelque chose*[1] in inciting Lord Queensberry on his malevolent activities.

Both Lord Russell of Killowen (in 1894 made Lord Chief Justice) and Sir Frank Lockwood,[2] the Counsel who conducted the Wilde prosecution, were hostile to Lord Rosebery: and it was Lord Russell's son, later Sir Charles Russell Bt. of the firm of Day and Russell, who furnished to Lord Queensberry the often tainted evidence of the male prostitutes by whom Wilde's conviction was brought about.

It always seemed to me that Lord Rosebery lost his nerve at the time of the Wilde scandal: the truth was that the suicide of his secretary, to whom he was bound by no common tie, and the chronic loss of sleep in addition to internal strife in his Cabinet had so gravely affected him that he allowed things to take their course; for I cannot but believe that a hint to Scotland Yard[3] might have enabled Oscar to leave the country, and once in Paris he would have been left unmolested, as pederasty is not one of the offences for which extradition could have been demanded from the French Government, at

---

[1] He was there for something.

[2] Sir Frank Lockwood, QC (1846–1897) English lawyer and Liberal Party politician.

[3] The London Police Department which is on the site of the Embassy of Scotland when a separate kingdom. E.B.

that time far from disposed to go out of its way to oblige *Perfide Albion.*

I remained on very intimate terms with Lord Rosebery after ceasing to act as his secretary until the date of my departure for East Asia, and during my visits to Europe in the ensuing years never failed to see this gracious and genial patron, my relations with whom must ever remain among the happiest recollections of my life, as I have already mentioned in my paper on Verlaine. Lord Rosebery became later (as I have said) a very intimate friend of my late brother-in-law, Sir John Findlay Bt., K.B.E., Lord Lieutenant of Banffshire, proprietor of the great Scotsman newspaper, and of my sister Harriet, Lady Findlay, D.B.E., [1] a leading conservative politician and a director of the Royal Scottish National Gallery.

As I have said, Lord Rosebery greatly liked my book China under the Empress Dowager and told my sister that he could not lay it down, rejoicing most unfeignedly in my "remarkable" success as an author, which, however, he kindly added, did not astonish him; but he added, with uncanny insight, that the story was left half-told and that many revelations might yet see the light regarding, my exact relations with that "enigmatic person", as he called Tz'u Hsi.

Mr. George Nathaniel Curzon, [2] that life-long neurotic and spinal invalid, whose frantic fits of hysterical weeping over imagined slights found a strange reproduction in a semi-sane member of H.M.'s secret service lately in China, appointed me

---

[1] Dame Harriet Jane Findlay , née Backhouse (1880–1954).
[2] George Nathaniel Curzon, 1st Marquess Curzon of Kedleston, (1859–1925), British Conservative statesman,, and Viceroy of India, 1899 to 1905.

for a season to be his private secretary. Despite his reputation of rudeness and inconsiderateness toward his subordinates (especially to servants who detested him, as Lady Oxford[1] says in her memoirs) I always found him relatively I Yü, to quote Confucius, easy going, except when confronted with a difficulty.

When in 1909 Lord Kitchener[2] visited Peking, he had heard of me as a *connaisseur de porcelaines et de céramiques*.[3] As is known, Kitchener was an inveterate collector and obtained many of his pieces as gifts by the simple expedient of asking for them from the owners: he and I procured several good specimens of Wu Ts'ai and yellow glaze, and after his return home I used to send to him periodic shipments of late Ming and Manchu porcelains, including some really wonderful Lanz Yao which actually reached Broome Park on the very day that his tragic death was announced.

Kitchener told me that Curzon had spoken, before the days of their final estrangement, of a "wayward genius" who had been his secretary and it seemed from the concomitant description, albeit no name was mentioned, that Curzon, *Georgius Superbus*, [4] was referring to me. When I mentioned to Kitchener that the Princess N.[5], (I do not name her, because by

[1] Emma Margaret Asquith, Countess of Oxford and Asquith, known as Margot Asquith (1864 –1945), British socialite, author, and wit; wife of Herbert Asquith, Prime Minister.
[2] Horatio Herbert Kitchener, 1st Earl Kitchener (1850 –1916), Irish-born British Army officer, colonial administrator, and national icon.
[3] Connoisseur of porcelains and ceramics.
[4] Proud George.
[5] Princess Zainab Nazli Hanim (1853–1913); a sophisticated Cairo hostess. Born in Constantinople, the daughter of a Ottoman-Egyptian prince, she married a Turkish ambassador Halil Şerif Paşa (Khalil Bey), and moved briefly to Paris with him. Upon his death she returned to Cairo, residing in a

the rule of Islam a woman who has carnal relations with a Giaour[1] is irrevocably doomed), so well known in *Le Cairo,* had said of him after *a nuit d'amour* with me during the Sudan campaign: *"Ce Kitchener, je l'aimais beaucoup, mais sais-tu mon cher, le sirdar n'avait point de force: it ne pouvait rien faire cette nuit-la."*[2] Kitchener roared with laughter: "Where there's no will my boy, there's no way."

Kitchener's predilections are well known and I will not expatiate upon them, not indeed having the right to throw stones at the memory of the dead, leaving that to a Lord Northcliffe[3] *et hoc genus omne*[4] which "blackens goodness" (or rather in his case genius) in its graves, as Watson once wrote of a famous lady and then withdrew his obvious allusion, a withdrawal that deceived none. Kitchener was *froid*[5] towards feminine charms: perhaps the potion that the chief eunuch used to offer to my jaded appetite might have acted as potently on his passions as it did on mine. *Quién sabe!*[6]

---

palace, the Villa Henry. She married secondly, in 1900, Khelil Bouhageb, later Prime Minister of Tunisia. In her palace she entertained the intellectual elite and celebrities. Enid, the wife of archaeologist and diplomat Sir Austen Henry Layard, wrote: "She is fond of intrigue as a true Oriental & by many is thought to be dangerous but I do not think she is dangerous. She is devoted to the English & is a great admirer of Lord Kitchener's. [24 February 1912, Journal of Lady Layard;
https://www.browningguide.org/lady-layards-journal/]
[1] A non-muslim.
[2] "This Kitchener, I loved him very much, but you know my dear, the Sirdar [Commander in Chief] had no strength: he could do nothing that night."
[3] Alfred Charles William Harmsworth, 1st Viscount Northcliffe (1865 – 1922), British newspaper and publishing magnate, including of the *Daily Mail.*
[4] And all of this kind.
[5] Cold.
[6] Who knows!

Revenons à nos moutons:[1] in September 1896 I had occasion to consult Dr. Cantlie, late of Hongkong (Sir James Cantlie[2] under whom Sun Wen – Sun Yat-sen[3] – had studied), in connexion with a mild attack of sprue[4] which I had contracted in Japan. After the incident of Dr. Sun's kidnapping by the Chinese Legation, when he was in real danger of being placed upon a Swedish vessel loading at the Albert Dock for Canton as a mental case travelling under escort, with the certainty that decapitation would be his lot on arrival at the destination, Dr. Cantlie communicated with me to request my good offices in inducing Lord Salisbury to insist upon his immediate release, since the arrest was illegal by the law of nations.

Dr. Sun had induced a British servant of the Legation to inform Dr. Cantlie of his desperate situation. I at once informed Mr. Curzon who was parliamentary under-secretary: he was almost speechless with rage and lost not a moment in communications with Lord Salisbury then on vacation at Hatfield House. The latter, for once, acted promptly, wrote a peremptory note to the Chinese Minister complaining that Li Hung-chang's[5] recent semi-state visit to Britain and his official reception by the Queen should have had as sequel so flagrant a contravention of international law and custom. Dr. Sun was at once released and I may fairly claim to have contributed to the happy issue in a secondary degree.

---

[1] Back on topic.

[2] Sir James Cantlie (1851–1926) was a Scottish physician; a pioneer of first aid in medicine.

[3] Sun Yat-sen (1866–1925), Chinese statesman, physician, and political philosopher, who served as the provisional first president of the Republic of China.

[4] A disease of the small intestine.

[5] Li Hongzhang, Marquess Suyi (1823-1901), Chinese politician, general and diplomat of the late Qing dynasty.

When Louis XVIII said: *"la ponctualité est la politesse des rois"*[1] (*'et le devoir des petits'*,[2] as he might have added), he was preaching an axiom which Kings, to do them justice, recognise and act up to. Their representatives are not always equally considerate. I remember a Lord Commissioner for Scotland who gave a banquet at Holyroodhouse to some two hundred guests and marked the 'command': 8:30p.m. punctual; yet, when the party mustered to offer royal respect to the King's representative and his wife, the noble couple delayed their arrival for two hours *sans un mot d'excuses*,[3] while the invited guests *avaient à faire antichambre*.[4] Gratitude for services is another obligation of royalty: "An attribute which becomes the throned monarch better than his crown." If it be so, Dr. Sun, as the future father of his country and its first president, proved himself worthy of the adage by thanking me in a special reception in September 1912 at the former Foreign Office Mansion for distinguished visitors here in Peking, for my services in the matter of his kidnapping sixteen years before, adding that my valuable help had certainly abridged his mental and physical sufferings during his unjust *emprisonnement* and that I was, as *Wilhelm der Zweite*[5] once remarked of Austria vis-à-vis Germany: "a chivalrous second with flaming sword" to Dr. Cantlie who might have had to wait some days before achieving an interview with Lord Salisbury, although the result in the and would have been the same.

---

[1] Punctuality is the politeness of kings.
[2] And the duty of the little.
[3] Without a word of apology
[4] Wait in a room apart.
[5] Wilhelm II of Germany.

In the spring of 1897, Sarah[1] sent to me at my *Hôtel* in the Rue de la Paix a message: *"Miens! j'ai d'importantes choses à te dire."*[2] The Empress Eugénie was staying at the Continental, Rue de Rivoli, on her way to Cap St. Martin: Sarah who was *une des intimes*[3] of H.I.M. had been with her the previous evening, had mentioned me as *un Anglais qui avait de l'esprit*[4] and had been in Russia on a special private mission to Nicholas II. "He must be the man of whom Maria Feodorovna wrote to me some time ago, saying *'Il avait beaucoup de gaieté et infiniment d'esprit'.*[5] Tell him to come tomorrow: I will receive him at 4."

When I presented myself and made *les trois révérences de règle avec le baisemain*[6] wherewith she honoured me, Empress Eugénie graciously expressed her welcome: *"Je suis heureuse de vous voir: venez vous asseoir. Ma chère amie, l'impératrice Marie, m'avait écrit que Leurs Majestés étaient bien contentes d'avoir fait votre connaisance."*[7]

Her salon on the first floor *donnait sur le Jardin des Tuileries,*[8] and Sarah had told me that the Empress would sit contemplating for hours together that place of memories. "Sorrow's crown of sorrow is remembering happier days", as Dante says[9]: although to her the memory was rather that of

---

[1] Bernhardt.
[2] "Mine! I have some important things to tell you."
[3] One of the intimates.
[4] As a sympathetic Englishman.
[5] He was very cheerful and infinitely witty.
[6] The rule of three bows with kissing.
[7] "I'm happy to see you, come and sit down." "My dear friend, the Empress Marie, had written to me that Their Majesties were delighted to have made your acquaintence."
[8] Overlooked the garden of the Tuileries.
[9] Tennyson's translation. E.B.

one who thinks of the dead, not regretfully but *dans le calme*[1] that religion brought to her, also, I think, a sort of expiation that she deemed to be Heaven's due for *la débâcle de l'an 1870.*[2]

Her first question concerned Charles James Fox: *"Je sais très bien que votre ancêtre était le grand ami de la France: l'empereur* (she spoke throughout of Napoléon I as the Emperor and of her husband as *l'emporeur mon mari*[3]) *lui avait témoigné beaucoup d'égards à l'occasion de sa visite à Paris."*[4]

"Mais oui, Madame, les papiers de mon arrière-grand-oncle racontent en détail sa réception par l'empereur qui l'honora de sa compagnie en faisant un tour des Champs Elysées,[5] saying: 'France and England as allies would rule the world: India for the latter and China for me! But your King is more obstinate than even Pitt!'"[6]

Fox writes in his letter to Lord Holland:[7] "I told to Napoléon George III's opinion of me which, as you know, is not of yesterday: how he had commanded me to return my seal of

---

[1] In the calm.
[2] The debacle of the year 1870.
[3] The Emperor my husband.
[4] "I know very well that your ancestor was the great friend of France: the Emperor had given him a great deal of consideration during his visit to Paris."
[5] Yes, madam, the papers of my great-great-uncle describe in detail his reception by the Emperor, who honoured him with his company by making a tour of the Champs Elysees.
[6] William Pitt the Younger (1759 –1806) British Tory statesman, the youngest prime minister of Great Britain in 1783 at the age of 24 and the first prime minister of the United Kingdom of Great Britain and Ireland.
[7] Stephen Fox, 2nd Baron Holland (1745 –1774) of Holland House, Kensington.

office by messenger, so as to avoid seeing me in person, a cavalier proceeding, but I think the king was ashamed to see me."

Eugénie interpolated: "Exactly what Louis XV did (at Dubarry's[1] request) to Choiseul,[2] writing to the latter his letter of dismissal with the apostille *"Pas de réponse"*[3] Tell me what impression the Emperor made on Fox?"

"He marvelled at his consummate grasp of a situation and even of English politics, so far as they interested him; his crisp, epigrammatic comments, the savour of his summing up of Pitt's jealous character, of George III's feminine petulance, his conviction that the Whigs were, if not in sympathy with himself, at least prepared to arrive at a permanent understanding with France, above all his flashing humour, made Fox say to his brother Henry: 'You cannot call him a man; he is a god.'"

"If Fox had but lived," said Eugenie, 'the King would have given in, just as he did during the American war of independence, and accepted the alliance with the emperor."

"In any case, Madame, George's increasing *accès de démence*[4] was about to force him (*nolens volens*[5]) out of affairs, and the

---

[1] Jeanne Bécu, Comtesse du Barry (1743–1793), last official mistress of King Louis XV of France
[2] Étienne François, Marquis de Stainville, Duc de Choiseul (1719–1785) was a French military officer, diplomat and statesman. He considered the Comtesse ordinary.
[3] No answer.
[4] Onset of dementia.
[5] Unwilling or willing.

Prince of Wales, as an old intimate of Fox, would certainly have listened to his counsels rather than to Lord Liverpool."

"Les torts de l'histoire,"[1] said the empress; it is a fascinating but futile study especially for me who lives with the past. For you the future: as the English say: 'the world's your oyster!' But now tell me about the Hodinsky plain tragedy: were the Tsar and the Tsaritsa, both of whom are superstitious, struck by the fateful resemblance with the firework display on the Place de Louis XV in honour of the Dauphin Louis Auguste's marriage in 1770 with Marie Antoinette, when so many hundreds of spectators were crushed to death?"

"I hardly know, Madame; but both the Impératrice Marie and the Grand Duchess Serge expressed to me their sense of the sinister omen and presage of all that the disaster coming hotfoot on the Coronation conveyed to them. In fact, the Princess Elizabeth said: *"Le Ciel se prononcera: je prie Dieu qu'Elle ne finisse pas mal. C'est un présage, un augure qui me remplit d'une horreur indicible!"*[2] "So she spoke to you in French? That is interesting, for she speaks both English and naturally German better than French. Elizabeth is a *voyante*[3] like the *pythonisse de Delphos*.[4] The imperial couple should surely have asked our ambassador to postpone his reception! (She said *'notre'*,[5] not *'de France'*)."

---

[1] The wrongs of history.
[2] "Heaven will pronounce: I pray God that She will not end badly. It is an omen, an omen that fills me with an unspeakable horror! "
[3] Psychic.
[4] High Priestess of the Temple of Apollo at Delphi i.e. the Delphic oracle.
[5] Our.

"Madame, that was what the Grand Duchess thought, also the Empress Marie when I had the honour to see her some weeks later."

"Well," said the Empress, "let us hope that it was a warning from God, a call for greater circumspection, *un appel au for intérieur.*"[1] Tell me, do you not fancy that *la jeune imperatrice ne s'entend tout-à-fait pas avec sa belle-mere?*"[2]

"*Madame, on m'a dit cela à Saint Petersbourg, mais naturellement je me trouve dans l'impossibilité d'en juger is verite.*"[3]

"*Espérons que non, au moins. Les Parisiens qui leur firent un accueil des plus enthousiastes l'automne dernier ont trouve l'imperatrice assez froide et peu sympathique, tout on rendant hommage à la généreuse personnalité de Nicholas II, qui a bien du charme mais par malheur il manque de force d'âme. Mais pour vous, Monsieur, vous êtes toujours célibataire, me trompé-je?*"[4]

"*Oui, Madame, et je dois le rester toute ma vie; it m'était arrivé un terrible malheur: la charmante Doris V...* (I told to H.M. the surname - which here I omit of purpose set - of my sweetheart) *avait promis de se marier avec moi mais elle devint éprise d'un*

---

[1] A call to the heart.

[2] "The young empress does not get along with her mother-in-law."

[3] "Madam, I was told this in St. Petersburg, but of course I find myself unable to judge it as truth."

[4] "Let's hope not, at least." The Parisians who gave them a most enthusiastic welcome last autumn found the Empress quite cold and unsympathetic, all paying homage to the generous personality of Nicholas II, who has a lot of charm but by misfortune he lacks the strength of soul. "But for you, Sir, you're still single, am I wrong?"

de nos amis qui l'épousa trois ou quatre jours avant la date qu'on avait fixée pour notre mariage. Et après leur lune de midi, cette pauvre Doris n'est cassé le cou au cours d'une chasse a renard au Yorkshire. Requiem aeternam dons."[1]

"Mon Dieu, quel triste événement: je vous exprime toute ma sympathie; voilà un attristant souvenir qui ne vous quittera jamais!"[2]

"My humble thanks to Your Imperial Majesty. Doris was a relation of Lord Ripon whom you may know." "Yes, indeed: *c'est un fort Catholique et un grand seigneur typiquement britannique: la reine fait grand cas de lui en dépit du fait qu'il est du parti libéral qu'elle déteste, comme du reste vous le savez déjà très bien."*[3]

"Oui, Madame, comme vice-roi de l'Inde il avait encouru l'hostilité implacable des marchands et des colons britanniques à cause de sa sympathie envers les indigènes, es qui ne cessait jamais."[4]

---

[1] "Yes, Madame, and I must remain it all my life;" A terrible misfortune happened to me: the charming Doris V. had promised to marry me but she became infatuated with one of our friends who married her three or four days before the date we had set for our wedding. And after their honeymoon, this poor Doris broke her neck during a fox hunt in Yorkshire. Eternal rest unto them."

[2] "My God, what a sad event: I express my sympathy;" "This is a sad memory that will never leave you!"

[3] "He is a strong Catholic and a great, typically British Lord: The Queen makes great case of him in spite of the fact that he is of the Liberal Party which she hates, as you already know very well."

[4] "Yes, madam, as viceroy of India, he had incurred the implacable hostility of British merchants and settlers because of his sympathy for the natives, which never ceased."

"Mme. Bernhardt me dit que vous promettez grandement pour la scène; est-ce que vous contemplez vraiment une carrière theâtrale?"[1]

"C'est bien aimable de la part de Mme. Bernhardt que de dire cela; mais je ne crois guère qu'il me serait possible, vu le fait que mes talents histrioniques laissent beaucoup à désirer, nonobstant ses enseignements précieux et ses conseils encourageants."[2]

"M'est avis que voue devriez plutôt vous vouer à le diplomatie; je vois bien que vous êtes sympathique au plus haut degré; c'est là une qualité assez rare quoique bien nécessaire parmi des diplomates. A propos, j'ai appris hier soir de Mme. Bernhardt que vous parlez très bien l'espagnol et possédez des connaissanoes approfondies de 'notre' (she said "our") glorieuse littérature?"[3]

"Madame, j'ai bien étudié le Castillan durant de longues années, cette langue, comme dit Charles-Quint, dont on ne sert en priant à Dieu et aux Saints. J'aime profondément ce pays où j'ai beaucoup voyagé et es peuple chevaleresque qui exerce sur moi un grand attrait."[4]

---

[1] "Mrs. Bernhardt tells me that you have great stage promise; do you really contemplate a theatrical career?"

[2] "It is very kind of Mrs. Bernhardt to say that, but I do not think that it would be possible for me, given the fact that my histrionic talents leave much to be desired, notwithstanding her precious teachings and encouraging advice."

[3] "I think you should rather devote yourself to diplomacy, I see that you are sympathetic in the highest degree, and this is a rare but necessary quality among diplomats. By the way, I learned yesterday evening from Mrs. Bernhardt that you speak Spanish very well and have a thorough knowledge of our glorious literature?"

[4] "Madame, I have studied Castilian for many years, that language, as Charles V said, which is not used in praying to God and the Saints." I deeply love that

"Est-ce que le Reine Marie Christine vous a reçu? Voilà une grande femme, l'incarnation du courage et d'un sentiment de patriotisme vraiment exalté."[1]

"Non, Madame, pas exactement: mais c'est vrai que j'avais l'honneur d'assister à une réception qu' avait accordée la Reine au corps diplomatique, quoiqu'en une très humble capacité, en tant qu'ayant des liens de parenté avec l'Ambassadeur d'Angleterre."[2]

"Je suppose que l'impératrice d'Autriche ne vous ait jamais recu: si vous visitez Vienne, vous n'avez qu' è faire savoir à l'ambassadeur de la Grande Bretagne ce que je vous dis, et il pourrait arranger les choses par l'intermédiaire du chambellan de Sa Maison: tenez, je vais écrire à mon amie, l'impératrice, un petit mot, et c'est certain qu'Elle vous fera un très bon accueil."[3]

---

country, where I have traveled extensively, and a chivalrous people who exert a great attraction on me. "

[1] "Has Queen Mary Christine received you? Here is a great woman, the embodiment of courage and a sense of truly exalted patriotism."

[2] "No, madam, not exactly: but it is true that I had the honor of attending a reception which the Queen had granted the diplomatic corps, albeit in a very humble capacity, through having ties of kinship with the English Ambassador. "

[3] "I suppose the Empress of Austria never received you: if you visit Vienna, you have only to let the British Ambassador know what I am telling you, and he might arrange things by the intermediary of the house chamberlain: I will write to my friend, the Empress, a short note, and it is certain that she will give you a very warm welcome. "

"Je me permets d'exprimer à l'impératrice tous mes sentiments de la plus profonde reconnaissance: vraiment, Madame, vous me comblez de bienfaits que je ne mérite assurément point."[1]

"De rien, Monsieur. Eh bien! j'espère pouvoir vous revoir: je vais écrire à l'impératrice Marie pour lui dire que (de mon avis) vous méritez bien (et sans la moindre ombre de flatterie) toutes ses louanges enthousiastes, car vous joignez à la sympathie l'esprit, ce qui est assurément exceptionnel! Maintenant, je vous dis bonsoir, comme j'ai l'intention de faire un petit tour une fois de plus dans ce jardin des Tuileries où, comme du reste vous pouvez vous le représenter, m'attendent toujours ces souvenirs inoubliables, pour la plupart, Dieu merci, heureux. Alors, au revoir, Monsieur," dit-Elle, en me congédiant d'un gracieux geste.[2]

The Empress impressed me, as she did so many others, with her wonderful carriage and grace, which in no way belied Winterhalter's[3] portraits of her in her prime. She was, when I saw her, in her seventy-first year but *sa démarche, sa belle prestance*[4] were akin to those of a woman still young in mind and body. It will always rejoice me to recall my meeting with

---

[1] "I allow myself to express to the Empress all my feelings of the deepest gratitude: truly, Madame, you fill me with blessings which I certainly do not deserve."

[2] "Well, I hope to see you again: I am going to write to the Empress Marie, telling her that (in my opinion) you deserve (and without the slightest shade of flattery) all her enthusiastic praises, for you share the sympathic spirit, which is certainly exceptional! Now I say goodnight to you, as I intend to take a little turn once more in this garden of the Tuileries where, as you can imagine, are always awaiting me unforgettable memories, for the most part, thank God, happy. "Good-bye, sir," she said, dismissing me with a graceful gesture.

[3] Franz Xaver Winterhalter (1805–1873) German painter and lithographer, known for his flattering portraits of royalty and upper-class society..

[4] Her approach, her beautiful presence

a great historical figure. I forgot to record that of all the great official events of her life, that which had left on her memory the deepest impression was the occasion when she performed the ceremony of opening the Suez Canal in 1869, Napoleon III having been unable to be present. I believe M. Paléologue says the same in *Les entretiens de l'impératrice Eugénie.* [1]

Candour obliges me to confess, not without hesitancy, *une bévue des plus formidables que j'avais faite au cours de cet entre-tien.* [2] I happened to mention the Honourable Mrs. Ronald Campbell, [3] *la veuve d'un officier britannique tut è l'ennemi en Afrique,* [4] since her son, Guy, [5] and I were *des camarades d'école.* [6]

"Mais oui", said the empress, *"elle m'accompagnait à l'occasion de mon pèlerinage à l'Afrique du Sud, pour visiter l'endroit où fut tué mon cher fils en l'an 1879."* 'Et moi (malheureux' de répondre': [7]

"Ah: Madame: ce lâche assassinat du prince impérial, cette lâcheté disgracieuse qui blessera à tout jamais l'honneur de

---

[1] *Interviews With Empress Eugenie* (1928).
[2] A most formidable blunder I made during this interview.
[3] Katharine Susanna Claughton (1849–1934), daughter of the Bishop of St Albans. Married the Hon. Captain Hon. Ronald George Elidor Campbell (1848–1879), Coldstream Guards, second son of the 2nd Earl Cawdor, who died in battle.
[4] The widow of a British officer killed by the enemy in Africa.
[5] Reverend Guy Ronald Campbell (1874–1950), Rector at Wilton. Married the Hon. Vere Annesley, and had issue.
[6] School friends.
[7] "But yes. She accompanied me on the occasion of my pilgrimage to South Africa, to visit the place where my dear son was killed in the year 1879. " And I (unhappy to answer):"

mon pays; ce poltron de Carey[1] qui l'abandonna aux sagaies des Zoulous en flagrante infraction de con devoir de militaire et d'homme de bien."[2]

"Monsieur, ne dites jamais ce mot d'assassinat; ma famille s'en était servie, elle aussi, au temps de sa mort et m'avait mise en grande colère. Mon fils tomba au champ d'honneur d'une manière digne de celui qui portait le beau nom de Napoléon. Quant à Carey, il l'a vraiment trahi, mais je crois bien que sa lâcheté fut due à une panique dont furent saisis et lui et l'escorte devant les sauvages, comme au cas du fatal sauve-qui-peut de Waterloo. Du reste, Carey mourut à l'Inde moins d'une année après mon fils, la proie (on me l'a dit) des remords et de la honte, entoura du mépris de tous. Dieu le pardonnera, mais pour moi c'est assez difficile que de faire la part de sa trahison déshonorante."[3]

---

[1] Jahleel Brenton Carey (1847–1883), British officer who became notorious for his alleged responsibility for the death in action of Napoléon, Prince Imperial (1856–1879), at the hands of Zulu warriors in South Africa.

[2] "Ah, Madam: that cowardly assassination of the Imperial Prince, that ungainly cowardice which will forever wound the honor of my country, that coward of Carey, who abandoned him to the Zulu spears in flagrant violation of military duty, good man."

[3] "Sir, never say this word murder, my family used it at the time of his death and made me angry." My son fell in the field of honor in a dignified manner and Carey, he really betrayed him, but I believe that his cowardice was due to a panic with which he was seized and he escorted him to the savages, as in the case of a fatal rescuer of Waterloo, and Carey died in India less than a year after my son, the prey (as I have been told) of remorse and shame, surrounded with contempt by all. God will forgive him, but for me it is rather difficult to share in his dishonourable betrayal. "

"Madame, qu'ai-je à vous répondre? Je ne saurais vous exprimer toute ma honte d'avoir osé, en un moment d'inadvertance, m'exprimer d'une telle malheureuse façon."[1]

"V. M. je vous demande pardon du tond de mon coeur et vous prie humblement d'oublier, si cela vous est possible, ma terrible erreur qui était certainement due à la haine et au mépris que m'inspira ce fripon-là."[2]

"Volontiers, Monsieur; je comprends votre noble courroux, ce qui témoigne d'un coeur généreux. N'en parlons plus."[3]

"C'est vrai, pensai-je, qu'on ne s'honore guère on blessant (bien que pas exprès) les sentiments d'autrui; d'autant plus cet amour maternel pour un fils infortuné."[4]

Sarah with her incomparable grace bade me take heart, as others beside the Duchess of Alba [5] and Eugénie's other Spanish relations (I think, but am not sure, that la Comtesse de Montijo was then still living) had said and written in the same sense. It distressed me to learn from Mme. Bernhardt's own lips that she too (*elle aussi*) was convinced of foul play and not

---

[1] "Madame, what have I to say to you? I can not express to you my shame at having in a moment of inadvertence dared to express myself in such an unfortunate manner."

[2] "V. M. I beg your pardon for my heart's heart, and humbly beg you to forget, if possible, my terrible error, which was certainly due to the hatred and contempt with which this rascal inspired me."

[3] "Gladly, Sir;" I understand your noble wrath, which is a testament to a generous heart. "Let's not talk about it."

[4] "It is true, I think, that we hardly honour ourselves in hurting (even if not deliberately) the feelings of others; all the more that maternal love for an unfortunate son."

[5] María Francisca de Sales de Palafox Portocarrero y Kirkpatrick (1825 – 1860), 12th Duchess of Peñaranda, 9th countess of Montijo; Eugénie's older sister. Married the 15th duke of Alba.

merely of cowardice on Carey's part: her settled belief was that he had received *un pot de vin*[1] from some one in a very high place to betray the prince and that *de louches négociations*[2] had preceded Carey's appointment to watch over 'Louis' (as [his] mother called him).

As everyone knows, the younger Rostand[3] wrote *une pièce de théatre*[4] accusing Queen Victoria as responsible, *perfide Albion*, faithful to her traditions, having thus (essentially speaking) killed the great Napoléon, equally by the act of a great London surgeon caused Napoléon III's death under chloroform administered on repeated occasions despite cardiac weakness, French medical opinion holding that it was incumbent to wait after the first lithotomy[5] before rushing matters, so that there was grave ground of suspicion; finally by alleging that Victoria feared the restoration of the Bonaparte dynasty as prejudicial to Great Britain and had arranged with Lord Chelmsford[6] (of all people) to contrive his assassination.

It seems to me incredible that Victoria, who loved Eugénie dearly and who remembered her and the Prince Consort's visit to Saint-Cloud as one of the happiest events of her life, should have been accused of sending him to his death in South

---

[1] A bribe.
[2] Shady negotiations.
[3] Maurice Rostand (1891–1968), poet, novelist and playwright; eldest son of noted playwright, poet and essayist Esmond Rostand.
[4] *Napoléon IV* (1928) by Maurice Rostrand.
[5] Surgical removal of gallstones.
[6] Frederic Augustus Thesiger, 2nd Baron Chelmsford (1827–1905), British Army officer who rose to prominence during the Anglo-Zulu War, when an expeditionary force under his command suffered a decisive defeat at the hands of a Zulu force. Despite this, he was able to score several victories, culminating in that of the Battle of Ulundi, which ended the War.

Africa; whither, in fact, she opposed his going from the beginning.

Sarah was always Anglophile but in those days Queen Victoria's anti-French attitude gave a certain colour to suspicions which, of course, Eugénie would have repudiated with horror, for she loved the Queen. Sarah told me of the Empress' belief in communications with the dead: the notorious medium, Home, [1] whom Browning mercilessly castigates as "Mr. Sludge the medium" owing to a *soi-disant* communication with the spirit of his dead wife, had been summoned to give a *séance* at the Tuileries which impressed the imperial couple by certain oracular predictions from the spirit world, apparently not wholly without resemblance to the things heard and seen by T'zu Hsi at the Tung Yüeh Miao (East Peak Temple).

Again, when the Duchess of Alba, her sister, died from cancer, her spirit appeared to Eugénie reproaching her in unmeasured vehemence for not warning her of the fatal nature of the malady: *"Pourquoi ne m'avais-tu pas avertie? Tu avais tort!"*[2]

I was still in Paris when a letter from Aubrey Beardsley informed me of his Baptism and First Communion: "I feel like a caller who has been waiting on the doorstep of a house, hesitant and fearful before knocking. And now the door is opened to me and I am basking in the warmth and radiance after wandering so far, so far. Dearest Trelawny, make up your mlnd and do likewise."

---

[1] Daniel Dunglas Home (1833–1886), famous Scottish medium.
[2] "Why didn't you warn me?" "You were wrong!"

Sarah very kindly brought about a meeting for me with Réjane:[1] it is pleasant to feel that the former truly admired Réjane's genius, especially as her art was exhibited in directions which did not impinge upon Mme. Bernhardt's field of work. Take her for all in all, I should have said that Sarah compared favourably as regards *jalousie de métier et l'absence d'une petitesse quelconque d'esprit*[2] with a Henry Irving or a Duse.

Réjane was delighted to learn of Aubrey's conversion and of his spiritual welfare, though naturally much concerned about his physical condition which had now become alarming. She gave to one of his portraits of her as Mme. Sans-gêne[3] a place of honour in her boudoir and spoke affectionately of Aubrey's haggard, sunken eyes and wistful, pathetic face with the narrow forehead and the long hair of the palest yellow hue.

"Eh bien, Monsieur, Sarah me dit que vous sortez de souche allemande, mais que, nonobstant ce fait-ci, voue êtes toujours un grand ami de la France."[4]

"Oui, Madame, je suis à tout jamais admirateur de ces qualités incomparables de clarté d'esprit et de logique que a toujours possédées la France; quant à l'Allemagne, si j'ose me comparer pour un moment au colosse qu'est Goethe, comme lui, je ne suis

---

1 Gabrielle Réjane (1856–1920), French actress.
2 Jealousy of craft and the absence of any smallness of mind.
3 The lead character in the historical comedy-drama *Mme. Sans-gêne* (1893) by Victorien Sardou and Émile Moreau, concerning incidents in the life of Catherine Hübscher, an outspoken 18th-century laundress who became the Duchess of Danzig.
4 "Well sir, Sarah tells me that you come from German stock, but notwithstanding that fact, you are always a great friend of France."

pas non plus l'adulateur aveugle de la Prusse, mais j'adore cette culture teutonique à un plus haut degré (en effet beaucoup plus) que celle de mon Albion qui manque toujours d'un système rangé ou plein de cohérence."[1]

"On m'a souvent priée de faire une tournée en Allemagne, mais je ne consentirais jamais à donner ces représentations à Berlin, bien que je ne soulevasse aucune objection à jouer à Dresde ou à Munich. Mais l'ambassadeur de France à Berlin ne me permettrait jamais cela, pas même au cours d'une tournée en Autriche. Eh bien! C'est plus fort que moi: je no pardonnerai jamais à la Prusse son pillage de Saint-Cloud en 1870 et par-dessus le marché la conduite du maréchal Blucher après la première occupation de Paris en 1814. Et Mme. Sarah dit la même chose: elle n'ira jamais à Berlin ni fera droit à la démarche d'y paraître que Guillaume II lui a gracieusement faite (et à moi aussi) à maintes reprises. Le jour viendra, Monsieur, où votre bonne reine comprendra, elle aussi, qu'elle se trompe affreusement au sujet des intentions peu amicales de son petit-fils envers l'Angleterre. Mais naturellement je n'en dis rien des autres membres de la féderation allemande; au contraire, je les respecte sincèrement, tout en adorant Wagner et ce pauvre roi de Bavière, cet infortuné qui était, lui aussi, un génie de race."[2]

---

[1] "Yes, madam, I am always admiring these incomparable qualities of clarity of mind and logic which France has always possessed, and Germany, if I dare to compare myself for a moment with the colossus Goethe, like him, I am not the blind adulator of Prussia either, but I adore Teutonic culture to a higher degree (in fact much more) than that of my Albion which still lacks a tidy system of complete consistency."

[2] "I have often been asked to tour Germany, but I would never consent to give performances in Berlin, although I have no objection to playing in Dresden or Munich. But the French ambassador in Berlin would never allow me to do that, not even a tour in Austria. Well! I would never forgive Prussia for her plunder of Saint-Cloud in 1870, and, above all, for the conduct of her

I had planned a visit to *Le Caire*[1] for that autumn (1897) and was given an introduction to the Princess N...[2] an Ottoman by birth who had married a cousin of the late Khedive. She was a near relative of Edhem Pasha,[3] the Commander-in-Chief in the recent Greco-Turkish war; I had not the honour of his acquaintance but he most kindly acceded to the request of the Ottoman ambassador in Paris, again through Sarah's kind contrivance, for His Excellency was decidedly *épris d'elle'*.[4]

I do not know what Edhem would have thought of our subsequent manoeuvres, I mean mine and those of the Princess with her consummate and developed carnality. A good deal in dispraise, I should fancy, since Islam prohibits extra-conjugal relations and all acts other than the natural coitus of man and woman, above all regarding as a cardinal sin the contact with a Giaour, the crime impossible to be forgiven. It was hardly the best season to visit Cairo, but I braved the heat. Worthy British men (and women) assured me there that a dinner party for erotic purpose with the Princess N. (I omit the remainder of her title, well known as it is, because she

---

tour into Austria, and, above all, the conduct of Marshal Blucher after the first occupation of Paris in 1814. And Sarah says the same thing: she will never go to Berlin, nor will she accept the invitation to appear there, which William II has graciously made to her (and to me too) on many occasions. The day will come, Sir, your good Queen, too, will understand that she is foolishly mistaken about the unfriendly intentions of her grandson towards England, but naturally I say nothing of the other members of the German federation; on the contrary, I sincerely respect them, while adoring Wagner and the poor King of Bavaria, the unfortunate man who was also a genius of his race."

[1] Cairo.
[2] Princess Zainab Nazli Hanim. See earlier note.
[3] Edhem Pasha (1851–1909), Ottoman field marshal; a leading commander in Greco-Turkish War (1897).
[4] Enamored of her.

made me promise never to reveal our liaison) spelled death to any non-Moslem.

Stories were rife of young British officers being lured to their doom by this amorous Circe and of mysterious conduits leading to the Nile, of corpses retrieved from the waters bearing concrete evidence of strangulation, of untrammelled luxury (or rather *luxure*[1]) as in the days of good Harun Al Rashid,[2] in a word the *bobards*[3] that my imaginative, if worthy, compatriots love to disseminate regarding Oriental tastes and the 'gorgeous' East that so few Britons ever take the trouble to understand.

I did not believe a word of these malicious reports but, as H. H. [4] was known to be violently Anglophobe, I wondered whether this her habit of mind might not have engendered Münchhausen-like legends of apocryphal occurrences. (In any case to murder poor me would have been an original way of honouring Edhem Pasha's eulogistic introduction.)

I received within an hour of the presentation of the latter's letter presenting a man he had never seen (nor heard of till he penned the latter) a card with the legend 'secret': *"La Princesse N. se trouverait honorée à un haut degré si Monsieur Edmond Backhouse avait la bonté le passer chez elle ce soir même pour faire la causette. La Princesse l'attend. Pas de réponse par écrit,*

---

[1] Lust.
[2] Harun al-Rashid, 5th Caliph of the Abbasid dynasty (c763–809); his empire extended from modern Morocco to India. A number of the stories in *The Thousand and One Nights* are based on Harun and his magnificent court at Baghdad.
[3] Blarney.
[4] Her Highness.

S. V. P."[1] Naturally, I respected the confidential nature of *l'invite* without attributing to it nor to her any sinister design, nor detrimental possibilities, any more than I did some years later when summoned to the presence of the Old Buddha for 'domestic' purpose to satisfy her *rut de femme.*

I was received by a bevy of Turkish (not Egyptian) slaves headed by a colossal majordomo who, so the Princess informed me, was a Circassian, white skinned, wrinkled and flabby, a eunuch who had been in the service of Abdul Hamid.[2] I bestowed, as custom required, most lavish *bakchich*[3] and received in return the equivalent (in Ottoman) of the designation Your royal and Imperial Highness.

As a fact, I knew Turkish and it was pleasant to hear the mellifluous sound, so gratifying to the ear, in comparison with Egyptian Arabic. We passed through a series of courtyards, ideal places of sojourn during a Cairene summer which, however, compareth favourably with the Peking 'canicule'. There was a spacious garden with a mosquito-rife pond containing, gold fish in abundance and *nenuphars*[4] now past their bloom; I thought of:

"In Bagdad's shrines of fretted gold
High-walled gardens green and old."[5]

---

[1] "Princess N. would be honored to a high degree if Monsieur Edmond Backhouse had the kindness to spend it at her house this evening for conversation." The princess is waiting for him. No answer in writing, S. V. P.
[2] Abdul Hamid II (1842–1918), 34th Sultan of the Ottoman Empire.
[3] Gratuities.
[4] Lillies.
[5] Tennyson. EB

273

Had there been *scintilla veritatis*[1] in the canards regarding the princess, the scene would have been adaptable to crime, but she was, I take it, of the type that loves *à tromper*[2] the male but not *à l'arranger* (or to make away with) her lovesick victims.

Shown on to the veranda where N. was sitting, she greeted me with effusion in a semi-sensual and wholly *spirituelle* fashion. The princess looked like a woman of forty; she wore what for that time was *une robe des plus décolletées*,[3] Monsieur Worth,[4] I should guess, being the name of her couturier: it was a rainbow gauze gown which clung to her lithe, little figure; she was bejewelled but not excessively so. Her tiny hands and feet (she was bare-footed except for black satin babouches), impressed one with their delicacy: she wore a large cabochon single emerald ring and another of pigeon-blooded rubies; her comely hair was done in the fashion of the nineties which I thought a pity; her features were attractive without great beauty, more because of the expression and the endless play *d'esprit et d'espièglerie*,[5] which bewitched the onlooker and charmed him like *le fumet*[6] of tokayan wine. She told me herself that she had been greatly loved, had had many affaires in Byzance long before her exile (as she termed it) *au Caire*.

"Mon parent me dit que vous parlez l'Ottoman"[7] (in those days none ever said "Turkish" which was deemed derogatory).

---

[1] A spark of truth.
[2] To decieve.
[3] A dress of very revealing neckline.
[4] Charles Frederick Worth (1825 –1895), English fashion designer who founded the House of Worth, and considered to be the father of *haute couture*.
[5] Of spirit and playfulness.
[6] The smell.
[7] "My relative tells me that you speak Ottoman."

"Mais tout de meme vous m'excuserez si je parle français. Je vais te tutoyer; tu ne m'en voudras pas, me trompé-je? Non, je le crois?"[1]

She told to me the anecdote about Sir Herbert Kitchener and his frigidity which she attributed to impotence, although given the right environment, he was no more incapable than the present writer in days of yore. While we regaled ourselves with apéritifs, though Islam stringently forbids alcohol in any shape or form (alcohol in Arabic meaning "powder to stain the eyelids" and not, as often stated, "the good") she ventilated her hatred of Britain, accusing Sir Evelyn Baring (Lord Cromer)[2] of having hired "medicine men" to poison the late Khedive, her cousin. "You English are a stupid race, or you would evacuate the country."

I asked her if she had ever met Oscar Wide, as the catchword was familiar to my ears; and she assured me that it was he who had taught to her the phrase *'Ce que les Anglais sont noix.'*[3] She was most curious about my Constantinople (as we should say now, Istanbul) erotic adventures and my agreeable associations with eunuch loves. "You find them (the eunuchs) softer than women, I suppose," making an appropriate, if lewd, gesture. *"Non, votre altesse, cela dépend comma de juste de la femme."*[4]

---

[1] "But still you will excuse me if I speak French." I'm going to 'tu' you. [i.e. speak on a familiar basis.] You will not be angry with me, am I wrong? "No, I believe it?"

[2] Evelyn Baring, 1st Earl of Cromer (1841–1917), British statesman, diplomat and colonial administrator.

[3] What the English are is nuts.

[4] No Your Highness, it depends on the woman.

The dinner was *un charmant tête à tête, la cuisine à l'Ottomane*, delectable sorbets and real Rahat-lakoum or candied fruits, *arrosé*, with abundant (if sweet) *vin de Champagne. Nous avions notre cocarde, tous les deux,*[1] before the end of the meal, and the love-feast started without delay almost before the eunuch slaves had completed *la débandade.*[2] I spare *au lecteur bénévole,*[3] equally *à la lectrice s'il y en a,*[4] the rehearsal of our amorous antics save only to say that we omitted no manoeuvre of the time-honoured lust-begotten *répertoire* and that H. H. in her delicious lubricity, surpassed even myself with suggestiveness and unchaste, if ornamental, devisings.

Certes,[5] she found me no Sir Herbert Kitchener, no Sirder whose militant appearance presented to her lust such ample promise, alas! devoid of fulfilment, even (as she complained) to the extent of accomplishing a mild *demi-élargissement*[6] (to use her phrase) of his person as she sought to titillate a most unmilitary *chybre.*[7] But I think that she knew of his homosexual predilections, for she denominated me as *un bimétalliste des plus séduisante,*[8] whereas Kitchener was wedded to obstinate *monisme,*[9] and at that time, omitting the epithet of seductive, I certainly deserved the honourable brevet of 'double standards' and was able to *faire mon devoir envers Son Alteese dans un aphrodisiaque quelconque.*[10]

---

[1] We were aroused, both of us.
[2] The scuttle of removing dishes.
[3] The voluntary reader.
[4] Equally to the reader if there are any.
[5] Certainly.
[6] Half-enlargement.
[7] Cock.
[8] A most seductive bisexual.
[9] Oneness.
[10] Do my duty to Her Highness in any aphrodisiac.

Her vocabulary *anent le soi-disant vice anglais* [1] was as complete as that of the most inveterate *flâneur des boulevards*: [2] we discussed Turkish terms (I beg pardon, "Ottoman") for homosexual ecstasies: sitting at the feet of a feminine Gamaliel, [3] I enriched my vocabulary which was already tolerably fluent and adequate regarding *les coins et les recoins de ce fatal penchant, quo j'admets, tout en rougissant jusqu'au blanc des yeux.* [4]

It was *une délicieuse orgie prolongée jusqu'a l'aube du jour* [5] and ceasing only with the arrival on the scene of n comely white-faced eunuch with the sweetened *café à la Turque.* *"Dis-moi une chose, mon cheri, ne préférerais-tu avoir affaire à celui au lieu de moi-même?" "Jamais, jamais, ma déesse." "Tu as toutes les perfections, c'est bien là la vérité!"* [6]

And so, to the palpable disproof of the common report that a European who entered the palace of Princess N. never emerged alive, excepting in the one case of Kitchener whom it would obviously not have paid to murder, I returned to Shepheards after a *déjeuner au complet* [7] with my new Siren. *"Si tu écris à S.E. le Pasha Edhem, ne dis rien de notre nuit*

---

[1] Concerning the so-called English vice.
[2] Dawdler of the boulevards.
[3] Elder teacher.
[4] The nooks and crannies of that fatal inclination, which I admit, blushing to the whites of my eyes.
[5] A delicious orgy extended to the dawn of the day.
[6] "Tell me one thing, my dear, would not you prefer to have to deal with the one instead of myself?" "Never, never, my goddess." "You have all the perfections, that is the truth!"
[7] A full breakfast.

d'amour: ça l'entêterait et la chose serait fatale à ma réputation de veuve."[1]

Had Abdul-Hamid got wind of the episode and possession of my person, he would have castrated me and scared my anus with a red-hot poker (*tisonnier*), *tout en pénétrant le rectum, fa tang ch'i tsui*: let the punishment fit the crime. I quite believed that what the whole *beau-monde* of Egypt whimpered as a matter of course *ferait esclandre, au cas où l'on l'ébruitait*,[2] replying: *"Mon ange, je te prie de t'en remettre à ma discrétion et à mon honneur: ce privilege sacré de ton amour sera toujours un secret inviolable: je sais me taire: par l'amour d'Allah ne t'inquiète pas sans rime ni raison."*[3]

It was a charming digression for me *"in mezzo del camin di nostra vita"*[4], a brief flirting episode which I recall with contentment *pas tout-à-fait dénué d'orgueil*.[5] *Moi, l'insulaire, j'avais réussi à lui plaire; n'était-ce qu'un rêve'*,[6] such as the *houris*[7] bring to the blessed ones in the Moslem abode of bliss? Byron could, ay and would, have evolved a canto worthy of Don Juan on our carnival of lust; my relative, Edward John Trelawny,[8] the intimate associate of both Lord Byron and

---

[1] "If you write to Pasha Edhem, do not say anything about our night of love: it would stubborn and it would be fatal to my reputation as a widow."

[2] Would make it scandalous, in case it was.

[3] "My angel, I ask you to trust me to my discretion and my honour: this sacred privilege of your love will always be an inviolable secret: I know how to keep silent: by the love of Allah do not worry rhyme or reason. "

[4] Dante. E.B. In the middle journey of our life.

[5] Not entirely devoid of pride.

[6] I, the islander, had succeeded in pleasing her: was it only a dream.

[7] Beautiful virgins.

[8] Edward John Trelawny (1792–1881) was a British biographer, novelist, adventurer. Son of Charles Trelawny-Brereton (a descendant of Sir Jonathan Trelawny, 2nd Baronet, who married Mary, daughter of Sir Edward

Shelley, whose artless *récits*[1] of his conquests (*un peu brodés, je n'en doute point*)[2] in oriental lands recorded adventures in Moslem countries, in less wealth of amorous detail but with greater vocabulary to depict the subtle charm of the century of women whom (so he says) he possessed with unabated lust.

Armed with a special introduction from Lord Salisbury to Sir Claude MacDonald,[3] the British envoy to China, and private recommendations to several heads of firms in Shanghai, I arrived at that city, once a centre of British influence and the bane of an iniquitous Semitic) opium traffic, early in April 1898. Despite a cordial missive from Sir Thomas Sutherland,[4] Chairman of P. and O. Company, I was insulted in a highly forward manner by a callow clerk fresh from England and his Board-school: he shouted at me across the counter in response to my courteous request for information regarding a Bill of Lading;[5] but when I showed to this rude young popinjay his chief's letter, he cringed and whined in abject apology, begging me not to report his unconscionable discourtesy to Sutherland.

Ah! ye heavy-paunched 'Taipans' and ye new-hatched unfledged clerks, where are ye today? Some among you are pining in internment camps under the Nipponese rod,

---

Seymour, 2nd Baronet. Author of *Adventures of a Younger Son* (1831) and *Records of Shelley, Byron, and the Author* (1878).

[1] Stories.

[2] A little embroidered, I do not doubt it.

[3] Colonel Sir Claude Maxwell MacDonald (1852–1915), British soldier and diplomat. Envoy Extraordinary and Minister Plenipotentiary at Peking, 1896–1900.

[4] Sir Thomas Sutherland (1834 - 1922) British banker and Liberal and Liberal Unionist politician; founder of The Hongkong and Shanghai Banking Corporation; Chairman of the P&O (shipping) Company.

[5] Document acknowledging receipt of cargo for shipment.

receiving in yourselves *la récompense due à votre égarement*.[1] Never again shall ye ride rough-shod over the rights of respectable citizens nor treat the Chinese people as a subject race. Ask the seven seas and the unfathomed caves of ocean where your argosies are today! You are one with Niniveh and Tyre. God has 'shroffed'[2] you, as you used to 'shroff' dollars when silver was the current coin of this realm of China. It shall be better for Sodom and Gomorrah in the day of judgment than for you, overweening and *outrecuidant*[3] survivals of a never-returning epoch, whatever the issue of the war, allied victory or defeat, for your day is done. You are weighed in the balances and found wanting before God and man.

And so I arrived during a howling sand-storm in time-honoured, secular Cambaluc,[4] to be well received by the British Minister, a tall, lean, lanky *militaire*[5] with an undue sense of his value as a diplomat, which in fact was 'nil', and with a conceited wife,[6] and, still more, a shrewish sister-in-law, Miss Armstrong, twin harpies who ruled him and shaped his every action.

It was the day of Kuang-hsü's[7] reforms, but I was set to work on Russian translations, Muscovy being then the paramount

---

[1] The reward due to your errors.

[2] Tested for value: a scroff is a banker or money changer in the Far East who tests and evaluates coin.

[3] Impertinent.

[4] Peking.

[5] Military type.

[6] Ethel, Lady MacDonald, née Armstrong (1852–1915). Widow of P. Craigie Robertson of the Indian Political Service, she married MacDonald in 1892. Made a Dame in 1935.

[7] Kuang-hsü (1871-1908) Emperor of China. In 1898 he attempted to stay the dynastic decline by sponsoring a series of reforms but they alarmed vested interests, and the same year, Empress Dowager Tz'u-his launched a

power in Peking: Port Arthur and Talienwan (Dairen) had lately been seized after Germany's occupation of Tsing-tao. The race for railway concessions had begun, and by MacDonald's direction I assisted the infant "Pekin" (sic) Syndicate in its successful efforts to obtain mining rights in Shansi. Both Lords Salisbury and Lansdowne,[1] then Secretary of State for War but later head of the Foreign Office, wished to send me up to Urga (now Ulan Bator[2]) as British agent; but the Russian authorities, though cognizant of the Tsar's favour to me, deprecated my going there on the untrue ground of "Mongol suspicions" of British "nativity" in that region. The matter was dropped until Japan's victories ended Russian hegemony and my residence in Outer Mongolia would have lost savour.

I made admittedly phenomenal progress with Chinese and enjoyed many delicious homosexual unions, which surely aided my linguistic processes, with fair Manchu scions of the aristocracy, usually reciprocal, sometimes passive but never purely and simply active, for the pastime of ascendancy never greatly appealed to me, unless specially demanded by my *vis-à-vis,* as in Cassia's[3] case.

Love came to me in many a fond disguise, or ever I first saw Cassia's dreamy everlasting dark orbs, Cassia of the long eyelashes and the arched brows, Cassia of the lovely sensual

---

coup d'etat against him. He was confined, and she resumed the office of regent, revoking all reform decrees. He remained in confinement until his death, one day prior to her own.

[1] Henry Charles Keith Petty-Fitzmaurice, 5th Marquess of Lansdowne (1845–1927), British statesman.

[2] Capital of Mongolia. Now Ulaanbaatar.

[3] Cassia Flower, Kuei Hua, a youth Backhouse meets in a male brothel in the first chapter of *Décadence Mandchoue.*

mouth calling for erotic ecstasies and the tireless ardour of supremest uncurbed passion, those pomegranate lips redder than any rose that blew, that delectable posterior whose fair line Charmides[1] or Hyperion[2] would have coveted, that deep, unforgettable *rigida* all a longing and a wild desire, *ineffablement provoquante.*[3]

> "Love and lust were born in May:
> Lust the echo of the spring,
> Love the bird upon the wing"

waited for me in Cassia Flower, my adored one, my radiant other self.

Before the siege of the Legations on June 20, 1900, I was travelling on a special Foreign Office mission in Inner Mongolia, and but for an insinuating manner with the Boxers, who were even then molesting Europeans, might well have lost my life in the solitudes of Gobi, as I Woe pursued by a small band of fanatics in their red uniforms, questioned, found innocuous, and allowed to go unmolested on my way.

The siege saw me a volunteer and Queen Victoria conferred upon me a medal and clasp: the daily fare of tough mule and the dreary task *en faction*[4] meet[*sic:* an apparent typo] bored me less than the enforced abstinence from the pleasures of a

---

[1] The handsome youth of Plato's *Charmides*.
[2] A synonym for radiant male beauty. From Greek mythology: the father of the sun-god Helios.
[3] Ineffably provocative.
[4] Of guard duty.

pathic, but I made up for carnal listlessness and asceticism later in amplest measure, for *crescit eundo*.[1]

Statistics are vain things; but I can recall (and could. write out in a sort of Homeric Catalogue) the names of eighteen *amants*[2] with whom I associated in dear dalliance between 1898 and 1899, when I first encountered sweet Cassia. After the relief of Peking, I was interpreter to General Gaselee[3] and served the cause of the Manchu Dynasty in that capacity, as well as earning the thanks of my government and a compliment from M. de Giers,[4] the Russian envoy, who always addressed me as Baron, by virtue of His August Master's imperial Letters Patent.

Field Marshall v. Waldersee's [5] Chief of Staff, General v. Schwartzkopf,[6] who perished in a fire at the Chung Hai[7] one May night [8] of 1901, honoured me with an invitation to the palace hall wherein he was later to lose his life in the effort to save his favourite Pekingese pug. (He spoke of my father – then still living – as 'Freiherr von Backhaus'.)

It was on the site of this apartment that I was later to have so many erotic adventures with the Old Buddha and on one

---

[1] It grows as it progresses.
[2] Lovers.
[3] General Sir Alfred Gaselee (1844–1918); commander of the British component of the international expeditionary force during the Boxer Rebellion.
[4] Mikhail Nikolayevich von Giers (1856–1924) Imperial Russian diplomat; Envoy to China November 1898 to September 1901.
[5] Field Marshal Alfred Ludwig Heinrich Karl Count von Waldersee (1832-1904).
[6] General Julius von Gross von Schwarzhoff (1850–1901).
[7] A palace complex west of the Forbidden City known to Europeans as the Winter Palace.
[8] It was the night of 17-18 April 1901.

occasion to receive a semi-playful chastisement at her hands for introducing dear Pao Ch'en into the Lake Palace for a love encounter, an offence punishable with death for him and with flogging for me.

Every syllable in these pages is under oath "So Help Me God", as if I had kissed the Testament in Court of Law. I would add that in academic relations with the students I was pure as ice and chaste as snow; my sexual interests were entirely outside the serious university pre-occupations.

Perchance my Ottoman princess erred not in denominating me a '*bimetallist*',[1] *fu pen wei lun che*, for in an active sense I must have *bûché* (seminal ejaculation) on thousands upon thousands of occasions, *me dépensant sans compter*,[2] upending myself beyond computation, *ce qui ne se montre plus*,[3] not indeed as the law of Islam enjoins, "the male shall recline horizontally over the woman and possess her from a spinal posture, neither standing nor sitting, without libidinous caresses of the sexual parts be it by hand, be it by lips or by mouth, but shall limit his activity to the direct intercourse of the male organ placed intromittently [*sic*] within *le vagin*."

---

[1] Bimetallism refers to a system of allowing the unrestricted currency of two metals (normally gold and silver) at a fixed ratio to each other, as coined money. It became a radical 19th century economic movement that desired to supplement the gold standard (which its proponents believed held the world economically hostage) with one based on silver, to boost silver-based economies, such as the United States and India. The word was also used to signify eccentricity or obsession, and as a synonym and euphemism for a dual nature and same-sex desire. Oscar Wilde uses it as a risqué private joke, including in *A Woman Of No Importance*, where Lady Hunstanton says: "Bimetallism! Is that quite a nice subject? However, I know people discuss everything very freely nowadays."
[2] Spending without counting.
[3] Which is no longer.

Tis a worthy injunction, were it ever fulfilled, *'omnium consensu capax imperii si nunquam imperasset'*.[1] As a child, I plead guilty to habituel *'shou yin'*, 'hand salacity', vulgarly called *'lo kuan'rh'* 'tube friction", the 'sin' of poor proverbial embarrassed Onan, at a tender age, or ever ejaculation was possible. This manipulation of which Sir James Paget[2] Bt. M.D. doubted the physical ill so much as the moral prejudice, continued during the years of my adolescence; until from being a 'well of loneliness' except for my lascivious thoughts which once, like my conscience today, never let me be, I sought conjunctivity whether as a medium for others' intrusive battering at the door or as an offensive weapon of inquisitive exploration toward a defined, if lascivious, goal. In the former case the fires of Etna smouldered, ay and burned within me; in the latter the waters, as of a Niagara, sought and found an outlet for pont-up imprisoned lusts.

Has this excess affected my character? Yes and no: it has occasioned a lesion to my will which is weak and to my judgment which is hesitant and nebulous; that it has affected my intellect and brain I still do not believe and have the authority of *des sommités médicales*[3] to support me who deny to me any cerebral degeneration. And I have over been veracious, kind-hearted, true to my own self. My cross, *fatale dono*,[4] is a woeful indecision, a halting between two opinions, a feebleness under pressure even from my own domestics whose truculence bullies and distresses (as when I was

---

[1] Tacitus on Galba. E.B.   If the Government is capable of consent orders.
[2] Sir James Paget, 1st Baronet (1814 –1899), English surgeon and pathologist
[3] Medical leaders.
[4] Fatal gift.

threatened with a beating – not erotic – only last summer, June 1943, surely the climax and the crown of insult from one whom I am powerless to terrify or to overcome, if I failed to provide two and a half dollars or eight pence for pressing needs in heroin, and I yielded to his blackmail and *chantage*,[1] like a poltroon[2]), a tendency to be brow-beaten by lesser men, pressmen, sharpers, *chevaliers d'industrie*;[3] to be made use of for selfish ends, a lovable (perhaps) but over-yielding good nature, *une débonnaireté*,[4] which consents to sacrifices of time, energy and money toward persons devoid of gratitude and devising their own aggrandisement.

Such, then, is Edmund Backhouse, who was by Curzon dubbed (so Kitchener said) a wayward genius! And he may be a bad judge who in his haste says that Curzon was wrong! Now evening comes, my moments are but few; 'the long day's task in done,' said roman Antony.[5] The river of my intellectual attainment (such as it is) is broad-widening to the ocean whither all the fertilising streams of the world must needs ultimately fall. "Bruised pieces go: you have been nobly borne", said Shakespeare; in my case at least consistently and without betrayal of my conscience, *pu pien ch'u chih*. This I know that, were I to live again, I would lead the same life except that I regret having so long postponed my Holy Baptism.

I am one of those of whom the Florentine[6] speaks, those who cannot submit their passions to reason: that which Meng Tzu[7]

---

[1] Extortion.
[2] An utter coward.
[3] Knights of industry.
[4] A goodness.
[5] *Antony and Cleopatra*, Act IV, Scene XIII. E.B.
[6] Dante.
[7] Mencius, born Mèng Kē (c385–c303BC), Chinese Confucian philosopher.

so aptly calls *hao jan chih ch'i*, that selfless exaltation which connotes the *chün tzu*, , the true gentleman. To Dante's vision those unhappy souls found place in the Inferno, but for me a place is prepared in Purgatory where for a long season I must undergo the searching fires of preparation and chastisement, or ever I pass into the divine celestial polity, witness of *l'amor che muove il sole e l'altre stelle*, the love that sways the sun and other stars. Amen: so be it, or as the Free Masonry which for me, Catholic, is now forbidden, "So Mote it be"!

Malicious persons have denied to me even legitimacy of birth, but, so long as my sovereign recognises me as his "trusty and well beloved cousin", I can cheerfully let the cur pack howl and yell, while I pursue my path even to the end, to the uttermost and to the last, strong in the knowledge of having never wilfully wronged a soul.

> "I strove with none, for none was worth my strife;
> Nature I loved and after nature art:
> I warmed both hands before the fire of life;
> It sinks and I am ready to depart."[1]

So may it be with me in my mortal hour "as one who wraps the drapery of his couch about him and lies down to pleasant dreams."

I have to cry *peccavi*, [2] for this subjective wealth of introspection uttered aloud to the reader: memories without candour, as Tolstoi said, are futile things and I have not spared expatiating the shady side of my walk through life, *cette*

---

[1] *Landon. EB
[2] Exclamation expressing guilt.

charmante promenade à travers la réalité,[1] as Chateaubriand calls it; but is it reality? Is it not rather a dream and a delusion, Dead Sea fruit without savour, a vision of power that entices and eludes, scarce other than the mirage I have so often seen in the Desert of Gobi, *k'ung chung lou ko,* castles in the empyrean?

It is repugnant to me to write in any boasting sense of my work and persistent industry: endowed with a remarkable memory, I made good use of my linguistic flair and acquired a knowledge, not always equally profound, of the following languages: French, German, Italian, Spanish, Portuguese, Dutch, Danish (and Norwegian), Swedish, Finnish, Czech, Magyar, Slovene, Serbian, Croatian, Bulgar, Roumanian, Greek, Turkish, Polish, Grusenian (Georgian, the tongue of Joseph Stalin), Russian, Persian, Sanskrit, Pali, Mongol, Tibetan, Manchu, Turki (Turkestan), Japanese, Chinese, Korean, Hebrew, Latin, Classical Greek, Arabic (Syrian), Icelandic, Gothic (Ulfrila's Gospel of Saint Mark), Armenian, Anglo-Saxon, Ladin (in a theoretical, philological sense), Breton, Cymric; one or two others such as Amharic, wherein I waded, but hardly swam *en pataugeant sans nager;*[2] and last and least that tongue which is for the moment (in China and Japan) an obsolete memory, a forbidden fruit, a dead language to which in happier days in the Far Past the name of English was accorded.

Sir Max Beerbohm, some time *mon comrade de collège*, who stayed with me at my London hotel and who often formed *pars*

---

[1] This charming walk through reality.
[2] Wading without swimming.

magna [1] of a *partie carrée* [2] with Oscar, Bozie and myself, incomparable alike as essayist and as cartoonist, once made a delicious caricature (to which the press took exception) of Edward VIII's ghost: the phantom of that august monarch (now in heaven) *loquitur*, as he revisits the glimpses of the moon, in this instance the Restaurant *maintenant fermé à jamais* [3] of the defunct 'Hôtel Edouard Sept' (the fat king's statue, I fancy, *toujours debout* [4] despite recent coolness (to say the least) *entre les deux empires,* [5] *eh bien* Bertie's gracious ghost *loquitur*: "After all it is this restaurant that is my truest memorial."

For my part I may without blushing asseverate that my sexual superfluities, be they frontal or *proctodaeal,* passive or active, are but *parerga* [6] as Plato says, or sideshows in vulgar parlance, a great part (indeed) of my life but not the foremost. I have been a most labourious worker, *une fourmi* [7] who merits comparison with the chiefest and most painstaking of my contemporaries, if indeed genius, as Dizzy said, is really the "taking of infinite pains". *Qui sait?* [8] Certainly not I, *moi qui parle,* [9] nay nor wiser heads than mine.

I have written innumerable papers and articles on divers subjects, political, literary, philosophical, philological, historical and social, for *The Times* of London, *The Westminster*

---

[1] A large part.
[2] A party of four persons.
[3] Now closed forever.
[4] Still standing.
[5] Between the two empires.
[6] Digression.
[7] An ant.
[8] Who knows?
[9] Me who speaks.

Gazette, The Pall Mall Gazette in the days of Mr. William Waldorf Astor (Lord Astor)[1] and Lord Frederic Hamilton,[2] *The Round Table* (regarding China and the Extreme Orient), *The Atlantic Monthly* of Boston, Mass., apart from local journals in Cathay. I was principal author of *China under the Empress Dowager* which achieved a huge success in Britain, U. S. A. and in Germany (in its German translation); I understand that Polish and Swedish translations were also successful, though the French version, *Tz'u Hsi* made a comparative 'four' and failure, despite kindly reviews.

I know from first hand that so good a literary judge as Lord Rosebery found it fascinating and "could not lay it down," (as he told my sister,[3] his friend) though he deplored certain *mal à propos* [4] personal touches which were not due to me (although I must *forcément* accept a joint responsibility) such as childish carping gibes at the wife of the American Minister to China, Mrs. Conger,[5] with other flouts and jeers which prostitute the narrative, though peradventure catering to public taste.

I wrote practically the whole (except the initial chapter) of *Annals of the Court of Peking* which also won a remarkable

---

[1] William Waldorf Astor, 1st Viscount Astor (1848–1919) Anglo-American attorney, politician, businessman (hotels and newspapers), and philanthropist.
[2] Lord Frederick Spencer Hamilton (1856–1928), Conservative M.P., editor, and author of best-selling memoirs.
[3] Dame Harriet Jane Findlay. See earlier note.
[4] Inopportune.
[5] Sarah Pike Conger (1843–1932), author, Christian Scientist, and leader of the Woman's Christian Temperance Union, who befriended Empress Dowager Cixi, and published in 1909 *Letters From China*, a collection of her letters and diary entries during her seven years there. Wife of Edwin Hurd Conger (1843–1907), American congressman and diplomat.

success and, like *The Empress Dowager*, was translated by a well known Chinese publishing house and gained a very large sale in China. So great a judge as the first Lord Cromer, Sir Evelyn Baring G.C.B., reviewed both books in *The Spectator* of London and lavished eulogies on the documentation and the depth of knowledge: he did not know China but he knew the spirit of the gorgeous East. Lord Plunkett,[1] a Celtic wit and scholar, told to my brother Col. Miles Backhouse[2] D.S.O. that he regarded the concluding chapters of *The Empress Dowager* as some of the most brilliant pieces of writing he had ever read. Sir Valentine Chirol,[3] foreign editor of *The Times*, wrote a five page review for that great journal entitled *The Mystery of the Forbidden City*, calling the work a revelation throwing a flood of light upon the Manchu Dynasty, lurid indeed, but luciferous. Be that my epitaph, even though but little illumination is shed upon *la vie intime de l'imperatrice*[4] which I have left to the present study to portray.

Rather reluctantly, I must add that to my old University Oxford I presented a collection of 30,000 Chinese and Manchu volumes; also, that in compliment to my work, I was elected *un membre de l'Academie Diplomatique de Paris* and specially invited to address that distinguished body; while London University offered to me its Chinese chair in 1913.

---

[1] William Lee Plunket, 5th Baron Plunket (1864–1920), Anglo-Irish diplomat and administrator. Governor of New Zealand from 1904 to 1910.
[2] Lt.-Col. Miles Rowland Charles Backhouse (1878–1962). Soldier and company director. Married Olive Buxton, and had issue.
[3] Sir Ignatius Valentine Chirol (1852–1929), British journalist, author, historian and diplomat.
[4] The intimate life of the empress.

Blague dans le coin! [1] I mention these egoistic facts as possessing a germane bearing on my career. I have written the greater part of an Anglo-Chinese dictionary and prepared endless material for a Chinese-English dictionary which will probably never see the light; also a work on the written language of China compiled by order of H.M. Foreign Office.

I may not say much about my semi-official preoccupations in Peking, but will mention that I was for some years Professor of Literature and Law at what was then the Imperial University. The number of official translations of documents not only in Chinese but in Japanese, Manchu, Mongol, Tibetan and Russian which I have made for the London Foreign Office and the British Embassy in Peking is legion and amongst others the Right Hon. Antony Eden[2] M.P. sent to me not long ago an official letter of thanks for recent translations in Japanese; whilst a former ambassador to Brussels, Sir Robert Clive [3] G.C.V.O., at the time *Chargé d'Affaires* at Peking, expressed to me in writing his warm approval of my sinological merits and tendered hearty thanks.

A certain Semitic correspondent of Reuter's in Peking charitably said of me (*more suo*) [4] that my life was a long camouflage, a wilful reclusion owing to a "guilty conscience", that I was too "proud" (what of?) to associate with other

---

[1] Joke in the corner!
[2] Robert Anthony Eden, 1st Earl of Avon (1897–1977), British Conservative politician who served three terms as Foreign Secretary, and was Prime Minister 1955 to 1957.
[3] Sir Robert Henry Clive (1877–1948), British diplomat. Counsellor at the Peking Legation from 1920 to 1923.
[4] In their own manner.

Europeans, that my *soi-disant* knowledge was an imposture and a *devanture*[1] which took in none save myself.

I deny the accusation *in toto*: none was ever more socially disposed (if time permitted) than I; none ever worked harder or more patiently. One does not proclaim to the world functional exotic proclivities, but apart from that reticence which is the debt due to convention and obligation, I have ever been candour and simplicity itself, though it is only now, at the end of my life that I lift the veil to represent my moral depravities as they were, ay and as they would be still, God forgive me, did the physical force (now extinct) therefore remain. "By their fruits we shall know them:" *kuan kuo chih shu*, is as true now as it was two thousand years ago.

"Praise me or condemn me," *chih wo tsui wo*, as China's sage said, let me then be judged by my work, imperfect, very surely, but still an abiding pleasure in senile retrospect. *Valgliami 'l lungo studio e 'l grande amore.*[2]

Saith the Chinese adage: *Kai kuan lun ting*, "when the lid is placed upon the coffin, judgment is fixed"; even as the Greek tragedian's "Call none happy until he be dead." Happiness is relative and I can assert with truth that, pleased as I was fifty years ago when Sam Lewis, the great Jewish usurer, brought to me gold Fr. 104,000 as a *boni* or *gain gratuit*[3] out of his million won at the tables by the money I loaned to him for love, I was even happier quite recently when a French publisher (*vive la France!*) of Peking forwarded to me F.R.B.$50, say £1

---

[1] Facade.
[2] Dante. E.B. Avail me the long study and great love.
[3] Free gain.

293

in English money, in purchase of an article I had composed on Cardinal Newman. And perchance the day may dawn when, *réduit à la besace*,[1] I shall be still more thankful to him or to her who allows me in charity, a tottering old man, to function as a *pousse-pousse*[2] and grants to me *en récompense*[3] the liberal *pourboire*[4] of say F.R.B.$3 over and above the regular tariff. *Salut à tombée majesté*,[5] as Dumas makes Athos say.

Truly it shall be better for Sodom and Gomorrah in the Day of Judgment than for the politicians who dragged the world into this unnecessary war, these Cleons[6] of the Commonwealths. Ay! but where is the Aristophanes to flay them with his lash, to chastise them with the scorpions of devastating ridicule, as in the *Knights* which mocks that sausage selling demagogue? "You have the Theban chorus yet; where is the Theban phalanx gone?"

And this shall be my list word, the conviction of an honest mind that sets no faith in fallacies, nor in windy oratory which dissembles and declines to face facts, for ever prophesying what it knows that it cannot perform; whose life is all a lie. *Vae victis!*[7] *C'est vouloir prendre la lune aux dents. A vrai dire, ce sont des mémoires d'outre-tombe que j'ai écrites, ce sont les*

---

[1] Begging. Literally: reduced to the bag.
[2] Rickshaw.
[3] In reward.
[4] Gratuity.
[5] Hello to fall majesty.
[6] Cleon was an Athenian general portrayed as a warmongering demagogue by Aristophanes and Thucydides.
[7] Woe to the vanquished!

dernières paroles d'une voix qui tombe, d'une lumiere qui s'éteint.[1]

As Raleigh[2] wrote his *History Of The World* being a prisoner of State in the Tower of London; as Bunyan[3] in his majestic prose-poem in a dungeon, and Defoe[4] his *Robinson Crusoe* with the bailiffs knocking at his garret door: so I, immeasurably their inferior in genius ("would I were equal to them in renown"[5]) am in a sense "equal to them in fate" an interned prisoner of war in far Cathay.

> "I have done, and may God forgive me!"[6]
> "So may the lord of life who sets
> On human things his seal of fire
> Make music of our vain regrets
> And crown our impotent desire."[7]

---

[1] It's wanting to take the moon with your teeth. To tell the truth, these are memoirs of the tomb that I wrote, these are the last words of a falling voice, of a light that goes out.

[2] Sir Walter Raleigh (c. 1552 –1618), English statesman, soldier, spy, writer, poet, and explorer.

[3] John Bunyan (1628–1688), English writer and Puritan preacher; author of the Christian allegory *The Pilgrim's Progress*.

[4] Daniel Defoe, born Daniel Foe (c1660 –1731), English writer, trader, and spy.

[5] Milton. E.B.

[6] Shakespeare, Henry VIII, Act II, Scene 1. EB

[7] Benson. EB

POSTSCRIPT
By Dr Reinhard Hoeppli

Sir Edmund Trelawny Backhouse then in his seventy-first year wrote in the first half of 1943 two works *The Dead Past* and *Décadence Mandchoue*, extraordinary in more than one sense, both entirely unsuitable for ordinary publication. The author who had been a resident of Peking for many years lived at the outbreak of the Pacific War very retired in the British Embassy Compound. The War imposed on him a few restrictions but fundamentally did not change his quiet life. On account of his age and failing health he was exempted from going with other allied nationals to the Civilian Internment Camp at Weihsien. In early summer 1943, he entered the French St. Michael's Hospital where he remained up to his death on January 8th, 1944.

The editor, who had never met Sir Edmund before the war, had been from 1930 to 1943 a staffmember of the Peiping Union Medical College. During the Pacific War he was, as Honorary Swiss Consul, in charge of American, British and Netherlands interests in Peiping and in this quality became acquainted with Sir Edmund. He visited him very frequently – for many months nearly daily – until his death.

The reader of *The Dead Past* and *Décadence Mandchoue* will learn in the first of the author's unhappy childhood and of his years in Europe, in the second of his life in China until the death of the Empress Dowager. The reader will form his own opinion but nevertheless may welcome some additional information about the author and his work based on the editor's personal experience and observations.

THE AUTHOR: According to *Burke's Peerage, Baronetage and Knightage* (96th edition 1938) and to *Who's Who* (edition 1937), Sir Edmund was born on October 2 1873; the same year was originally given in his last passport but evidently at his own request changed to 1872. He told the editor that the last mentioned year was the correct one but never properly explained why *Burke's Peerage, Who's Who* and the first entry in his passport gave 1873.

Comparatively few, especially among foreigners knew him personally, although his name was familiar as that of co-author (with J. O. P. Bland) of *China under the Empress Dowager* (1910) and *Annals and Memoirs of the Court of Peking* (1913). It was also known that he had (together with Hillier and Barton) published an excellent Anglo-Chinese Dictionary. He had the reputation of a 'recluse' who particularly disliked the contact with foreigners; even queer habits in this respect were reported. He was said to turn around when, walking on the city wall, he saw a foreigner coming towards him, and to cover his face with a handkerchief when passing a foreigner in a rickshaw. These reports, even though they may be exaggerated, indicate not only his dislike of foreigners but also an eccentric mind.

When one lives apart from others, especially when one shows strange habits, as a rule rumours, mainly of an unfavourable kind, develop.

Sir Edmund had the reputation of being homosexual; another, sinister rumour spoke of a murder committed in his own house on one of his Chinese staff. It was whispered that he had at one time translated documents for the Soviet Embassy in Peking, and that after the raid on that Embassy in 1927, these activities had been found out by the Japanese, who later in their turn had forced him to translate for them.

A particularly ugly rumour which, if it represented the truth, would deprive him of his character as a gentleman, had it that after the death of the Empress Dowager, Sir Edmund, in connection with some palace eunuchs who had stolen a very valuable jacket of the late Empress adorned with beautiful pearls, tried to cheat a staff member of a foreign bank who had paid in advance an agreed price, but in consequence of a cleverly staged theatrical coup never obtained the object, while Sir Edmund or his family eventually had to refund the irritated prospective buyer.[1]

It may be added here that when the editor's rickshawman, a Manchu, after the outbreak of the Pacific War, saw for the first time Sir Edmund, he mentioned spontaneously that there was a rumour that this old man in bygone days had been a lover of the Empress Dowager. This statement was made long before *Décadence Mandchoue* was written.

Those various rumours – whether false or true – have been mentioned only, because they indicate the highly complex personality of the author. The impression the editor got when meeting Sir Edmund first was that of a distinguished looking old scholarly gentleman dressed in a shabby black, somewhat formal, suit who had a definite charm and spoke and behaved with exquisite slightly old-style politeness. His long white

---

[1] See Trevor-Roper, A Hidden Life, pp156-157.

beard gave him a venerable aspect, his walking was slow and somewhat unsteady, so that one feared he might fall down. His bands were well-shaped and white, slightly feminine; they moved nervously and often showed tremor. His eyes were remarkable for the very different expressions they were able to show in rapid succession, as the editor could observe in the course of many visits. They might at one moment have the quiet look of an old scholar, quite in line with beard, dress and refined politeness; suddenly they became the eyes of a monk in religious ecstasy, to change again into the eyes of an old salacious profligate with a very clever cunning look, which gave the face a certain resemblance to that of Aretino on Titian's painting in the Pitti Palace in Florence. It was his eyes which betrayed that fact that the first and dominant impression of an old scholar represented only a part of his personality. Gradually after somewhat closer contact one obtained an entirely different aspect: that of a person who notwithstanding age and ailments, still harboured a strong sexuality and who, after some external inhibitions had been overcome, revealed with lascivious pleasure the erotic part of his personality. In such moments, he presented occasionally the very picture of an old satyr enjoying happy memories.

By preference he was wearing a long Chinese gown of dark colour which made him timeless in the sense that he might have looked in place in a Roman house at the time of the late emperors, in a Renaissance setting, and in the studyroom of one of the Jesuit fathers at the time of K'ang Hsi. When sitting on the verandah of his residence in the British Embassy Compound, he used to wear a black Chinese cap with a large piece of rose-quartz fastened to its front part in the old Chinese fashion. During the hot summer months, he was wearing a light yellow Chinese gown of grass-cloth.

He was a gourmet who occasionally indulged in small luxuries such as strawberries and asparagus out of season which he could hardly afford in view of his very limited funds. He was also fond of good wine, especially red Bordeaux and Burgundy. As far as the editor could ascertain, he had never indulged in opium-smoking, but took daily much caffein in crystals and during the last year of his life sleeping-powders and pills in large quantities.

His conversation was always interesting dealing as [a] rule with a great variety of topics, but giving preference to historic matters, literature and erotic subjects. He was a bibliophile who had given a very large collection of Chinese and Manchu books and manuscripts to the Bodleian Library in Oxford.

His memory was prodigious, his gift for languages extraordinary. It was therefore somewhat surprising to find occasionally an exaggerated sensitiveness in a man whose knowledge of languages was so great that he could afford to make a mistake. He whose Chinese, including calligraphy, was very good, but who unavoidably sometimes made small mistakes when writing Chinese characters, took it more or less as a personal insult if the editor's Chinese secretary corrected them. His ability to converse with great facility in different languages, together with a certain pride and perhaps wish to show it, induced him to introduce words of some other language, especially French, into his English conversation. It was very fascinating to hear him speak of the past, he brought back scenes of bygone days with many details, and when on winter afternoons, sitting in half-darkness in his arm chair, he spoke of people dead since long, they seemed as if by magic to return to life and to reveal some of their secrets, charming, scandalous, and even horrible as they may have been.

There can be no doubt that nature had given Sir Edmund not only a prodigious memory but also an extraordinary power of imagination. This last made his stories particularly vivid and fascinating, but obviously represented to a certain extent a danger to their truthfulness.

What had Sir Edmund been doing during all these years in Peking where he had first arrived in 1898? This simple question is not quite as simple to answer. For some time he was a Professor in the University of Peking, later he seemed to have been connected in a semi-official character with the British Embassy. There were several indications that he belonged to the British Intelligence Service.

For example, his knowledge of persons who had to all appearances nothing to do with him, was often very great. When once his conversation with the editor turned to a famous Peking murder case, which apparently had not been solved, Sir Edmund not only explained it in detail as a case of mistaken identity, but gave the names of the culprits, their subsequent fate and death, the source of his information, and also the reason why at that time the prosecution had to be stopped.

Anybody with a lot of highly dangerous knowledge is likely to feel not safe. Sir Edmund sometimes seemed to be subject to some fear, and this may also explain to a certain extent his highly unusual attitude towards England and the allies on one side, and towards Germany and Japan on the other. In addition, there can be no question that he harboured a strong and lasting resentment' against the British and the country of his birth. The original manuscripts of *Décadence Mandchoue* and *The Dead Past* give numerous examples which, at the editor's request, were later omitted or changed when the manuscripts were typed.

Some explanation may be found in Sir Edmund's family milieu in Cornwall which contrasted markedly with his tastes and interests. His mother was a Salisbury – Trelawny a member of a very old Cornwall family which traced its history back to Edward the Confessor. On the paternal side there was a link with Germany dating from the eighteenth century. Sir Edmund's family was related with that of Charles James Fox, the famous statesman whom he greatly admired and counted among its members a number of officers in the Army and Navy. Two of his own brothers were distinguished admirals while another brother had held a position in the Army.

It is rather likely that Sir Edmund, while still a boy, showed already qualities which were alien to his family, and possibly a good deal of the illtreatment by his parents of which he so bitterly complains in *Tangled Skein* may have been due to an antagonism, perhaps subconscious, between the very uncongenial personalities of parents and son. Also to his brothers he must have seemed strange at an early time. "Did you dream this, Edme" as he quotes himself, was the retort of one of his brothers to whom he had spoken.

It is probable that Sir Edmund felt somewhat a stranger in his family and among the members of the British aristocracy of his time, who in turn most likely sensed and resented it, without appreciating Sir Edmund's unusual qualities. His wish to leave the uncongenial British atmosphere was very likely one of the reasons why he went to China, where he found just the milieu he was looking for, and which corresponded to his interests and tastes. His admitted dislike of British society seems in China to have gradually developed to a dislike of foreigners in general, as mentioned before. The editor has during the Pacific War never heard from any Englishman, especially not one of high education and good social standing, such unkind remarks on Great Britain, the British Government and the British character in general as made by Sir Edmund. On the other side, there was nobody in the Peking British community who spoke so highly of Germany and Japan. It may be of interest to add that while Sir Edmund himself did not hesitate to blame the British, he did not like to hear other people attacking them; he was even very sensitive about this point. There can be no doubt that he was very fond of Germany, especially the cultural past of that country with which he was connected by ancestral links. In [regard to the] Japanese, he appreciated their politeness and admired their courage in war. He seemed to enjoy Japanese victories just as if he was a Japanese and recorded with sadistic pleasure the various defeats of the allies, especially of the British, during the first period of the war. It has to remain an open question whether this peculiar attitude represented his real feelings, or was possibly the result of a constant hidden fear of a real or imaginary danger from the Japanese authorities. Concerning France and the French, he always, from the beginning to the end, manifested a liking, dwelling with delight in many conversations on interesting periods in French history and on French cultural achievements; the last Valois, as might be expected, was among his favourites. Likewise for Russians he had only good words, but it has to be pointed out that when speaking of Russia he had the old imperial Russia in mind.

Sir Edmund who was never married, became a Catholic in [the] summer [of] 1942, and subsequently signed by preference 'Paul' Backhouse. He had evidently since long contemplated to enter 'Holy Church' as he called it, and the general political situation probably precipitated his step. He felt alone, somewhat lost and looked for a shelter. The beautiful ceremonies impressed and attracted him, just as they have attracted so many others. In addition, it is very likely that he hoped that by accepting the Catholic faith he would be provided by the church, not only with money which he always needed, but eventually also with some peaceful abode, secluded and sheltered, such as a monastery with an old garden where he could sit and contemplate, removed from the world and safe. He expressed this wish on several occasions and mentioned 'Monreale' near Palermo, with its beautiful old garden and its exquisite architecture as a model for his dream of a peaceful place of retirement before the end.

He was deceived in this respect. Not only did the Church not provide funds but also his dream of a sheltered peaceful life in a monastery-garden could not be realised and for good reasons. The Catholic Church enjoyed certain privileges during the Japanese occupation, but was always closely watched and had to be very careful in all relations with 'enemy' nationals. "Monseigneur always says: the Lord will provide", Sir Edmund once complained, speaking of visits by the Bishop of Peking whom he had evidently approached with a request for funds. The Lord did not provide and therefore the much-criticised British Government had after all to continue to help him with relief payments.

Sir Edmund's Father Confessor was Irish and not highly cultured: "better suited to convert coolies than people like myself," to use one of Sir Edmund's judgments about this priest who, like many of his compatriots, hated Great Britain. It is very likely that he and Sir Edmund met on common ground in their criticism of England and their love for Germany. His Father Confessor brought Sir Edmund many of the well-known small religious pictures on cards so dear to the lower classes in Catholic countries who place them usually in religious books. Sir Edmund kept them on his table for months while at the same time he wrote some of the most immoral chapters of *Décadence Mandchoue*.

During the last months of his life, he seemed to have lost to a certain degree his admiration for Catholicism and especially a good deal of his former respect for the priests. "They come pestering me all the time with their impertinent indiscreet questions, I wished they would leave me alone", he remarked on several occasions. Anyhow he ended his life in peace with his church, receiving the sacraments of which he once remarked "if they don't help, they will at least do no harm".

To draw the conclusion from such remarks that he was, with regard to the Catholic Church, a hypocrite pure and simple, would do him unjustice. He certainly had a sincere liking for the Catholic religion, but his nature was such that he might mock and be devoted, even be a believer to a certain extent, and all that at the same time; some element of superstition may likewise have played a role.

It would have been easy for Sir Edmund as far as his earthly possessions were concerned to give up everything and to enter a monastery because he had hardly anything left. He who in his youth had been evidently quite wealthy died, as far as his possessions in China were concerned, practically a beggar. The same scholar who had presented the Bodleian Library in Oxford with about 30,000 books and manuscripts died with only such few personal belongings as some worn Chinese and foreign clothes – a fur coat was the only article of some value – an old Victorian travelling clock and a small collection of books, all, with one or two exceptions, cheap editions and practically valueless. He had hardly any linen, no watch, no cufflinks and apart from the piece of rose-quartz fastened on his Chinese cap and mentioned before, no jewellery of any kind. A red leather case containing the document of his succession to the baronetcy was somewhat incongruent with the other items.

Most important of the things he once possessed was his library, the loss of which he often deplored. A gold watch, several valuable manuscripts, such as an autograph letter by Marie Antoinette, were other items he mentioned on various occasions. How could he lose all this and evidently much more? His answer always was "thanks to unfaithful servants and treacherous friends". But why did he never try to recover at least some of his property, especially as he obviously knew those who had robbed him?

What seemed to have happened was that apparently in 1939, while the Japanese conducted an anti-British and anti-American propaganda in Peking, which however to all of the editor's knowledge never led to looting, let alone attacks on the life of ordinary civilians, Sir Edmund for unknown reasons was suddenly seized by such a fear that he left his house in the West City and only with a few of his belongings took refuge in a German boarding-house within the precincts of the Ex-Austrian Legation Compound in the Legation Quarter. This alone represents a somewhat strange act, but much more strange is that subsequently he to all evidence never again entered his former house, leaving and abandoning everything – and all this happened about two years before the outbreak of the Pacific War!

According to statements in his autobiography he had sent already many years before his end some of his belongings for safekeeping to Lloyds Bank in London. Among them should be found the diary of Li Lien-ying, the famous chief eunuch of the Empress Dowager. This diary contains, according to Sir Edmund, references to his visits to the Forbidden City and therefore might substantiate and verify one of the most interesting parts of *Décadence Mandchoue*: the author's intimate relations with Tz'u Hsi.

Little need be said of his outward life from the beginning of the Pacific War to his death. At the outbreak, he lived in a single room, very modestly furnished in a house of the British Embassy Compound, some of these houses having been rented by British nationals. He had one servant whom he treated with great consideration, but who in return often played the role of the master. Easy to understand that notwithstanding Sir Edmund's age, rumours developed, especially as opium-smoking and heavy drinking did not cause the dismissal of Pien, the 'attendant', as Sir Edmund always called him. It should however be stated that with all his shortcomings, Pien knew well Sir Edmund's little peculiarities and wishes, and tried in general his best – provided he was sober – to serve him well. He was, notwithstanding the occasional rough treatment of his master, quite attached to him, although he had not been very long in his service. On the occasions of Sir Edmund's death and funeral he showed a great grief which was certainly genuine.

Sir Edmund on account of high blood pressure, dizziness, prostatic hyperplasia [1] with urinary troubles, entered the French St. Michael's Hospital on April 6, 1943 and remained there to his end, occupying a small room on the ground floor of the east wing. This hospital, being under the administration of Catholic sisters, with priests visiting patients nearly every day, formed in some way a kind of substitute to the monastery which Sir Edmund had hoped would give him shelter. In fall 1943, the editor as well as others noticed a certain change in his behaviour, he became irritable, his usual exquisite politeness left him occasionally; he was often gloomy and spoke of his approaching end. On the occasion of his last birthday, after having received some wine from the editor, he returned his card with *"mille remerciements de votre très génereux cadeau. Vous êtes bien bon pour mot. C'est aujourd'hui mon dernier anniversaire."*[2] On Christmas 1943, he became suddenly unconscious, fell, and after having regained consciousness, showed asymmetry of mouth and difficulty in speaking. These symptoms improved but were followed by others such as bluish and black patches on his legs indicating disorders of his circulation. Two days before the end, the temperature rose suddenly and at January 8th, 1944 at seven o'clock in the morning Sir Edmund died without pain and having been conscious nearly to the end. The medical certificate gave "Softening of the Brain" as the cause of death.

After a service in St. Joseph's Church – the Tung Tsang – he was buried on January 10th, 1944 in the Catholic cemetery of

---

[1] Prostrate enlargement.
[2] A thousand thanks for your very generous gift. You are very good at your word. Today is my last birthday."

Chala outside P'ing Tze Men, near the burial places of some of the famous Jesuit fathers of K'ang Hsi's time.

A few hours after his death, a young Chinese called at the Swiss Consul's office and inquired whether the contents of Sir Edmund's last will and testament were known, as Sir Edmund whom he had met for the first time a few weeks before in the French Hospital, had promised him that he would leave his by his testament a beautiful large diamond.

It is hardly necessary to add that no such diamond nor any other diamond existed and nothing was mentioned of such a legacy in the testament. The latter left practically everything to his family in England besides three modest legacies to three of his servants, the last one "Pien" being one of them.

Sir Edmund's personality is, in the editor's opinion, to some extent typical of certain highly gifted homosexuals whom he has met in the past, and shows the abnormal sexual instinct merely as one of several characteristics. There exists as a rule a great, rather feminine sensitiveness. Partly by force of circumstances, partly also by natural inclination, there is often found a lack of directness and a tendency for mystification, which in the worst cases may produce insincerity and direct lies.

Politeness, often exaggerated, is partly an expression of the personality, but is primarily used and doubtless often deliberately, to keep others at a distance. Sir Edmund's somewhat old-style but exquisite politeness has been mentioned before. It even extended to ordinary communications concerning small unimportant matters, and hardly a letter or a brief note was received by the editor which did not begin with "Much revered", "My dear and deeply revered", or "My dear and deeply honoured".

A tendency to indulge in eccentric habits is likewise often found. Whereas, on the one side dignity and social standards are carefully maintained, and people of the higher classes are often treated haughtily, there is at the same time a tendency to become rapidly intimate with members of the lower classes – well understood, not necessarily always in order to indulge in sexual practices. Servants, especially males, are usually treated well and with consideration by such homosexuals: Sir Edmund showed this attitude very pronounced. The world of imagination, even if not based on such extraordinary natural gifts as in Sir Edmund, is often cherished and cultivated, partly perhaps because in the sexual sphere indulgence is not always easy, and therefore has to be supplemented by wishful dreams which subconsciously are also applied to other realms. Sir Edmund's creative imaginative power was astonishing: he used it very frequently and, as in the story of the bequeathed large diamond, sometimes merely for its own sake, "l'art pour l'art" because nothing could be gained. Fear is another characteristic, and this was very definite in Sir Edmund, although in his case one may assume that he had possibly stronger reasons than mere blackmail for homosexual practices.

Powerful gifts of the intellect are often, as experience shows, coupled with particularly strong sexual instincts in 'normal' individuals; Sir Edmund is a good example that this rule also applies to homosexuals.

Last but not least should be mentioned a certain kindness and good-heartedness, not seldom observed in them. It may in the first moment seem a paradox that a person who has a number of characteristics which are not particularly attractive, should be fundamentally good-hearted, nevertheless this is true as the editor could observe on various occasions. This good-heartedness in the case of Sir Edmund was the chief secret of his charm. It was immediately felt by most people of the lower classes, but also by his equals in society, and perhaps subconsciously induced then to overlook certain weaknesses which they would not have forgiven in others.

A person of Sir Edmund's complex type, living an extraordinary life in a highly complex environment will be judged differently according to the viewpoint of the critic. The editor, refraining from any judgment, wishes only to state that he regards himself fortunate to have come in contact with Sir Edmund, who having moved for many years in a vanished world brilliant in art and literature, and at an extraordinary oriental court. could in his conversation bring all back so colourful and vivid that persons who belong to history whom he had once met, seemed alive and spoke through him.

Although his imagination may occasionally have interfered with his memory, his conversation had such fascination that he who had known personally Verlaine, Mallarmé, Beardsley, Pater and Wilde, not to speak of Tz'u Hsi and her court, could by a few remarks, give their peculiar atmosphere and characteristics. Of Mallarmé, he once remarked that he had just a little the touch of the "bourgeois", a remark which possibly gives the truth and represents an observation the young, rich English nobleman was liable to make when meeting the school-teacher Mallarmé.

Sir Edmund, with all his shortcomings, was most extraordinary, and perhaps never revealed his personality completely. The editor also after many months of nearly daily contact with him, fully realized how little he fundamentally knew him, and never realized it more than when he saw him for the last time, in his coffin. REQUIESCAT IN PACE!

THE WORK. Most of Sir Edmund's literary work in the past consisted of translations of official documents for the London Foreign Office and the British Embassy in Peking, of no interest to the general public, and remaining in consequence more or less unknown except to a few. Besides, he wrote many articles on different subjects for the London *Times*, the *Westminster Gazette*, the *Pall Mall Gazette* and the *Atlantic Monthly*, apart from articles for journals in China. He had also prepared a wealth of material for a Chinese-English Dictionary which however was never published.

It has been mentioned before that he was the co-author of an excellent Anglo-Chinese Dictionary and of two other publications, *China under the Empress Dowager* and *Annals and Memoirs of the Court of Peking*. These two works are not publications on history in a strict scholarly sense and were not intended to be. However, even if this is admitted, there remains the somewhat unpleasant fact that *China under the Empress Dowager* is in the main based on a diary (supposed to have been that of Ching Shan, a high government official) which according to recent research of Prof. J. J. L. Duyvendak of the University of Leyden must be regarded in its presented form as a forgery; Sir Edmund claims to have found and translated it. It must be admitted that a diary of Ching Shan may have existed and that it may have been used. The diary as published in *China under the Empress Dowager* is however

315

according to Duyvendak certainly a forgery and it is only natural to suspect Sir Edmund as either having committed the forgery, or having translated the text as an authentic document while knowing that it was a forgery. On rare occasions, because Sir Edmund being very sensitive by nature was particularly sensitive on this point, the editor tried to induce him to give an explanation. The result was that he always declared that he had found the diary as he translated it and had acted in good faith. Asked whether, in the light of recent research, he still regarded the diary as genuine, he answered evasively in terms such as "I did not falsify it," and did not commit himself. In the editor's opinion – but this is merely a personal impression – Sir Edmund did not himself commit the forgery; whether he suspected or even knew that the diary was not genuine was impossible to judge on the basis of Sir Edmund's conversation. Should he have been an accomplice, his somewhat redeeming virtue would have been that he acted in the interest of two persons be admired and cherished, the Grand Councillor Jung Lu and the Empress Dowager Tz'u Hsi.

China under the Empress Dowager, when compared with *Décadence Mandchoue,* contains besides the diary another questionable part: the report on the death of Kuang Hsü and Tz'u Hsi. The end of both is stated to have been due to natural causes and is described quite in detail. Just on account of these details, the average reader will not suspect that the actual facts – according to *Décadence Mandchoue* – were entirely different. There have been since long strange rumours about the coincidence of these deaths and some suspicion of foul play had been voiced. The reader of *Décadence Mandchoue* will find this suspicion fully justified, as both Kuang Hsi and Tz'u Hsi according to this work were murdered. The emperor is said to have been strangled not poisoned. When the editor mentioned the old rumour that Kuang Hsü had died after having eaten poisoned tarts, Sir Edmund declared that such an attempt had been made but had failed. A scholar with access to the Archives of the British Foreign Office will have no difficulty to verify Sir Edmund's statement in *Décadence Mandchoue* as he personally told the editor that he at that time had fully informed the British Government. There remains the question why he intentionally distorted facts. The answer is simple: Sir Edmund for various reasons wished to continue his life in China; publication of the true facts concerning the death of Kuang Hsü and Tz'u Hsi would have made his further life in China impossible and *"Pékin veut bien une mess"*.[1]

Annals and Memoirs of the Court of Peking has no bearing on Sir Edmund's two last works with which we are concerned and therefore need not be discussed.

The editor realises that he is responsible for the existence of *The Dead Past* and *Décadence Mandchoue*. Both represent essentially collections of the various stories which Sir Edmund told him on his frequent visits during the first year of the Pacific War. Whatever the historic value of these stories may be, it seemed regrettable that they should be lost, and in order to preserve them and to have at the same time a good pretext to provide him with additional funds from his private means the editor suggested to Sir Edmund to write the most interesting of his experiences, and to sell the manuscripts to him as would a professional writer.

---

[1] Peking wants a mess.

Sir Edmund had a great facility in writing, sending the editor in rapid succession sheets covered with the thin, highly nervous products of his penmanship, rather difficult to read. There was in consequence the additional advantage that he could fill many hours of his long days by an occupation which cost him little effort and at the same time gave him a certain pleasure by enjoying once more in memory the unusual and remarkable scenes of his past life. There can be no doubt that he was really benefitted by this occupation, his temporary improvement being so obvious that various visitors remarked upon it.

He wrote *Décadence Mandchoue* between December 1942 and May 1943, to be followed by *The Dead Past* which he had completed at the end of June. Considering that he had no possibility to consult books and had no literary help whatever, solely and entirely relying on his memory, one had to admit that the creation of the two works, especially in the comparatively short period of slightly over 6 months, represents a rather remarkable achievement at the age of seventy.

The Dead Past contains, besides *Tangled Skein* – in principle a mere autobiography – separate essays on Verlaine, Mallarmé, Beardsley and Pater, which furnish considerable further autobiographical material. The most sensational one is the essay on Verlaine, who according to Sir Edmund, was for one term his teacher in French at St. George's School in Ascot. The appreciation of Beardsley's work, by emphasising the essentials of his art. proves that Sir Edmund who not very frequently spoke of purely pictorial problems, had a fine feeling for the beauty of line and the essentials of a drawing. The editor regards the essay on Pater as the best one, as it is evidently based on a longer and deeper connection between author and subject than is the case in the other essays.

Décadence Mandchoue consists of a collection of twenty chapters dealing with happenings at the Manchu court or with persons directly or indirectly connected with it. The Empress Dowager stands in the centre of interest; the author took part in most of the related scenes, but a few are based on reports of eye witnesses. The whole gives excellently the atmosphere of a decadent court society just before its end. From a historic point of view, the most important chapter is that dealing with the death of the emperor and the empress dowager, already referred to.

The most fantastic part of the whole work is that describing the author's intimate relations with Tz'u Hsi. Who, among those who read Segalen's[1] *René Leys*,[2] will in this connection not remember the French author's book; but even *René Leys* is supposed not to be based entirely on imagination. Should the existence of intimate relations between Sir Edmund and the

---

[1] Victor Segalen (1878–1919), French naval doctor, ethnographer, archeologist , writer, poet, explorer, art-theorist, linguist, literary critic and nomad. Married Yvonne Hébert, and had issue. Seglan's death at the age of forty-one remains a mystery: his body was discovered in a Breton forest. Alongside it lay a copy of Shakespeare's works opened to *Hamlet*.

[2] A novel cast in the form of the diary of a Frenchman in Peking in 1911, the final year of the Qing dynasty. It was inspired by Seglan's infatuation with Maurice Roy, the handsome bilingual teenage son of the director of the French postal service in Peking, and is a meditation on fact, fiction and storytelling, and as well as a discreet exploration of sublimated homosexuality. Roy becomes the mysterious character of the title, who is engaged as a language teacher by the narrator, who is obsessed with the mysteries of the Forbidden City. Ley reveals that he is connected with the Imperial Court, being the head of a secret police force, and a lover of Empress Dowager Longyu, wife of Zaitian, the Guangxu Emperor, and last Empress of China. But are his stories true or imagined?

Empress Dowager be proved, we have the grotesque fact that a man who in general had only homosexual interests became for several years not only a sort of lover of an old Manchu woman – admitted she was the all-powerful Empress Dowager – but that stimulated and fortified by Li Liege-ying's 'love philters', he performed to the physical satisfaction of a woman who certainly had experience and knew how to choose.

The explanation, in the editor's opinion, rests in the pleasure the Empress Dowager found in the company of a clever, witty, amusing foreigner, always respectful and discreet, who as far as the purely physical side of the question is concerned, perhaps just on account of his perverted sexual instincts was able by clever devices to provide enjoyment even for an old oversexed woman like Tz'u Hsi. Sir Edmund told the editor on several occasions that it was chiefly his conversation which made him to be treated as a 'favori' and it is most likely that this statement gives the truth.

With regard to *The Dead Past* and *Décadence Mandchoue* the fundamental question presents itself immediately. How far do the two works give the truth; do they to some extent possess historic value or are they simply products of the author's fertile imagination?

Sir Edmund's status as a scholar is uncertain, chiefly on account of the publication of the forged diary of Ching Shan. But even being fully aware of this, there is no doubt for the editor that Sir Edmund in writing *The Dead Past* and *Décadence Mandchoue* firmly believed he was stating the truth.

Evidently realising the extraordinary character of his work, he, on various occasions in the text, again and again pledges his word that he gave the truth and nothing but the truth. How far he subconsciously deceived himself, eventual future investigations may show.

Sir Edmund's memory, extraordinary as it was, was imperfect like every other faculty of man. Whether old age had weakened it, or had allowed his equally extraordinary imagination occasionally to get the better of it, is impossible to decide. It is certain in any case that in some instances which could be checked, his memory was at fault.

As an example may be quoted in *Décadence Mandchoue* (The Mantle of Cagliostro) the reference to the event – supposed to be historic – when Cagliostro in a dark room showed Marie Antoinette in a crystal the guillotine and her own body with the head severed. This scene is not historic but evidently confused with one in Alexandre Dumas'[1] novel *Joseph Balsamo*. There Cagliostro shows to Marie Antoinette in a grotto at the country house of the Baron de Taverney in a globe shaped carafe filled with water her own body under the guillotine and her head falling into the basket. Just as Sir Edmund mentions in his story, Dumas makes the Dauphine cry out before she faints.

There is the possibility, not to say likelihood that Sir Edmund's memory led him still to a confusion of other scenes which he knew from books with those he had himself witnessed. This particular kind of confusion has to be considered especially, as

[1] Alexandre Dumas, born Dumas Davy de la Pailleterie (1802–1870, French author.

Sir Edmund was a great reader. An example is in all probability also the description of his conversations with members of the former Russian Imperial Family. There is no reason to doubt that he had been presented to the Czar, the Empress Dowager and the Grand Duchess Sergius. It is however not very likely that these high-placed persons opened their heart about unhappy events in their family and sinister forebodings to a young foreign visitor whom they met for the first time, even if this foreigner had been introduced by the British Ambassador. It is more likely that in this case Sir Edmund, either based on his knowledge of members of the Imperial Family, made them say words which they might have said to others more intimate with them, or that, deceived by his memory, he reported as having witnessed conversations of which he had read long ago perhaps in some memoirs.

It is more or less obvious that events as described by Sir Edmund could not have occurred in exactly the same way as related by the author, even if given with all details. In *Décadence Mandchoue* (the Mantle of Cagliostro), the Empress Dowager in a very lengthy séance sees in the crystal all important events of her past life. It is extremely unlikely that the old despot would have tolerated – not to say enjoyed – the recollection of past events well known to her and to a high degree unpleasant, when she was eager to see the future. It is still less probable that she spoke in a loud voice and somewhat explained her former actions before the rather mixed assembly.

In *Décadence Mandchoue* (The Lovers Doom), Sir Edmund in the first description of the remnants of the unfortunate couple killed by lightning, and subsequently burned in the conflagration, spoke of a small heap of white ashes. After the

322

editor had pointed out that remnants of persons burned in the fire of a building as a rule have a very different aspect, he readily changed his former description and presented it more in line with the usual picture seen on such occasions.

In the absence of proofs to the contrary a reader of *The Dead Past* and *Décadence Mandchoue* may hold the opinion that both works are entirely products of an extraordinary, rather morbid, imagination. Assuming for a moment that future research would demonstrate the correctness of this opinion, *The Dead Past* would lose most of its value but *Décadence Mandchoue* even as a work of imagination, would keep the merit of giving extraordinarily well the general atmosphere of Tz'u Hsi's court, especially as far as the erotic side is concerned. In a certain sense, the author's achievement would be still more extraordinary if all the colourful vivid, and in their way fascinating stories, had been created by the author's imagination, especially if one remembers his age and the absence, of any literary or other help.

The Empress Dowager shows a considerable resemblance to Catherine II of Russia[1], the 'Semiramis[2] of the North' with the difference that in Peking death and not banishment to Siberia waited for the unfortunate 'favori' who had done his duty. Also, apart from her enormously developed sexuality, Tz'u Hsi is most remarkable especially on account of her courage and rapid decisions in cases of personal danger. Her well-known ambition and enjoyment of power becomes frequently evident, just as a certain kindness, when her personal interests were

---

[1] i.e. Catherine The Great (1729–1796).
[2] A mythological Assyrian warrior queen. Inspired by the real queen, Shammuramat (811–808BC).

not involved, otherwise the life of her fellow human beings meant nothing whatever to her and she pronounced horrible death sentences between topics of ordinary harmless conversation. It is easy to understand that most of her subjects who had to deal with her lived in constant fear, as even a small accident might mean the loss of life. As usual at the former courts of oriental despots, she had a few devoted friends also among the servants and with all his shortcomings Li Lien-ying shows the redeeming virtue of perfect loyalty and sincere attachment to his mistress.

In the editor's opinion, *The Dead Past* and *Décadence Mandchoue* are not purely imaginary but are fundamentally based on facts. How far these facts have been distorted by a confused memory, and to what extent purely imaginary happenings have been added, can only be judged by a future critical examination, which will have to make use of all available documents. Concerning *The Dead Past,* it should be possible to verify whether Verlaine was actually for a brief period teacher in St. George's School in Ascot. His life has been thoroughly checked, but even so, there remain evidently still some *lacunae*, unrecorded periods, especially concerning his visits of England[*sic*].

It seems incredible but is not impossible that Sir Edmund, who was charmed and fascinated by Verlaine's personality and work, and who spoke frequently of him, had reached a stage when, misled by his imagination, he believed he had had at school Verlaine as a teacher of French. It would have been pointless, had he deliberately invented this story and had intentionally told a lie. Should future research show that Verlaine had never been a teacher in Ascot, we have the curious fact, well known however to alienists, that a person

324

not only sincerely believes in some event which never took place, but is even able to give about it a wealth of intimate details.

The editor is obliged to M. R. de Margerie, Counsellor of the French Embassy in Peking for informing him of a somewhat similar case concerning Chateaubriand, who in general may be regarded as an author who honestly tried to present the truth. Joseph Bédier[1] in his *Etudes Critiques* could nevertheless show that Chateaubriand in his *Memoires d'Outre-Tombe* relates in all sincerity as witnessed, events at which he could not have been present. Sir Edmund therefore with regard to this point finds himself in good company.

The reason why the editor, with regard to Verlaine's teaching in St. George's School in Ascot, feels slightly suspicious, is that Sir Edmund when he first told of his personal relations with Verlaine, also mentioned that he had met Rimbaud at Mallarmé's residence in the Rue de Rome on the occasion of his visit to Paris in [the] company of his teacher. Sir Edmund, one has to keep in mind, was at that time a schoolboy who might have noticed some special external peculiarities of Rimbaud, but who could obviously not grasp his genius, and had fundamentally hardly any reason to remember details of an unknown stranger whom he had accidentally once met. He gives nevertheless a rather detailed description of his face, remembering even the colour of the eyes and mentioning a slight limp.

---

[1] Joseph Bedier (1864–1938) French writer and scholar and historian of medieval France.

The editor by a number of questions was able more or less to ascertain that this meeting could not have taken place. Sir Edmund apparently realising this left in the manuscript the description of the nearly impossible meeting, but some days later added a few lines about a cobbler 'Rimbot', a friend of Verlaine whom he had also met. In his conversation, he admitted that he had possibly confused this cobbler with the famous Rimbaud in some other recollections which he had told the editor, without however including them in his essay on Verlaine.

It will be easily understood that on such an occasion the editor, with all respect due to Sir Edmund, somewhat wondered to what degree his stories could be regarded as representing facts, considering the extreme facility by which the author introduced on the spur of the moment conveniently new persons, and altered the situation after his former statements had become untenable.

With regard to *Décadence Mandchoue* it will be possible, provided permission is given to use certain documents in the Archives of the British Foreign Office, to check Sir Edmond's report on the death of Kuang Hsü and the Empress Dowager. The author's intimate relations with Tz'u Hsi can in all probability likewise be examined. Sir Edmund mentions a letter by Sir Edward Grey[1] referring to his relations with one, not to be named. A copy of this letter and other documents concerning this point may be found and may allow a final judgment as to the correctness of Sir Edmund's statements.

---

[1] Edward Grey, 1st Viscount Grey of Fallodon (1862–1933), better known as Sir Edward Grey; British Liberal statesman.

Apart from their possible historic value, *The Dead Past* and *Décadence Mandchoue* are valuable also as material for research in sexual perversions. In this connection it may be pointed out that Sir Edmund was not only essentially homosexual but that he was apparently also very fond of sensations provoked by flagellation active and passive to judge from *Décadence Mandchoue*. He on several occasions referred in this respect to the Mignon of Henry III[1] of France for whom he had a special liking.

The two works furthermore represent a wealth of material for a psychological study of the author's highly complex personality.

It is obvious that an ordinary publication of both *The Dead Past* and *Décadence Mandchoue* is impossible. Should in some future an opportunity offer, the editor has the intention to have both works privately printed in a very small edition, and to have them distributed to some leading libraries of several countries for the eventual benefit of research.

For the time being, the editor has prepared four typewritten copies of each manuscript to be given after his death to the Library of the British Museum in London, the Bodleian Library in Oxford, the Bibliotheque Nationale in Paris and Harvard College Library, Cambridge, Massachusetts, U.S.A. each library to receive one copy of both works. The original manuscripts and the first typewritten copy of each work with corrections by the author's hand are to be to the Bodleian Library in Oxford. By this arrangement, the editor hopes to serve those

---

[1] Henry III (1551–1589), King of France from 1574 until his assassination in 1589. Noted for his male favourites, his mignons.

scholars for whom the two works may be value and to prevent their use by unauthorised persons.

R. HOEPPLI
Peking, February 1946.

Specimen of the Author's Handwriting

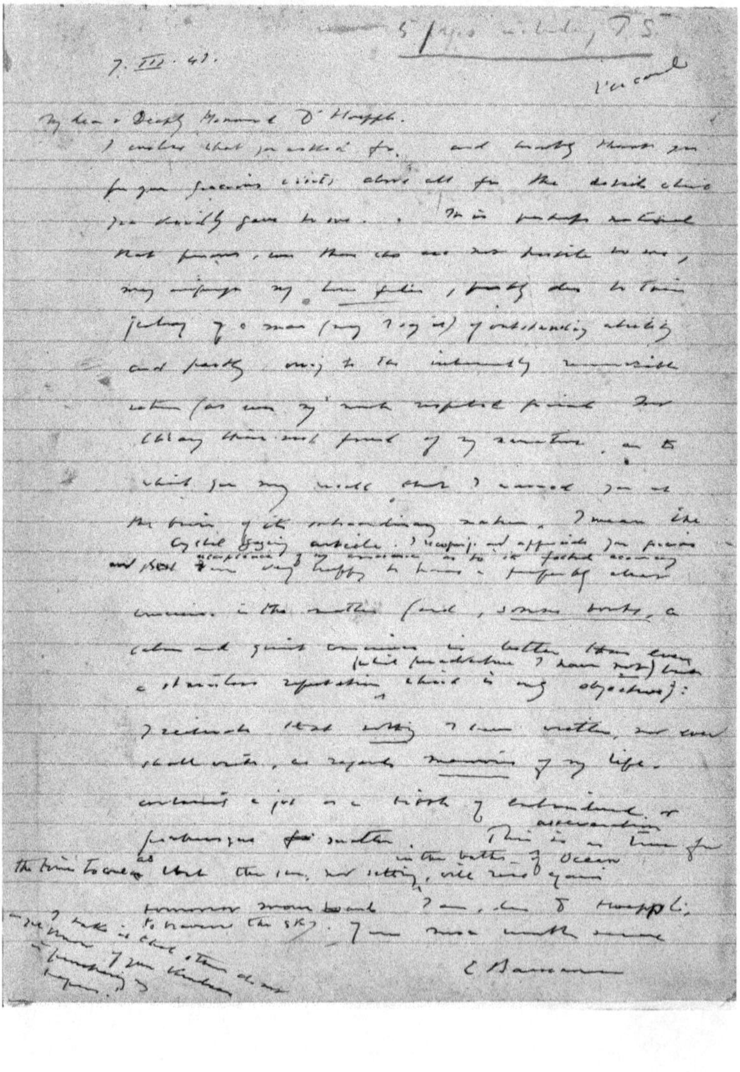

The Author on His Death Bed.

8 January 1944.